# FROM MAGIC TO SCIENCE

*Frances Butler*

PLATE I

VISION OF THE FALL OF THE ANGELS

From a MS. of Hildegard's *Scivias* at Wiesbaden, written at Bingen about 1180. See p. 232.

See p. 232.

[*Frontispiece*

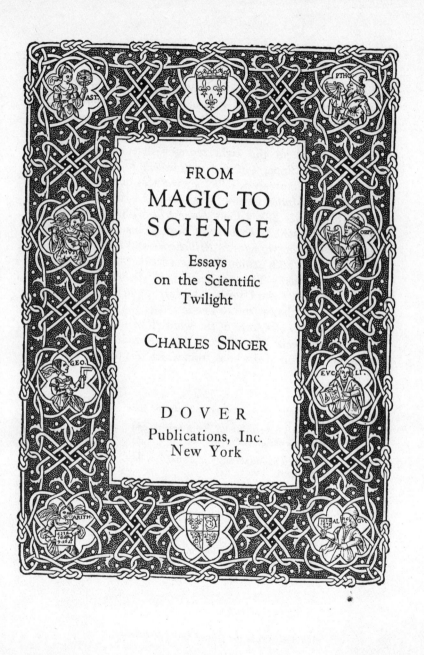

FROM
MAGIC TO
SCIENCE

Essays
on the Scientific
Twilight

CHARLES SINGER

DOVER
Publications, Inc.
New York

THE historiated border on the title page is from a work that appeared just four hundred years ago, the *Cosmotheoria* of Jean Fernel, printed at Paris in 1528 by Simon de Colines. Of the figures in the interlacings, those on the left symbolize the sciences themselves, those on the right representative exponents of the sciences. In the uppermost row *Astronomia* holds an armillary sphere and to her corresponds *Ptolemy* with his quadrant and book. In the next tier *Musica* fingers the zither and is faced by Orpheus twanging his harp. Below them *Geometria*, with her compass and right angle, is opposite to *Euclid*, who displays his book of diagrams. In the lower margin two figures, *Arithmetica* and *Alkhowarizmi*, i.e. 'he of Khorasan,' both exhibit boards inscribed with the so-called 'Arabic' numerals. The application of these numerals was known as *Algorism*, a word formed by corruption and compression of the name of Alkhowarizmi. The letters in the right lower panel are an abbreviation of a form of the word *Algorism*.

We have to thank Messrs. E. P. Goldschmidt & Co., Ltd., of London, for the loan of the book from which this border was taken.

Manufactured in the United States of America

GRAHAMO WALLAS
AUCTORUM DOCTORUM
JUCUNDISSIMO
STUDIOSORUM UNIVERSITATIS
AMICO FIDELISSIMO
SAPIENTIAE
CULTORI DILIGENTISSIMO
VERITATIS
PERQUISITORI ET INDAGATORI AVIDISSIMO
DONO DO DEDICO

## DR. CHARLES SINGER HAS ALSO PUBLISHED

1. The Cures of the Diseased in Forraine Attempts of the English Nation, London, 1598. *Reproduced in Facsimile with Introduction and Notes. Oxford : Clarendon Press*, 1915.

2. Studies in the History and Method of Science, First Series. *Oxford : Clarendon Press*, 1917 (*out of Print*).

3. Studies in the History and Method of Science, Second Series. *Oxford : Clarendon Press*, 1921.

4. Greek Biology and Greek Medicine. *Oxford : Clarendon Press*, 1920.

5. Early English Magic and Medicine. *Oxford University Press* (*for the British Academy*), 1920 (*out of Print*).

6. Greek Science and Modern Science : a Comparison and a Contrast. *London University Press*, 1921.

7. The Discovery of the Circulation of the Blood. *London : G. Bell & Sons, Ltd.*, 1922.

8. *With Professor Henry E. Sigerist.* Essays on the History of Medicine presented to Karl Sudhoff on the occasion of his Seventieth Birthday. *Oxford University Press*, 1923.

9. *With the Hon. Th. Zammit, C.M.G.* Neolithic Representations of the Human Form from the Islands of Malta and Gozo. *The Museum, Valletta, Malta*, 1924.

10. *With Professor Karl Sudhoff.* The Fasciculus Medicinae of Johannes de Ketham, Alemanus. *Facsimile of first Edition of* 1491 *with Introduction and Notes. Royal Folio. Oxford University Press*, 1924.

11. *With Professor Karl Sudhoff.* The Earliest Literature on Syphilis. *Lier & Co. : Florence*, 1925.

12. The Fasciculo di Medicina, Venice, 1493, with . . . a Translation of the ' Anathomia ' of Mondino da Luzzi, etc. *2 volumes, folio. Lier & Co. : Florence*, 1925.

13. The Evolution of Anatomy. *London : Kegan Paul*, 1926.

14. *With Dr. Edwyn Bevan, O.B.E.* The Legacy of Israel. *Oxford : Clarendon Press*, 1927.

15. Religion and Science considered in their Historical Relationships. *London : Ernest Benn, Ltd.*, 1928.

16. A Short History of Medicine. *Oxford : Clarendon Press*, 1928.

# AUTOBIOGRAPHICAL
# PREFACE
# TO DOVER EDITION

OF the seven articles in this collection one was written more than 45 years ago and the others more than 30 years ago. Thus, there are in them things which I would now express differently. Yet, upon reading them again, most seem to have stood the test of time rather better than I had expected.

In 1893, when I was a student, I attended the lectures on elementary chemistry by William (later Sir William) Ramsay. He was then actively engaged in his great work on the inert gases of the atmosphere but he always found time to chat with the practical class of the beginners. It was on one of these occasions that he first turned my mind to historical studies. Ever since that little talk, with a man whom I well knew to be great, I have taken an interest in this aspect of science. But how I came to devote myself to it is in part told by this collection and by this new preface to an old book. I have had the great pleasure of living to see my own field of studies develop into an accepted discipline, mainly through the influence and work of men well known to me. Osler, Allbutt, D'Arcy Thompson, Sherrington, Richard Gregory, F. W. Oliver, Sudhoff, Garrison, Meldrum, Wolf, Loria, Cajori, DeLaunay, Sarton, Sigerist, O. G. S. Crawford, Gordon Childe, Sherwood Taylor are among the men, now dead, who come immediately to my mind as those who have done much to advance the subject and from whom I have learned.

*The Visions of Hildegard of Bingen* was begun in 1912. I was then working as a pathologist and my wife and I spent that year at Heidelberg. We became inter-

viii PREFACE TO

ested in Hildegard because she was alleged (wrongly)
to have conceived the idea of living contagion, a subject
on the history of which Mrs. Singer and I had been
working. The University librarian at Heidelberg obtained on loan for me the Wiesbaden codex of her *Scivias*
of the second half of the 12th century. I recognized at
once that the figures, reproduced as Plates XI, XII,
XIII and on the cover resembled descriptions by patients
of what they had seen during attacks of migraine. Omit-
ting the bodies and faces from these pictures, they will
be recognised by neurologists as good representations
of the fortification figures and scintillating circles often
experienced in bouts of this disease. This Essay contains, I believe, the first recognition of the phenomena
of migraine as the basis of mystical visions. Certain
visions of Hildegard, however, were what I called 'reconstructed'. Thus, I have shown that by a mental process, she has in one case put together no less than four
visions which came to her at four separate times. This
is revealed in the *Heavenly City* of Plate XIV.

Hildegard and her visions came to occupy much of

our time during the next two years and these visions
turned us finally to historical studies. With that in view
we visited the Institute for the History of Medicine at
Leipzig and its director, Karl Sudhoff. He introduced
us to the technique of medieval manuscript research and
we began to study palaeography. At the same time, we
made friends with the bibliographer, A. C. Klebs, and
learned of his methods of dealing with early printed
books.

The Essay on Hildegard with its illustrations and the
blocks for them were ready by the end of 1913. Early
in 1914 I was invited by Osler to take a very minor post
at Oxford because, as he pointed out, it would give opportunity for historical work. I accepted gladly. He
saw my article and urged its publication on both clinical
and historical grounds.

In June, 1914, my wife and I visited Wiesbaden to see the Hildegard manuscript again. We went on to the Hildegard country in the neighborhood of Bingen, around the western tributaries that flow there into the Rhine. We learned from the German papers that war between Germany and France was then threatening. Since they carefully excluded reference to any chance of involvement of England, we decided, in our innocence, to remain where we were. Towards the end of July, however, travellers' cheques ceased to be payable in German currency. We therefore left at once for Holland, the nearest neutral country. This involved a most trying journey across the line of German mobilisation. During this difficult progress we gathered a small party of English and Americans. All of us were nearly penniless and had been forced to abandon our luggage. Mine, alas, contained the manuscript of this Essay. We reached England, exhausted and hungry, on August 1st, 1914. War was declared three days later.

The next few weeks were spent in rewriting the text of this Essay from memory. I rather think that I improved it. Mrs. Singer reinserted the references and saw it through the press while I was in the army. The book, of which it was a part, and to which Osler afterwards wrote a preface, was at once accepted by the formidable, learned and lovable Charles Cannan, then the Secretary of the Clarendon Press. I must mention his reaction to my first book. After about two minutes silence he said, "I suppose I'll take that stuff of yours. Might be worse," and he answered a few timid questions by impatient negative grunts. Although I came away from his presence depressed, his secretary was quite buoyant. "The old man has taken to you," he said. "He isn't often so chatty." I didn't feel that way, but he said, "He is like that. Wait a minute and you will hear him be much ruder to a very big swell." And it was so. I became sincerely attached to Cannan and I owe him my real start as a writer. I wish there were space here for more anecdotes of that remarkable man who could say more in fewer words than anyone that I have ever met. The curious reader will find a few such anecdotes in the account of him by one of his assistants in the *Dictionary of National Biography*. I would strongly recommend it for good reading about a great eccentric who would be better known but for his passion for anonymity.

The book was published in 1917 when I was an army medical officer in Macedonia. It immediately sold out and has become something of a bibliographical rarity. War conditions prevented a second edition, but, for reasons entirely hidden from me, it has been translated into Japanese with coloured plates added. My opinion of the quality of the Japanese text would not be important but the coloured plates in Cannan's words, "might be worse." The form of the Hildegard Essay before the reader is somewhat shortened from the original. Bibliographical references and controversial material are omitted. The plates are not coloured but it would have been impossible (except in Japan!) to reproduce them in this state as nearly all the blocks have disappeared in the course of two wars. The original coloured photographs are at the Warburg Institute in London. The presence of that magnificent home of the Muses on British soil is due to the events which led up to World War II. Incidentally, this Essay was the main factor in bringing me the D. Litt. of Oxford on the motion of Sir Frederick Kenyon, then Director of the British Museum, and of A. C. Clark, then Corpus professor of Latin.

The article *Science under the Roman Empire* has behind it a war of a different kind. Until 1920 Greek was a compulsory subject at Oxford. Directly after World War I, Gilbert Murray, who then favored the abolition of Greek as a compulsory subject, had arranged a series of introductory lectures for students of the humanities on aspects of Greek life. He invited me to speak on Greek science. Soon after, Murray changed his views on compulsory Greek and joined with Mr. R. W. (now Sir

Richard) Livingstone in defending it. Later, at the
voting of the assembly of faculties, the case for compulsory Greek was finally lost. I had voted with the majority against Livingstone and Murray. That night while
dining with Livingstone, I urged that since Greek had
ceased to be compulsory, he should edit a volume of
essays on the value of Greek studies. In a surprisingly
few days, he had assembled a team, in which I was included, for his *Legacy of Greece*. It all seemed to run
naturally from the pen, proved to be a 'best seller', and
is still in active circulation. There are evident gaps in
it, but its power is due to Sir Richard's skilful editing
and to the speed and drive which he inspired in the
contributors.

Obvious sequels were *The Legacy of Rome,* edited by
Cyril Barley (1923) and *The Legacy of Israel,* edited
by Edwyn Bevan and myself (1927). To both I contributed. Both took much longer to plan and are better
rounded and more carefully written than *The Legacy of
Greece,* but their writing may lack some of the urgency
of their forerunner. Both sold very well and are still
current. In the volume before the reader, the first Essay
is a modified form of my contribution to *The Legacy of
Rome.*

*The Dark Ages and the Dawn of Science* had grown
out of lectures delivered at summer schools, chiefly to
teachers. The first printed form appeared in 1923 in a
composite volume edited, like the others of a series, by
F. S. Marvin. I had been writing since 1913 for works
edited by that stimulating and invincible optimist, last
of the English Comtians, and through him had come in
contact with H. G. Wells. Though I did not share
the philosophy of either, we were all conscious of a
need for a history of science. For this we made a plan
in which I was to treat the twilight period. I never took
kindly to the plan, which did not mature. Should anyone read the Essay as here presented, let him remember
that it was written before the mighty works of Sarton,

Thorndike and Tannery were fully available. Without their labours no such project as we had attempted could have succeeded.

The next three Essays, *The Lorica of Gildas, Early English Magic and Medicine* and *Early Herbals* may be considered together. In 1919, while preparing lectures at Oxford on the history of biology, I had found that, from Palaeolithic times and throughout Antiquity, figures of plants had been much fewer and less naturalistic than those of animals. The reverse might have been expected since a static plant would seem easier to portray than a moving animal. This led me to seek prehistoric plant-pictures. They are remarkably few, but the search brought me into closer contact with Elliott Smith, Flinders Petrie and his assistant, Dr. Margaret Murray among my colleagues at University College, and with O.'G. S. Crawford who called on me for the first time in 1919. Helped by them, I searched Egyptian and Mesopotamian art, but found few drawings of plants other than the most conventional. In 1905 I had made a prolonged visit to Egypt, before joining an expedition to Abyssinia, and had, thus, a superficial knowledge of Egyptian art. A second journey up the Nile in 1909 added to my little knowledge of the subject. Finally, in 1923 I made a long visit to Egypt for the third time; on this occasion with Mrs. Singer and in the service of Thomas Cook and Son. It is now known, mostly from the skilled copies made by Mrs. Nina de Garis Davies, and works by Petrie and others, that there are a certain number of naturalistic representations of plants from ancient Egypt. But at that time these were less known and, considering the vast wealth of Egyptian art, they still seem conspicuous by their rarity. The same is true of Mesopotamian art.

This conclusion led me to examine classical and medieval representations of plants. Of these I had already some knowledge from the herbals in the British Museum and the Bodleian. We visited Vienna for a first-

hand study of the greatest and most beautiful of all
herbals, the venerable Juliana Anicia Dioscorides
(c.512) and of its hardly inferior cousin, the Neapoli-
tanus of about two centuries later. We went also to Leyden to see the almost equally remarkable Voss Latin
Apuleius of the seventh century. I also acquired a copy
of the fantastically inconvenient facsimile of the Juliana
Anicia. Its elephantine tomes were — to perpetrate
a mixed metaphor — the albatross around my neck for
months. I studied a few pages of them each day. They
set me fully on the study of medieval herbals.

Sudhoff had thought of working on the same line but
had abandoned it. He had collected photos of many
fragments of very early herbals. He most generously
sent me copies of these. I collected systematically photos
of almost all illustrated early medieval herbals in great
European libraries and especially those in Paris, the
British Museum and Oxford. On one occasion I drove
to Cheltenham with the gigantic Juliana facsimiles to
compare them with the princely tenth century Greek
Phillips MS. of Dioscorides which now adorns the
Pierpont Morgan Library in New York.

The first product of these researches covered the more
ancient period and appeared in 1921 in Vol. II of my
*Studies in the History and Method of Science*. I attempted a wider survey in *The Edinburgh Review* of
1923 and a still more general one in the present volume.
In 1927 appeared a more intensive treatment of the subject, containing new material, in the *Journal of Hellenic
Studies* as the "Herbal in Antiquity." I hope to produce
a new and extended version in book form. That article
included a reproduction of a sheet of a papyrus herbal
of about 400 A.D. found by excavation at Antinoe by
John Johnson, later Printer to the Oxford University
Press. Apart from being the earliest fragment of a herbal
that has been found, it is of value as linking the Greek
and Latin herbal traditions. The article also provides
an account of the surviving fragments of the work of

Krateuas of the first century B.C. He was, so far as we know, the first to illustrate a herb list.

I do not suppose that any man's estimate of his own work is of much value, but I regard the article in the *Journal of Hellenic Studies* and the account of Hildegard as my best contributions in the department of medieval studies. I was able to draw on my research for these works in writing the *Short History of Biology* which, however, did not appear till 1931. Its preparation, which extended over many years, brought me the help and friendship of Dr. Agnes Arber who had produced her fine *Herbals* in 1912. I was able to rely much on her knowledge and experience, but her published work begins with 1470, by which date mine closes. In plant identification I relied chiefly on A. J. Wilmott of the Botanical Department of the British Museum of Natural History. His early death deprived me of a willing and efficient mentor. In all my work I have been helped by my wife and much of it has been done in close collaboration with her.

The *Lorica* is a most extraordinary anatomical vocabulary in the surprising form of an extremely emotional prayer. It seems to have been composed to direct the Almighty to the particular bodily members of the suppliant which He should specially protect. Its interest is in the extraordinary variety and obscurity of its linguistic sources. It is couched in what is, in effect, a special literary dialect of Latin, characteristic of a small body of writings, the so-called *Hisperic Literature* produced in the Celtic West of Britain in or about the seventh century. Despite its origin, it had become part of the Anglo-Saxon medical literature.

Inevitably, in my work on herbals, I came on the Anglo-Saxon examples. In one of these a version of the *Lorica* is embedded. This led me to a study of the remains of pre-Norman English folklore which had been admirably collected in the sixties of the nineteenth century. By the twentieth century folklore had taken its place among anthropological studies. R. R. Marett, who then led the anthropological school at Oxford, encouraged me to continue working on the English material. When I joined the staff of University College, London, in 1920-21, I met J. G. Grattan, then Reader in Anglo-Saxon, who was busy on certain Early English charms while I was occupied with the Anglo-Saxon medical work known by the invented title *Lacnunga* which contained the *Lorica.* The knowledge that I had acquired of these out-of-the-way matters was summarized in a paper to the British Academy which is substantially reproduced here. In 1925 Grattan became Professor of Anglo-Saxon at Liverpool University, but during the next 25 years we met from time to time and continued our collaboration. He died in 1951. Our joint work, *Anglo-Saxon Magic and Medicine illustrated specially from the Semi-Pagan Text 'Lacnunga'* was published in 1952.

The last of these Essays appeared in much its present state as an "Historical Revision" in *History* in 1925. The story of the medical school of Salerno will always be surrounded by a slightly mirth-provoking fog. It is entirely appropriate that Dame Trot and the Prince of Salerno should still entertain the children at the old fashioned pantomime at Christmas when and where they are as real as Jack of the Beanstalk and Cinderella. But even these mythical figures must have come from somewhere, and the search for their source may reveal something of man's adventure on earth, however fanciful or even frivolous the legend. One attempt at solution of the problem lies before the reader.

The story of Salerno has been most skilfully treated more recently by Professor Kristeller. Our article treats only of one Salernitan legend. Its more documented version by Mrs. Singer and myself appeared in *Essays on the History of Medicine presented to Karl Sudhoff on the occasion of his Seventieth Birthday,* edited by Sigerist and myself in 1924. As Sudhoff was born 103 years ago, there can be few outside Germany who knew him in his most active years. Memories of him may be

welcome. In putting them on paper I reflect firstly on
how much I owe him, notably in this volume, and secondly that it is senseless to present a portrait that bears no
likeness to its original. In actual fact, the most evident
things about Sudhoff were his good looks and his faults.

In his prime he was a singularly handsome man, tall,
rather portly, well groomed, with nicely cut beard and
beautiful, welcoming, laughing blue eyes. (In fact, he was
without a sense of humor.) I always thought of him as
a personification of the traditional picture of Faust. His
learning was immense and no one who understood him
(which *was* difficult) could fail to spend five minutes in
his company without learning something worth while
from him. He seemed to be able to read all languages
but was intelligible only in his own which, unfortunately,
he spoke much too fast. He was a tireless worker himself,
discerning at putting younger men on lines of research
suited to them and generous in giving them access to his
own material. This was one side of the man. One did not
have to be long with him to discover that he was a man
of many sides but that this was perhaps his most genuine
side.

Outside his special interest (which was far from being
narrow) he was a mere child, and not a very good or
intelligent child at that. Politically he was infantile, per-
sonifying states and nations as children do, talking of
them as children do, and flying into passions as children
do. I very soon learned that it was best not to discuss
anything with him outside his own *Fach*. He was quite
unbelievably vain — a very caricature of a German professor. One extremely hot summer day my wife and I
visited the Leipzig book-fair at which he was showing
some ancient books. On the grounds there was a swimming bath. We made straight for it, and doubtless
dallied too long to give adequate attention to Sudhoff's
exhibit. In the evening he asked me, almost before we
had greeted each other, what I had enjoyed most in the
fair. I answered, tactlessly but quite truthfully, that it

was the swimming bath. He took it badly and showed signs of going into a tantrum, but Mrs. Singer averted this by assuring him, tactfully but quite untruthfully, that it was his exhibit. I noticed, however, that she did not pass his searching examination as to what it contained, very well. So she, too, ended the day in disgrace. Sudhoff was a great man with both food and drink and could be trusted to say all the wrong things in an after-dinner speech. So vain a man and so fragmented, he was a natural victim of Nazi propaganda, and it is charitable to draw a veil over his later years.

I translated two of Sudhoff's works into English. This pleased him and he was much pleased also with his *Festschrift* which was edited by Sigerist and myself. I rather think that had he himself been asked to choose who should produce this volume, his selection would have fallen on us. As soon as he received the volume, which he did with genuine emotion, he sat down to write to the contributors indicating the errors that they had made. Only a German professor could have thought of that one! He produced an immense amount of good work, especially on the Middle Ages, and threw new light on a mass of documents that had been neglected until his time. His work on Paracelsus is not likely to be replaced, nor that on medieval anatomy and surgery. He had no capacity for wider historical perspective and no literary power, so that no one would — or indeed could — read his works for their general survey value or for their style. He had considerable knowledge of current medical matters and had acted for several years at Frankfort as a general practitioner, but I cannot believe that he was a very good one. Nevertheless, he was a great researcher and anything that I myself have done of that kind I owe largely to him. I am glad of this opportunity to acknowledge it. But a much older sage has reminded us that wisdom and learning are not the same thing. And, when all is said, is not each of us a very imperfect vessel?

1958 Charles Singer

# PREFACE

THE main part of each of these Essays has been printed at various times during the last ten years. Some of them are now accessible only with difficulty. Since they are scattered through various publications and since they represent, in fact, the continuous development of a single line of thought, it has seemed advisable to collect them together. All the Essays except the first are considerably modified from the form in which they originally appeared.

The conception that the universe is a rational system, working by discoverable laws, seems to have first appeared as a definite belief among the Ionian Greeks in the sixth century B.C. If we had records sufficient to trace the inception and early development of this idea, there would surely be few topics more fascinating or more worthy of study. Alas ! the material is wanting and the history of Ionian philosophy is little but guess-work. Nevertheless, the process by which a rational conception of the world comes gradually to possess the mind is one which touches us all nearly, whatever may be our philosophy. Anything that may throw light upon it is worthy of consideration. The only adequate historical record that we have of the rationalization of thought, affecting an entire civilization, is to be found in the documents which display the passage of the medieval into the modern way of thinking  The history of that process, when it can be written in proper perspective, should provide an absorbing theme.

For the development of this theme we are far better placed than for the study of the Ionian rationalization. The material is very abundant and the medieval scholar has seldom to regret the scarcity of his documents. Nevertheless, but little progress has been made towards the proper digestion of the available material from the point of view that we are discussing. The medievalist is seldom a man of science, not infrequently he has his own axe to grind, and it is only in recent times that adequately trained medieval scholars have given their attention to the development of rational conceptions of the material world.

It is manifest, looking back on the Middle Ages, that they represent a process of slow decline from the intellectual efficiency of classical antiquity, and that this decline is followed by a recovery. The brilliance of the recovery in some departments and in some periods, e.g. of Art and Philosophy in the thirteenth century, must not blind us to its extreme slowness in the observational sciences. It is the twofold process of decline and recovery in the observational sciences that the author has set himself to trace. These Essays deal, however, only with the earliest and first steps in the recovery. They do not claim to trace the later steps and the author has here little to say of developments after the twelfth century. More detailed treatment of the later medieval period must be reserved for another volume, though some of these Essays block out the general line of treatment of the later period. Here some sort of attempt is made to trace the collapse of ancient science into the swamp of magic and the first attempts at recovery from that hideous slough.

The first Essay appeared in its present form as the article on *Science* in the volume on *The Legacy of Rome* edited for the Clarendon Press by Mr. Cyril Bailey in 1923. This Essay traces the decay of the rational spirit in the Roman world. It is hardly our purpose here to discuss all the causes of that decay. One important cause is certainly the failure of the active process of scientific research. The mind, ceasing to be ventilated by new knowledge, turned inward on itself and we can perceive early but very definite symptoms of more complete decay.

The second Essay on *The Dark Ages and the Dawn of Science* was originally contributed to a volume of essays

entitled *Science and Civilisation* edited by Mr. F. S. Marvin
and published by the Oxford University Press in 1923.
The article as there printed has been considerably modified.
It is an attempt to trace, in barest outline, the entire course
of medieval science, and as such is the key to the volume.
The author recognizes, however, that it is impossible in
the short space of such an article to give more than the
most general sketch of so large a subject, and that on many
points the present state of our knowledge is really inadequate
for definitive statement.

Much of the material of the third Essay, *The Lorica of
Gildas the Briton*, was contributed to the *Transactions of
the Royal Society of Medicine* (*Historical Section*) in 1920.
This Essay has been considerably altered from its original
form. In it we touch bottom in our series. The text
which is here treated represents the most extreme magical
degradation of the classical and ecclesiastical traditions.
In the other Essays no attempt is made to set forth a full
text, the attention of the reader being directed rather to
general movements and tendencies. Here, however, it
seemed to the author that he was dealing with a type
of material of which few of his readers could have had
any experience. Such magical and superstitious practices
as crop up from time to time in our every-day life we are
accustomed to treat with a smile. They seem to us harm-
less foibles, and few realize the degradation involved when
the mind becomes saturated with such material and deluded
with such hopes. The miserable theurgy of the *Lorica of
Gildas the Briton* exhibits to us Science, Theology, and
Literature in the last stages of decomposition. Though
Celtic in origin, the most ardent Celticist will hardly
claim that it adds radiance to the Celtic glamour.

The Essay on *Early English Magic* was originally read
before the British Academy and was published in the
*Proceedings* of that body in 1920. It has been rearranged
and somewhat abbreviated from its original form. The
material that is discussed is, in many places, little above

the Lorica, which was in fact freely used by the Anglo-Saxons as a protective charm. The main interest of Anglo-Saxon magic appears to the author to be the evidence that it provides for the mingling of cultures even at a very early date, and in a simple state of society. It happens that the diverse sources of Anglo-Saxon magic are relatively easily traced. These sources are set forth, but special emphasis is laid on the Teutonic element. This is stressed not because the Teutonic element is very large—for it is not—but because it forms a useful contrast to the classical and ecclesiastical elements that are more extensively discussed elsewhere in this book.

There is a reflexion to which a perusal of these two Essays, one on a Celtic and the other on an Anglo-Saxon theme, may perhaps incline the reader. A type of medieval enthusiast exists who would have us believe that the world would be well lost if we could only return to the intellectual habits of our forefathers. Books and articles are written on early Irish learning, on the Carlovingian revival, on the British and early English Churches and on like topics, in a tone which would lead undiscerning readers to believe that the Learning, the Civilization, the Culture, or the Humanity of those days are comparable to our own. Progress to these writers is but illusion, and that which has been shall again be. To those disposed to think on these despairing lines we may recommend a perusal of the material with which we have here to deal. It may be objected that we have chosen the lowest and rejected the highest manifestations of the medieval spirit, and that these are but the products of local ignorance and perversion. But the manuscripts from which we have taken this material are, in fact, for the most part of exquisite monastic workmanship. They were valuable and valued possessions, written by highly skilled scribes among a people with whom even literacy was rare. If we were really to exhibit the lowest manifestations of the medieval spirit we should have to go beyond the written page with which these Essays deal, and should be exhibiting customs comparable to those of West African savages. But all ages and all civilizations have their savage as well as their saintly side. To gain a true view of what Europe was thinking and feeling during the Middle Ages, the reader would be well advised to refuse to fix his gaze either on St. Francis, St. Thomas, and Dante on the one hand or on the bestial practices of the medieval peasantry or on the cruelty and wrong wrought by the Inquisition on the other hand. In placing the Lorica of Gildas, the history of the herbal and the Anglo-Saxon magical material by the side of St. Hildegard and the School of Salerno, it seems to the author that he has presented a favourable and not an unfavourable picture of the medieval mind.

In thinking of the Middle Ages it is always necessary to remember that the knowledge of the day was not only perverted and corrupted in quality but that it was also extremely small in extent. Indeed, we suspect that this latter element has given one of the main interests to medieval literary studies. Our civilization is nowadays so complex and all parts of our world are so inter-dependent that it would be extremely difficult to trace the sources of any modern writer and to provide any exact demonstration of the degree to which he is original. With the medieval writer the case is different. Even the most learned of medieval writers—even Albertus Magnus himself—knew so piteously little compared to a modern scholar that it is possible, with sufficient application, to trace all the sources of his information. Albertus was among the best, not the worst, of medieval men of science, and yet, in what is perhaps his most important scientific contribution, the *De Animalibus*, it has been possible to trace almost every sentence to its source. It is precisely this fact which makes medieval literature such an interesting medium for demonstrating cultural movements.

The fifth Essay in the volume, that on *Early Herbals*, appeared in its original form as an article in the *Edinburgh*

*Review* in 1923. The author there expressed those general views which he developed in detail—producing the evidence for his conclusions—in an elaborately illustrated article in the *Journal of Hellenic Studies* in July 1927. The Essay in this volume contains a number of these illustrations, together with some others. The history of the herbal is continuous from Greek to modern times. An immense number of manuscripts survives, and the author has examined scores of them. The herbals provide a peculiarly favourable medium for tracing the passage of tradition from people to people. Their texts are simple, their motives are obvious, such ideas as they contain are of an easily comprehensible order, and the tradition of the figures with which they are adorned can be traced even more readily than the tradition of the texts themselves. The entry and recession of the magical element can be closely watched in these herbals. We have been able to do no more than touch the fringe of a very large subject, but we would recommend the study of the herbal to the young folklorist as a little trodden and very attractive field.

The sixth Essay, on *The Visions of St. Hildegard*, appeared originally in 1917 in Vol. 1 of the author's *Studies in the History and Method of Science*. It went out of print very rapidly and has not since been republished. This particular article aroused a good deal of criticism, but the theory of the pathological basis of these visions has, we believe, been generally accepted by those who have read it with any knowledge of the condition known as ' Migraine.' The article has been rearranged and largely rewritten. Most of the criticism directed against the article had to do with the author's rejection of the genuineness of certain works ascribed to Hildegard. The matter turns on points that are not likely to engage the reader of this volume, and their discussion is here omitted. The chief interest of Hildegard's visions are (*a*) the cosmic theory on which they are based, (*b*) the extremely involved presentation of that theory, (*c*) the remarkably close way in which the minia-

tures of two manuscripts visualize the text and suggest a
living tradition arising with the prophetess herself, and (d)
the pathological basis of the visions.  On all these points
the author's conclusions seem to him to have stood the test
of time and he therefore reproduces them in much their
original form.

In the scheme of this book Hildegard is of importance as
representing an early attempt at something like a coherent
philosophy, intended to cover the appearances of the
material universe.  As such her work is, in fact, Science,
and with her we have left the Dark Ages and the Dawn
has begun.  In placing this view before the reader we
would ask him not to be deterred by what is, for us, the
extremely bizarre manner of presentment of her views.
She is feeling her way to a rational explanation of her
world, and the fact that her solution is not our solution and
that she is grotesquely wrong on matters of fact, should
not blind us to her intellectual merits.  The same criticisms
could, after all, be made of Aristotle or of any other early
thinker.

There is another point in the history of science of which
Hildegard provides an interesting illustration.  As is
pointed out in more than one place in this volume, the
important event in the history of science in the Middle
Ages is the arrival of the Arabian learning.  It was the
Arabian influence that finally set the intellect of Western
Europe on the high road to the Renaissance.  This volume
deals with the earlier medieval period, the pre-Arabian
age, the ' Dark Age ' as we may call it, and Hildegard marks
the parting of the ways.  She has had no access to an
Arabian writer, even in Latin translation, but she does live
in a world in which indirect Arabian influences are beginning to make themselves felt.  Some of these influences
we have been able to trace.

The volume closes with an Essay on *The School of
Salerno and its Legends*.  This article was contributed by
Mrs. Singer, in collaboration with the author, as an ' His-

torical Revision ' to the issue of *History* in October 1925. At Salerno was the first institution in Europe that had the semblance of a University. It was but a semblance. Nevertheless, the small amount of first-hand observation that was going on at Salerno as early as the eleventh century marks the first upward trend of the human mind from the degradation of the Dark Ages. Moreover, the school of Salerno exhibits the new Arabian influence at an earlier date than any other centre of learning. These are facts which can hardly be gainsaid. But the glamour of Salernitan history has proved a centre around which legends have clustered. Some of these, which are still widely spread, have utterly corrupted many accounts of the history of the school. In any event that history is extremely dim, but it becomes at least a little less dim by the dispersal of the cloud of legend. The somewhat humorous element which seems to cling to Salerno, and to lend the stories of it a peculiar aroma, make it a not unsuitable theme on which to end.

The author has to thank first of all Mrs. Singer, whose name appeared as a collaborator in the last Essay, but who has, in fact, been his collaborator in them all. For permission to reproduce these essays he expresses his thanks to Mr. Cyril Bailey, Mr. F. S. Marvin, the Clarendon Press, the Council of the British Academy, the Council of the Royal Society of Medicine, the editors of the *Edinburgh Review*, of the *Journal of Hellenic Studies* and of *History*, and to Messrs. Longmans & Co.

CHARLES SINGER.

UNIVERSITY COLLEGE, LONDON.
  *May*, 1928.

# CONTENTS

# PLATES

# FIGURES

# FROM MAGIC TO SCIENCE

# I

## SCIENCE UNDER THE ROMAN EMPIRE

## § 1.  *The Roman Attitude to Nature*

THE scientific idea, the conception of a reasonable universe, came to the peoples of Central Italy at a much later date than that at which it began to influence the Greeks of the Eastern Mediterranean and of Southern Italy. With the Romans pure science always remained somewhat of an exotic ; it was applied science that attracted them. The determining factor in the development of science within the Empire was the absorption of the Kingdom of the Ptolemies, whose capital, Alexandria, was and long remained the scientific head-quarters of the world. Yet despite the stimulus that followed on the contact with Alexandrian thought, Rome produced no great creative scientist. It is in the distribution and dissemination of the Greek wisdom rather than its development that we see the rôle of Rome.

Yet though Rome cannot be said to rival Greece in pure science, it must be allowed that in an allied department her achievements are remarkable. Among the Greeks art, in its highest development, excelled in idealistic representation—as did science in abstract reasoning. Man, the main theme of the Greek painter and sculptor, became godlike; the lower creation is less often represented, and when it is, the beauty of the animal is reflected from the nobility of its master [Fig. 4]. As for plants, they are practically omitted from Greek art save in connexion with ornament.

Now this contrasts profoundly with the development of art at Rome. The character of Augustan art was determined by the character of the Augustan country gentleman. The great Roman landowner, like his representative nearer home, was no great hand at philosophizing ; least of all was he given to what would have seemed to him that useless spinning of arguments about the essential nature of things which provided a leading motive in Greek scientific literature. But if no philosopher, he was a lover of the countryside, an observer by temper in that field which the Greek had taken to investigating because he believed it to lie on the road to knowledge. He had it in him to become a shrewd and close-observing naturalist, one who paid attention to the habits of plants and animals perhaps more than to the minute details of their form, but seldom given to general ideas about them.

This Roman spirit, slow to acquire any appreciation of the scientific attitude, yielded little in the way of scientific results. Yet the art which Rome produced in the Augustan age is instinct with the study of bird and beast and flower and tree. Nature is treated as she had never been before. The affection of Virgil for his bees, his cattle, and his herbs recalls the power and faithfulness with which creatures and plants are represented in Augustan art. Thus panels of the tomb of the Haterii in the Lateran Museum [Figs. 2 and 3] render to perfection the habit of a young wind-blown wild-rose. The buds are particularly natural, but the opened flowers strangely show four petals instead of five. At the top of one of the pillars three bees may be seen drinking from the hollow in the capital, while a fourth has been seized in the claw of a bird. Two other birds—perhaps ' Bee-eaters,' *Merops apiaster*—pursue bees among the branches below. The scene might have been prepared to illustrate passages in Virgil's fourth *Georgic*.

There are many instances of the faithful imitation of nature in Augustan art. It would not be easy to find any parallel in Greek art of the best period to the treatment of plants in some of the metal work of Pompeii [Fig. 1]. Even the brutality of a Cato finds reflection in the procession of fatted sacrificial beasts on the altar of Domitius Ahenobarbus [Fig. 6]. Compare the ewe and her young of the well-head at Vienna [Fig. 5] with the noble head of the Parthenon steed [Fig. 4], and you have the contrast epigrammatically set forth. The feeling of the Augustan artist is that of one studying nature as something quite outside man ; it is the sheep herself who tends her young ; her love is not a sentiment reflected from mankind.

FIG. 1.—Silver bowl ornamented with vine-shoots. From Pompeii, after Overbeck.

The Augustan artist has produced a nature study. The Greek has wrought a creature that sets forth the glory of the god.

When Hellenism first began to influence Roman thought, about the time of the second Punic war (*c.* 214 B.C.), Latin literature had as yet no scientific element. During the period between 200 and 189 B.C. Rome broke the power of Alexander's successors and established her protectorate throughout the Eastern Mediterranean. The influence of Greek ideas now grew rapidly. With the triumph after the battle of Pydna (168 B.C.) numerous Greek hostages, educated and of good family, came to Rome, and the library of the Macedonian king which was brought with them made a nucleus for the infiltration of Roman society by Greek wisdom.

For long there were those who struggled against this development without being able to stem it. Among them was Marcus Porcius Cato (234–149 B.C.). He prepared a sort of encyclopaedia for the use of his son, in which he endeavoured to show that the old Roman literature could hold its own against this newfangled material from Greece. Of that treatise only fragments have survived, but in his book *De re rustica* we possess the oldest Latin prose work that has come down to us. Its contents are very miscellaneous, relating principally to rural economy, but dealing also with cookery recipes, magical formulae, medical prescriptions, and much other strange material which shows how little scientific was the traditional Roman attitude.

Although the relation to science improved as time went on and all educated men learned Greek and were affected by Hellenic philosophy, it is probable that the general scientific principles of the Greeks as expressed in the writings of the Hippocratic, Aristotelian, and Alexandrian schools were seldom understood even by educated Romans. The prevalent attitude towards nature among the Latin-speaking upper classes, whether Italian or provincial, was expressed by the Stoic creed. That system, based on a rigid conception of the interrelation of the different parts of the world, provided little stimulus for the acquisition of new knowledge or for anything in the way of research. Thus, in place of knowledge accumulating progressively on a basis of a wide and far-reaching theory, we get either a type of exact but intellectually motiveless observation or a rejection of all knowledge not of practical importance.

There have been various attempts to explain why the Romans did not continue the scientific work of the Greeks. It is a strange phenomenon, for the value of the experimental method was still being demonstrated by the achievements of the Alexandrians. That school continued its activities under Roman rule and was the ultimate source of the only important Latin medical work that has come down to us, the *De re medica* of Celsus. It has been said that the

FIGS. 2 AND 3.—PILASTERS IN LATERAN MUSEUM

Birds pursue bees among branches of wild rose.
Compare Virgil, *Georgics*, iv. ll. 8–29.
See pages 2 and 3.

Roman mind could find no time from conquest and administration to attend to scientific matters, but this will not explain the whole matter, for there were those among the
Romans who were able to answer the no less exacting claims
of philosophy, of literature and, above all, of rhetoric.
Much too has been made of the view that regards the
scientific pause as due to the lack of instruments of precision.
This, however, hardly explains the facts, for scientific instruments are at least as much the result as the cause of the
application of scientific method.    The matter seems
rather to have lain deep in the Roman character.    It was
wrapped up in the nature of the favourite Roman philosophy,
Stoicism.    It needs to be considered in general relation to
the Roman psychology and is not improbably related to
the Roman obsession for Rhetoric.

In general we may say that Roman science appears at
its best in the department of ' Nature Study ' and at its
weakest in ' Pure Mathematics.'    The success or failure
of the Romans in any scientific field may be roughly gauged
by its nearness to one or other of these disciplines.    The
gauge must be biased, however, by the Roman desire for
' useful studies.'    There was for instance, as we shall
see, a special development in certain departments of
Geography (p. 40).

## § 2. *Latin Works on General Science*

We have several works by Latins which deal with the
implications of science in general.    These, however, seldom
involve any expert knowledge of natural phenomena, and
are concerned rather with the philosophical relations of the
science of their day than with science itself, as we understand that word to-day.    Of such works the most striking
and widely read is the *De rerum natura* of Lucretius
(*c.* 95–55 B.C.).    The man is aflame with his theme and
exhibits a veritable missionary zeal.    Yet, however magnificent as literature may be the work of Lucretius, and how-

ever important as our best representative of Epicurean views, it is too close an imitation of Greek philosophy to be of the highest value for our immediate purpose. It neither records first-hand observations nor does it represent an attitude of mind that can be considered as typically Roman. Lucretius, nevertheless, is interesting for us as the only Latin writer who gives us a complete and coherent scheme of natural knowledge.

The attention of the scientific reader of Lucretius will naturally be drawn to his atomic view of matter. The atomic conception was very ancient and had been taught by Leucippus (*fl. c.* 450 B.C.), Democritus (*fl. c.* 410 B.C.), and Epicurus (342–270 B.C.) among the Greeks. Lucretius, following these writers, explains the origin of the world as due to the interaction of atoms, and this interaction, he believes, is without the intervention of any creative intelligence. This is not the place to discuss the position of the gods in the Lucretian scheme, but we may note that even mental phenomena are for him of atomic origin and there is no real existence save atoms and ' the void ' (*inane*). ' Nullam rem e nilo gigni divinitus unquam.' *Nothing is ever begotten of nothing by divine will.* Everything springs from ' semina certa,' *determinate units.* The genesis of all things is typified by the generation of organic beings and the species of plants and animals give us models for all processes and natural laws. This conception of generation has its converse. ' Haud igitur possunt ad nilum quaeque reverti.' *Things cannot then ever be turned to naught.* Such an attitude involves that ' indestructibility of matter ' which, despite modern changes in our conceptions, is the historical foundation on which our chemical and physical knowledge has been built.

The resemblance of the Lucretian theory to modern atomic views is, however, more apparent than real ; not only are the atoms of Lucretius of different shapes and sizes but also he knows nothing of the definite laws by which they are held together as molecules, he has no inkling of the real

nature of chemical combination, and he is without that
' doctrine of energy ' that is so characteristic a feature in
all modern physical theory. Moreover, his work had little
direct influence on the development of the modern doctrine.
Epicurean thought has not, in fact, historically been very
favourable to scientific development. The atomic view of
matter was practically lost during the Middle ·Ages, and
Aristotelian philosophy, which involved the doctrine of
the continuity of matter, was paramount for centuries.
Atomic views, it is true, were known to a few ' Arabian '
philosophers, e.g. Averroes (1126–98) and Maimonides
(1135–1204), but their general standpoint was abhorrent
to the scholastics. Lucretius was rediscovered by the
scholar Poggio in 1418 and deeply affected the philosophy
of the Renaissance. The influence of that philosophy
waned with the great physical synthesis of the seventeenth
century with which the name of Galileo (1564–1642) is
associated. Atomic views continued to be held by a few
isolated thinkers, but modern scientific atomism arose
almost independent of the ancient sources. John Dalton
(1766–1844), the father of modern atomism, was probably
not directly influenced by Lucretius.

Yet there is one scientific department in which the
influence of Lucretius on Renaissance philosophy may be
said to have borne more direct fruit. Lucretius concludes
his work with a description of the plague at Athens in 430
B.C., and in describing this visitation he follows very closely
the account of Thucydides, and the Lucretian version is
of interest as having contributed something to modern
views of the nature of infection. In discussing the nature of
the plague Lucretius demands ' What is its cause ? ' and
he answers—working out his atomic theory here also—that
' just as there are seeds (*semina*) of things helpful to our life,
so, for sure, others fly about that cause disease and death.'

Now in the sixteenth century Lucretius, whose work had
been printed as early as 1473, was studied by an eminent
Veronese physician, Girolamo Fracastoro (1483–1553).

That acute investigator had absorbed much from the ancient atomic philosophy.    Pondering on the nature of epidemics —of which he was a close and accurate student—Fracastoro developed a theory that such diseases were due to *seminaria*, ' seed-stores,' the separate *semina* or ' seeds ' of which reproduced their like in infected victims to whose bodies they were carried by *fomites* or ' foci of infection.'    These ' seeds of disease ' of Fracastoro bore some analogy to the Lucretian atoms.

Fracastoro followed Lucretius in denying any essential distinction between the living and the non-living.    For him vital phenomena were explained as a product of atomic activity.    Such views became widely diffused in the sixteenth century, though they were seldom fully understood. As a result of misunderstanding ' atom ' became a synonym for ' living mite ' or ' animalcule ' and is thus encountered in the writings of Shakespeare, for instance (see *As You Like It*, III. v. 13, and contrast with III. ii. 246).    Much of Fracastoro's theory can be read into Lucretius, but the Renaissance physician developed it with newly acquired knowledge and with a skill peculiarly his own.    The theory of infection remained much where Fracastoro left it until quite modern times, when it assumed a new meaning at the magic touch of Louis Pasteur (1822–95).

Some have seen in Lucretius the beginnings of a theory of evolution.    He certainly exhibits a *scala naturae*, a ' ladder of life ' somewhat similar to that which may be discerned in the writings of Aristotle.    The earth produces out of herself first plants and then animals of ever higher and higher type.    ' Even as down and hair and bristles are first formed on the limbs of beasts . . . so the newborn earth raised up herbage and shrubs first, and thereafter produced the races of mortal things.'    This idea of ' spontaneous generation ' was almost inevitable until the realm of minute invisible life had been explored by means of the microscope which was not invented until 1608.    It is thus no wonder that Lucretius follows Aristotle and all antiquity

Fig. 4.—HEAD OF PARTHENON STEED
See page 3.

[Between

FIG. 5.—EWE AND LAMB. From a well-head at Vienna.
See page 3.

in assuring us that ' even now many animals spring forth from the earth, formed by rains and the heat of the sun.'

Did Lucretius take the matter further and did he have any conception of lower forms passing into higher forms ? In a sense he certainly did. Moreover, he invoked for the process a mechanism for the clearer explanation of which the world had to await the arrival of Darwin. Yet notwithstanding our familiarity with the idea of ' survival of the fittest,' the Lucretian view of the manner in which the more perfect creatures reached their present state must sound very strange to modern ears :—

' Many monsters earth then essayed to create, born with strange faces and strange limbs ; the man-woman, between the two, yet not either, sundered from both sexes ; things bereft of feet ; things without hands ; things dumb ; things blind ; things locked together by the clinging of the limbs so that they could not move nor avoid calamity nor take what they needed. Monsters and prodigies she would thus create, yet vainly, since nature forbade their increase, nor could they reach the bloom of age nor find food. . . . Many races of living creatures then perished nor could beget nor propagate, *for whatever animals now feed on the breath of life, either craft or courage or speed has preserved their kind from the beginning of their being.*'

When we turn to the phenomena which Lucretius has chosen for special description we cannot fail to be struck with the fact that he has been drawn to those which present something of the magnificent, dramatic, or cataclysmic. There is nothing of the quiet and minute observer about him. Thunder and lightning, water-spout, volcano and thunderbolt, suffocating vapours and great pestilences— these are the themes he selects for description. Almost the sole exception is his account of the magnet. This has a special interest because the passage drew the attention of William Gilbert (1540–1603), physician to Queen Elizabeth. Gilbert's *De magnete*, the first important work on experimental science to be printed in England, appeared in 1600.

He quotes Lucretius on the magnet and exhibits Lucretian influence (see pp. 109-10).

The remarkable composition of Lucretius takes an isolated place in Latin scientific literature. More characteristic are the *Rerum rusticarum libri III* of Varro and two works of the first Christian century, the *Naturalis historia* of Gaius Plinius Secundus (A.D. 23-79), the most complete and extensive work of its kind that has come down to us from antiquity, and the *Quaestiones naturales* of Lucius Annaeus Seneca (3 B.C.-A.D. 65).

Marcus Terentius Varro (116-27 B.C.) was born at Reate in the Sabine country, where the old Roman qualities are supposed to have lingered longest. He was educated by L. Aelius Stilo, the first systematic Latin philologist and antiquary. Later he went to Athens and came under Platonic influence ; he exhibits, however, throughout his works some Stoic leanings. Varro wrote encyclopaedically on the sciences and his works were the prototype of the numerous mediaeval works on the ' liberal arts.' He distinguished *nine* of these studies, namely, grammar, dialectic, rhetoric, geometry, arithmetic, astronomy, music, medicine, and architecture. Of these the last two were not recognized by Cassiodorus (A.D. 490-585), Martianus Capella (c. A.D. 500), and Isidore (A.D. 560-636), who handed down the tradition to the Middle Ages, and the number of liberal arts was thus reduced to seven (see pp. 68-9).

Varro, like Cato, tried to collect Latin learning and set it over against the Greek. Of the works of Varro unfortunately only two have been preserved, the *Res rusticae* and a part of the *De lingua latina*. If Varro depends on Cato, he develops a surer judgement based on more experience and knowledge. As a friend of Julius Caesar, whose literary and scientific tastes he shared, we should expect from him this higher and more tolerant standard. He was employed by Caesar in arranging the great stores of Greek and Latin literature for the vast library which he intended to found.

The *Res rusticae* was written by Varro in his eightieth year.  In the first book he devotes himself to the general theme of agriculture, in the second he discusses cattle and farm animals, and in the third bees, fish, and a number of wild creatures.  The old scholar records, to some extent, his own experience, but he has collected his material mainly from the writings of others.  He thus already exhibits the derivative tendency which is so marked among later Latin writers on scientific topics.  His interests are wider than might perhaps be expected, nor does he confine his discussion to his own country but makes comparisons with other districts and lands.  The presentation is enlivened by humour and the scene does not lack animation, though the mechanism of the dialogue often works stiffly.  He uses every opportunity to bring in etymology, and he rejoices in artificial separations and divisions, so that in general the work gives one very much the impression conveyed by many treatises of mediaeval origin.  Yet his style is always lucid and is sometimes vigorous and racy.

Among the more pleasing of the pictures that Varro draws is that of the life of bees.  This, however, is far inferior in accuracy to that set forth by Aristotle (384–322 B.C.) in the *Historia animalium*, and contains nothing that is not to be found in the poetic account of Varro's younger contemporary, Virgil (70–19 B.C.).  Among the more remarkable passages in the work is one in which sanguine observers have perceived an anticipation of the modern discovery of the nature of malaria.  ' In building houses,' he says, ' you must avoid the neighbourhood of marshy places . . . because when the marshes begin to dry they engender a multitude of invisible insects which are introduced into the mouth and nostrils with the inhaled air and occasion serious illnesses.'

Varro, along with the other Latin agricultural writers, early drew the attention of the scholars of the Renaissance. His work was transcribed by some unknown Veronese humanist as early as 1329.  Cato, Columella, and Palladius

were soon added to form a collection *Scriptores rei rusticae.*
After the invention of printing this collection was widely
circulated.   The first edition appeared at Venice in 1472,
and many subsequent issues, bearing the names of distinguished scholars, poured from the presses during the
hundred years which followed.

In the next writer we have to consider, the elder Pliny,
the Greek leaven has worked further than in Varro.   Pliny
was born at Como in A.D. 23 and was educated by P. Pomponius Secundus, a poet and military man who inspired him
with a love of learning.   He studied botany in Rome in
the garden of Antonius Castor.   Coming under the influence
of Seneca he studied philosophy and rhetoric, and practised
as an advocate.   Pliny saw military service in Germany,
visited Gaul, and became a procurator in Spain.   After
a stay in Rome during which he completed his *Natural
History*, dedicating it to Titus, he was appointed by Vespasian
prefect of the fleet at Misenum.   He was stationed there
at the time of the eruption of Vesuvius which overwhelmed
Pompeii and Herculaneum in A.D. 79, and he owed his
death to his desire to observe that phenomenon more
closely.   Pliny's education, his career, his opinions, and his
character are all typical of the Italian tradition of his day.
As a writer this erudite and much travelled man exhibits
great industry and an interest in natural phenomena that
is quite uncontrolled by any real scientific standards.
Learned and curious, Pliny is entirely devoid of critical
faculty.   In his *Naturalis historia* he collected an enormous
amount of material, entirely unsifted, and this work his
nephew rightly spoke of as an ' opus diffusum, eruditum,
nec minus varium quam ipsa natura.'   By Gibbon it was
described as ' that immense register where Pliny has de-
posited the discoveries, the arts and the errors of mankind.'
It was drawn from about 2,000 works—most of them now
lost—by 146 Roman and 326 Greek authors.   The *Natural
History* of Pliny, to which we shall frequently refer, may

FIG. 6.—FROM THE ALTAR OF DOMITIUS AHENOBARBUS (LOUVRE). See page 3.

12]

be divided into eight sections which are intended to cover
the whole of physical knowledge. The character and
relative length of these sections is significant. They are
distributed thus :

| (1) | Book | 1. | Introductory. |
|-----|------|-----|---------------|
| (2) | ,, | 2. | Cosmology. |
| (3) | ,, | 3–6. | Geography. |
| (4) | ,, | 7. | Anthropology. |
| (5) | ,, | 8–11. | Zoology. |
| (6) | ,, | 12–19. | Botany. |
| (7) | ,, | 20–32. | Medicine. |
| (8) | ,, | 33–37. | Mineralogy and Art. |

The main thought that goes through Pliny's book is that
nature serves man. Natural objects are hardly described as
such but only in relation to man. All things have their
' uses.' ' Nature and the earth,' he says, ' fill us with
admiration . . . as we contemplate the great variety of
plants and find that they are created for the wants or enjoyment of mankind.' This world of wonder is, however,
effectively without a God and works by rule—though it is
a somewhat crazy rule which these disordered, credulous,
wonder-loving volumes set before us. ' It is mere folly to
inquire into the nature of God . . . ridiculous to suppose
that the great head of all things regards human affairs.'
Yet in this world in which he lives man himself occupies
a quite peculiar and not always enviable position. ' While
other animals,' he says, ' have an instinctive knowledge
of their own powers . . . only man is helpless without
instruction. He alone desires honours and possessions . . .
he alone provides for his grave and even for his future after
death . . . All other animals live at peace with their kind
. . . but verily with man, most of his misfortunes are
man's doings.'—Man the beast of prey ! *Lupus est homo
homini, non homo quom qualis sit non noscit,* ' A man is not
human but vermin to a stranger '—so Plautus (died 184 B.C.)
had written long ago.

Many of the matters on which Pliny expresses a judgement would have been impressed on him in the manifold
life of Imperial Rome.    Many of the animals he discusses
were brought to the capital from the furthest ends of the
earth, for the arena or for the kitchen.    So too with plants.
Pliny describes a botanic garden kept by a Roman for the
purpose of ascertaining the medical and allied properties
of herbs.    In descriptions of living creatures Pliny goes
back to Aristotle and Theophrastus, but there is no systematic  building  of  the  subject  and  he  is  scientifically  far
inferior to his sources.    Medical plants are treated in greatest
detail and he holds the view that all plants have their own
special medical powers.    The thought that nature exists
for man constantly recurs.    His philosophy, which accords
in  general  with  the  Stoic  scheme,  is  largely  drowned
and  lost  in  his  love  of  detail  and  is  often  submerged
in rhetoric.

Seneca (3 B.C.–A.D. 65) has gone over to the Greeks even
more fully than either Varro or Pliny.    Lucius Annaeus
Seneca was born at Cordova and his mother appears to have
been a native Spanish lady.    At an early age he came to
Rome and there he spent practically all his life.    He came
under Stoic influence and made his mark as an advocate.
Seneca became praetor and consul, acted as tutor to Nero,
and is said to have amassed a colossal fortune.    After his
pupil's accession he showed himself subservient to that
monster's designs.    Nero ultimately turned against him,
and Seneca, having been ordered to prepare for death,
anticipated his sentence.    His end is described in a powerful
passage by Tacitus.
A provincial and a member of one of the newer families,
a brilliant rhetorician with a passion for philosophy, of
which he was an eloquent but unsystematic exponent,
a man whose undoubted balance and judgement had been
earned in affairs rather than in action, with an interest in
nature rather in its cosmical than in its detailed aspects,

Seneca provides in many respects an interesting contrast
to his contemporary Pliny.  If inferior in character, Seneca
is the larger-minded of the two.  His work is less typical
perhaps of the Roman attitude, but it is the more philosophical and far more critical.  Yet his *Quaestiones naturales*,
even more than the *Naturalis historia* of Pliny, is borrowed
material.  The number of direct observations that it contains
is small.  Seneca is distinctly less credulous than Pliny,
but just for this reason he fails to preserve so much interesting material.  The chief importance of his work is that it
exhibits the attitude to nature of the more philosophical—
and, we would add, *rhetorical*—Romans of his day.

Seneca is a Stoic, but does not hesitate to criticize the
opinions of the school to which it is evident he is but loosely
attached.  The subject of the *Quaestiones naturales* is a
general account of natural phenomena, but as such it is
ill arranged and imperfect.  It deals chiefly with Astronomy
and Meteorology together with Physical Geography, exhibiting a special interest in earthquakes and allied phenomena.  Seneca fell into that trap which had caught so many
Greeks before him, the confusion of philosophy with
science.  It was a habit of many ancient writers that they
would only consider phenomena in relation to their conception of the world scheme as a whole.  Even the medical
system of antiquity suffered from this tendency, though
Celsus assures us that it had been his master Hippocrates
himself ' who first separated medicine from philosophy.'
Our author, who was called by Dante ' Seneca morale,'
was especially interested in Ethics, a moralist first and physicist or scientist afterwards.  Physics—which for him meant
a general description of the Universe—led to a knowledge of
man's destiny and through that to a consideration of man's
duty.  ' Some moral significance,' he tells us, ' should
be attached to all studies and all discussion.  Whether we
seek into the secrets of nature or treat of divine things, the
soul must be delivered from its errors and from time to
time reassured.'

At the end of each book Seneca sums up the moral to be derived from the phenomena investigated. This is often of the most distant and strained character. Thus, terminating his discussion of the phenomena of light, he asks, ' What were nature's purposes in providing material capable of receiving and reflecting images ? ' And he answers, ' Firstly her motive was to show us the sun with his glare dulled, since our eyes are too weak to gaze at him direct, and without something to reflect him we should be wholly ignorant of his shape . . . Secondly we should be unable to see or investigate that conjunction of the two heavenly bodies by which the daylight is wont to be inter-rupted [in eclipses], unless we could examine the reflections of sun and moon in basins on the ground with comparative freedom. Thirdly mirrors were discovered in order that man might know himself.'

Such a point of view appealed greatly to the Middle Ages. It was a standpoint very acceptable to the mediaeval Church, by which Seneca was regarded as a Christian. He was included by St. Jerome among the *scriptores ecclesiastici*, and is frequently quoted by later Christian writers. But this exclusively ethical attitude is inconsistent with the effective advancement of knowledge and has been one of the greatest enemies of science. In spite of the nobility of his sentiments, in spite of his lip-service to the advancement of knowledge, in spite of his belief in human destiny, Seneca's ethical attitude could do nothing to stay the downfall of ancient wisdom. To that downfall and to Seneca's relation to it we shall later return.

The works of Pliny and Seneca differ from those of most of the authors that we have to consider in that they were not ' discovered ' by the Renaissance humanists. Pliny and Seneca were indeed never lost, and their works formed part of the reading of the Dark and Middle Ages. For the understanding of mediaeval thought a knowledge of these authors is necessary.

## § 3. *Medical and Veterinary Knowledge*

The original native Roman medical system was quite devoid of scientific elements and was that of a people of the lower culture. Interwoven, as is all primitive medicine, with ideas that trespass on the domain of religion, it possessed that multitude of ' specialist deities ' which was so characteristic of the Roman cults. Thus Fever had three temples in Rome, and was supplicated as the goddess *Febris* and flatteringly addressed as *Febris diva, Febris sancta, Febris magna.* Foul odours were invoked in the name of *Mephitis,* to whom a temple was erected at a place where asphyxiating fumes emerged from the earth. Lassitude was implored as *Fessonia. Uterina* guarded the womb, and *Lucina,* assisted by a whole group of goddesses, had charge of childbirth. The entire pantheon of disease and physiological function was presided over by the *Dea Salus,* whose temple was on one of the summits of the Quirinalis. She was the deity who took the public health under her supervision.

Some of the surviving records of the original Roman medicine are of even lower material. Cato the Censor assures us that the ancient Rome, which he lauded, was *sine medicis sed non sine medicina,* ' healthy without doctors.' He advised that to a sick ox be given three grains of salt, three laurel leaves, three rue leaves, and various other threes for three consecutive days, both patient and physician fasting and the drug being given when both were standing erect. For human patients his panacea was cabbage. He sought to reduce dislocations by reciting over them the euphonious formula,

> Huat hanat huat ista pista sista domiabo damnaustra.

Students of folk-lore have shown that magical jingles can often be traced back to a forgotten tongue, but that of Cato suggests the expletive *lingua franca* still used by the victims of such accidents !

The entire external aspect of Roman medicine was grad-

ually changed by the advent of Greek science. There is
evidence, however, that the change hardly penetrated below
the upper classes. Thus in medical works of the fourth
and fifth centuries of the Christian era we still encounter
numerous survivals of the older material. There are also
many references in St. Augustine's *De civitate dei* which
show that the ancient beliefs were widely current in Italy
even among the well-to-do of his day. After the fall of
the Empire they lingered among the barbaric peoples that
entered into its heritage. Nor are they yet extinct, for prescriptions and practices of Pliny, of Marcellus Empiricus,
and of Sextus Placitus Papyriensis may still be traced in the
folk-customs and folk-beliefs of our own land and in the
sayings and doings of continental peasantry.

Notwithstanding the large medical field that the Western
Empire provided, and the wide acceptance of Greek medicine by the upper classes, it is remarkable that the Latin-
speaking peoples produced no eminent physician. During
the Republic medical education had been entirely a matter
of private teaching. The relation of pupil and master
exhibited by the Hippocratic oath was evidently that which
prevailed under the early Empire. The initiate declared,
' I will reckon him who taught me this Art as dear to me as
those who bore me. I will look upon his offspring as my
own brethren and will teach them this art, if they would
learn it, without fee or stipulation. By precept, lecture,
and every other mode of instruction, I will impart a knowledge of this art to my own sons, and to those of my teacher,
and to disciples bound by a stipulation and an oath, according to the Law of Medicine, but to none other ' (see p. 22).
Despite the Ionic Greek dress in which this formula is
known to us, there is evidence that it is of Imperial date
and of Roman rather than of Greek origin. The very
form of the oath suggests the arrangements which were
gradually made for medical instruction at Rome. The
first important teacher there was the Greek Asclepiades

of Bithynia (died *c.* 40 B.C.), a contemporary of Lucretius and like him an Epicurean. Asclepiades introduced the atomic view of Democritus into medicine. He deeply influenced the course of later medical thought, ridiculed the Hippocratic attitude of relying on the *vis medicatrix naturae*, ' the healing power of nature ' which he regarded as a mere ' meditation on death,' and urged that active measures were needed for the process of cure to be *cito, tuto, iucunde,* ' seemly, swift, and sure.' He founded a regular school at Rome which continued after him.

An outline of the history of this school and of others formed in Rome can be made out with some approach to clearness. At first the school was the mere personal following of the physician, who took his pupils and apprentices round with him on his visits. At a later stage such groups combined to form societies or colleges, where questions of the art were debated. Towards the end of the reign of Augustus or the beginning of that of Tiberius, these societies constructed for themselves a meeting-place on the Esquiline, the so-called *Schola medicorum.* It had a president with the title of *archiatrus* and a secretary known as the *tabularius* or *scriba.* Finally the emperors built halls or *auditoria* for the teaching of medicine. The professors at first received only the pupils' fees. It was not until the time of Vespasian (emperor A.D. 70–9) that medical teachers were given a salary at the public expense. The system was extended by Hadrian (117–38) and Alexander Severus (222–35).

Thus Rome became a centre of medical instruction. After a time subsidiary centres were established in other Italian towns. From Italy the custom spread and we meet traces of such schools at the half Greek Marseilles, as well as at Bordeaux, Arles, Nîmes, Lyons, and Saragossa. From Marseilles, which had been the home of the geographers and astronomers Pytheas and Euthymenes, came the physicians Crinas and Charmis. The latter, though accustomed to bathe his patients in ice-cold water in the depth of winter, received one of the highest medical fees mentioned in antiquity. Marseilles too was the home of Demosthenes, the most renowned of ancient oculists, who lived under Nero, and whose works were much sought after and survived at least as late as the fourteenth century. Bordeaux did itself no great honour in giving to the world Marcellus Empiricus, who had high office under Theodosius I (379–395) and Arcadius (396–408), and has left us a book which represents wellnigh the low water-mark of superstitious folly. For the most part, however, these provincial schools produced workaday medical men, few of whose writings have come down to us. They were perhaps largely training places for the army surgeons. That ,class seldom had literary interests, though Dioscorides, one of the most prominent physicians of antiquity and one who earned the respect of Galen and has deeply influenced the modern pharmacopoeia, served in the army under Nero. Dioscorides, however, wrote in Greek, and his work was probably not translated until the sixth century.

Before we leave the topic of medical instruction it will be in place to say a word concerning the study of anatomy. The practical study of that subject had been carried on at Alexandria, beginning with Herophilus and Erasistratus about 300 B.C. Physiology had been experimentally studied, and the terrible charge of vivisection of human beings is made against the school of Alexandria by Tertullian (c. 155–c. 222) and Augustine (354–430), who are supported by the very damning evidence of Celsus. Dissection of the dead body was still practised at Alexandria towards the end of the first century B.C., but it is probable that it had ceased by the middle of the second century A.D. It is clear that it was on the bodies of animals that Galen (A.D. 130–200), for instance, relied for his anatomical knowledge. Considering the indifference to human life which the Romans often exhibited, considering their brutality to slaves and the opportunities offered by gladiatorial combats, considering the obvious value of anatomical knowledge for surgical practice and the organization of the military medical service of the Empire, it is truly remarkable that the anatomical knowledge of antiquity was thus allowed to lapse. It did not revive until the rise of the mediaeval universities (p. 94).

We may now turn to the literature of medicine. The earliest scientific medical work in Latin is the *De re medica* of Celsus which was prepared about A.D. 30. It is of great interest as our one adequate representative of the surgery of the Alexandrian period. Written in excellent Latin, it is in many ways the most readable and well-arranged ancient medical work that we have. All the evidence, however, points to this work of Celsus having been a compilation if not a translation from the Greek, and the sole surviving part of a complete encyclopaedia of knowledge. Many of its phrases are closely reminiscent of the ' Hippocratic Collection.' The ethical tone is high and the general line of treatment sensible and humane. Celsus, though almost unknown to the Middle Ages, was the first classical medical writer to be printed, his work appearing at Florence in 1478.

The treatise of Celsus is divided into eight books. It opens with an interesting account of the history of medicine containing a comparison of the rival sects of the so-called ' Dogmatic ' and ' Empiric ' physicians. The first two books deal with diet and the general principles of therapeutics and pathology, the third and fourth discuss internal diseases, the fifth and sixth external diseases. The seventh and eighth books, devoted to surgery, are perhaps the most valuable. Celsus professes himself a follower of Asclepiades of Bithynia (died *c.* 40 B.C.), but, unlike his master, he by no means despises the Hippocratic *expectant* method of ' waiting on the disease.' In many matters his comparative boldness as a surgeon will draw the attention of the modern medical reader. Thus he describes plastic operations on the face and mouth, and the removal of

polypus from the nose.   He tells too of the very dangerous
operations for extirpating a goitre and of cutting for stone.
He gives an excellent account of what might be thought
the modern operation for removal of tonsils.   Noteworthy
also is his description of dental practice, which includes
the wiring of loose teeth and an account of what appears
to have been a dental mirror.   An idea of the surgical instruments in use in his time can be obtained from those which
have been recovered from Pompeii, some of which are displayed in Fig. 7.   At the top is shown a pair of forceps of
a form used in removing a long uvula.   Below, from left
to right, are arranged a long forceps with pointed ends, a
small pair of scissors, a pair of dental forceps, and a small
pair of tweezers.   To the right there is placed a pair of blunt
forceps above and an instrument for scarification below.

The remaining Latin medical writings that we possess
are not of high scientific value.   Surviving works are ascribed to Antonius Musa, the medical attendant of Augustus.
The attribution, however, is spurious, and, after Celsus,
the first Latin medical author whose writings have survived
is probably Scribonius Largus, a physician of the so-called
' Empiric ' school.   He practised at Rome under Claudius,
whom he accompanied in A.D. 43 on his expedition to
Britain, and he was physician to the Empress Messalina.
His receipt book is derived entirely from Greek sources
of the lower type.   He follows the unscientific method,
which became very popular in the Middle Ages, of beginning
with the head and working down to the feet, entirely dis-
regarding the relations and functions of the organs.   This
method of classifying diseases by their position in the body
is very ancient and is encountered in an Egyptian medical
papyrus of about 1700 B.C.   Scribonius is the earliest
writer who makes mention of the so-called *Hippocratic oath*,
and has been praised because some of the unguents that he
employed for wounds had antiseptic qualities.

After Scribonius Largus the most ancient Latin medical
work is that of Pliny.   He was a scorner of medical science

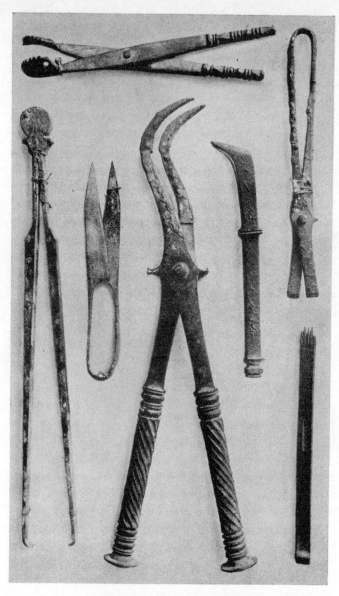

FIG. 7.—SURGICAL INSTRUMENTS FROM POMPEII
By the courtesy of Prof. K. Sudhoff.
See page 22.

and the starveling Greeks who practised it. 'Medicine, in spite of its lucrativeness,' says Pliny, ' is the one art of Greeks that the serious Roman has so far refused to cultivate. Few of our fellow-citizens have been willing even to touch it, and if they do so they desert at once to the Greeks . . . Unfortunately there is no law to punish ignorant physicians, and capital punishment is never inflicted on them. Yet they learn by our suffering and experiment by putting us to death.' The collection of Pliny, which was to be a substitute for the works of these wretched Greeks, consists of a vast series of remedies built on the supposedly firm ground of ' experience.' It is based on no theory, it is supported by no doctrine, it is founded on no experiment. Yet it is the prototype of the medical output of the next fifteen hundred years. The cry of Pliny for ' experience ' as against ' theory ' has been plaintively echoed by the ' practical ' man down the ages. Yet there are subjects and there are conditions in which the man without a theory may be the most unpractical of all. Medicine is such a subject and disease is such a condition.

When ' experience ' is invoked in medical matters by Pliny and by later writers, the absence of the parallel to the ' experience ' of many other affairs of life is often missed. In other matters the so-called experience is usually under some sort of control, and therefore in fact approaches the character of ' experiment.' Experience is thus frequently but the result of a series of *observations provoquées*. With clinical medicine, so long as it is uncontrolled by the ancillary sciences, this can seldom be the case. A single instance from Pliny will suffice. ' The herb dittany,' he says, ' has the power to extract arrows. This *was proved* by stags who had been struck by these missiles which were loosened when they fed on this plant.' Had Pliny made any effort to verify such a statement ? He had take his ' experience,' in fact, from an interpolated and spurious passage of a work by Theophrastus, and he omits to mention his source. Prepossession with the idea of the value of such experience led Pliny and the ages which followed him into innumerable absurdities into which it would be profitless to follow them. But if the multitudinous remedies of Pliny are always useless and often disgusting, yet his book contains some valuable material for the history of medicine, culled from many sources now lost. His very discursiveness and love of gossip are our gain, and though he can do nothing to advance medical knowledge he gives us much insight into medical practice in antiquity.

The latter medical writings in the Latin language are hardly worth notice here. Some, such as those of Priscianus (*c.* 380), Marcellus (*c.* 400), and (pseudo-)Apuleius Barbarus (? *c.* 400), contemptible in themselves, are of interest for the influence they had on after ages. One writer, Quintus Serenus Sammonicus (*c.* 250), is remarkable for having introduced into Latin the foolish custom of writing medical works in verse. He is also the first to record the famous device or charm known as the *Abracadabra*. Another late Latin medical writer, Vindicianus (*c.* 400), less futile than most, was the friend of St. Augustine. Important for a special reason is Caelius Aurelianus, a Numidian physician of the fifth century. His work is of philological interest and is also noticeable as one of the few remnants of the so-called ' Methodist ' school. It is, however, a translation from the Greek Soranus and not a native work. The last Latin medical writer of antiquity is probably Cassius Felix, an African, whose language is interesting but whose work, written in 447, consists only of extracts from earlier writers.

Veterinary medicine was a topic on which the Roman agricultural interests concentrated considerable attention. An important source for much of their material was a work by the Carthaginian Mago (*c.* 200 B.C.), which was translated into both Latin and Greek. The earlier Latin works on agriculture—Cato, Varro, Columella—naturally include many passages which discuss the treatment of sick animals, and there is evidence that they draw largely on Mago.

The *Georgics* of Virgil (written 31 B.C.) is really a manual of agriculture in verse. In the third book of the *Georgics* Virgil deals with the care and breeding of animals, and he speaks of epizootic diseases such as scabies in sheep, foot-rot, anthrax, rabies, and sheep-rot. Much veterinary information may be gleaned from the works of Pliny. A curious collection of remedies for diseases of cattle has come down to us under the name of Gargilius Martialis (*c.* A.D. 200) ; it is interesting as an example of late Roman veterinary medicine with little or no Greek influence. The agricultural writer Palladius, who flourished in the fourth century, gives an account of the points of horses and describes how to tell their age by the teeth. The work exercised some influence on the Middle Ages and was translated into English as early as 1420.

By far the best known and most complete Latin veterinary work is the *Digestorum artis mulomedicinae Libri IV* by Flavius Vegetius Renatus (383–450), who is known also as a writer on military topics. The treatise is remarkably scientific and well arranged, considering the period at which it was composed ; especially noteworthy is the contempt expressed in it for incantations and other superstitious practices. It had been studied by Petrarch and was the first veterinary work to be printed (Rome, 1487). Vegetius has been called the ' father of veterinary science ' ; it is certain, however, that he was a compiler, and among his sources is the *Mulomedicinia Chironis* translated from Greek by one Claudius Hermerus (*c.* 300 A.D. ?). The work of Hermerus survives and is of great philological importance as a record of Low Latin linguistic forms.

§ 4. *Hygiene and Organization of Public Health*

If in Medicine itself the Roman achieved but little, in organization of medical service, and especially in the department which deals with the public health, his position is far more honourable. All the writers on architecture—Varro,

Vitruvius, and Columella—give much attention to the orientation, position, and drainage of buildings, and from an early date sanitation and public health drew the attention of statesmen. Considering the dread of the neighbourhood of marshes on the part of these practical sanitarians and in view of modern knowledge of the mosquito-borne character of malaria, it is entertaining to find the mosquito net (*conopeum*) ridiculed by the poets Horace, Juvenal, and Propertius !

Sanitation was a feature of Roman life. Rome was already provided with cloacae or subterranean sewers in the age of the Tarquins (6th cent. B.C.). Similar conduits have been found in excavations in Crete of Minoan date, but there is evidence that the idea reached Rome from

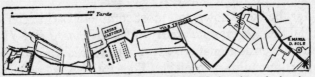

FIG. 8.—Plan of the course of the Cloaca Maxima through the city to its outlet in the Tiber.

Etruscan sources. Tradition is probably just in referring the construction of the *Cloaca maxima* itself, the main drain of Rome [Figs. 8 and 9], to the period of monarchy.

The growth of hygienic ideas is seen in the interdict by the ' Law of the Twelve Tables ' (450 B.C.) against burials within the city walls. It is noteworthy that this order is made without reference to any physician. The same absence of professional medical intervention may be noted in the instructions issued to the aediles to attend to the cleanliness of the streets and to the distribution of water. Nor is any medical help or opinion invoked by the ancient *Lex regia*, attributed to Numa, which directed the opening of the body in the hope of extracting a living child in the case of a pregnant woman who had died. It is the origin of the so-called ' Caesarean section,' the method by which Caesar himself is said to have been brought into the world.

Fig. 9.—OUTLET INTO TIBER OF THE CLOACA MAXIMA, THE MAIN SEWER OF ROME

From an engraving by Piranesi.  See page 26.

At the date of these decrees physicians in Rome were either slaves or in an entirely subordinate position. Their status was greatly improved by Julius Caesar, who, Suetonius (c. A.D. 120) tells us, ' conferred citizenship on all who practised medicine at Rome . . . to make them more desirous of living in the city and to induce others to resort to it.' The finest monument to the Roman care for the public health stands yet for all to see in the remains of the fourteen great aqueducts which supplied the city with 300,000,000 gallons of potable water daily. No modern city is better equipped in this regard. The Roman military writer Sextus Julius Frontinus (c. A.D. 40–103) has left us a good account of these aqueducts and their history in his *De aquis urbis Romae*. The distribution of water to individual houses was also well cared for, and excellent specimens of Roman plumbing may be seen in the British Museum [Fig. 10]. A large number of other sanitary devices have survived in many sites and are particularly well seen at Timgad in Algeria [Fig. 11].

Under the early Empire a definite public medical service was constituted. Public physicians or *archiatri*, as they were later called, were appointed to the various towns and institutions. Alexander Severus (222–35) organized the medical service of the imperial house. The archiaters of the palace were sometimes promoted to provincial governorships, as happened to Ausonius (c. 320), father of the poet, who became prefect of Illyria, or to Vindicianus (c. 400), the friend of Augustine, who became proconsul of Africa. At a yet later date the first archiater of the sacred palace was invested with the function of judging disputes between physicians. ' We decorate you from this moment,' says Cassiodorus (490–585), to one of them in his usual pompous and roundabout style, ' with the honour of being head of the archiaters, that you alone among the masters of health may be pre-eminent, and that all those who exercise their ingenuity on the subtleties of mutual contradictions may refer to your judgement. Be you the arbiter of this exalted art, and adjudge the conflicts of those who have formerly taken only their passions for judge. In healing them you will heal the sick if you terminate their quarrels prudently. It is a great privilege for you that these able men should be submitted to your authority and that you should be honoured among those whom all the world reveres.'

In Greek lands state physicians had been known for many centuries and are mentioned by Herodotus (c. 484–425 B.C.). In the days of the Empire the custom of appointing district

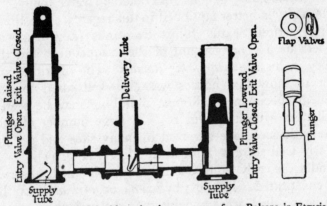

FIG. 10.—Diagram of double action bronze pump from Bolsena in Etruria, now in the British Museum. The pump is worked by alternating plungers raised and lowered by a single rocking beam which, for simplicity, is here omitted. The bottoms of the cylinders in which the plungers move were connected by pipes with the water supply and are furnished with flap valves opening upward. When the plunger was raised a vacuum was created and the water lifted the valve and rushed in. When the plunger reached the highest point the valve fell again and retained the water. When the plunger descended it forced the water from the cylinder into the central delivery tube through another flap valve in the horizontal pipe.

physicians spread early from Italy to Gaul and to the other provinces. A statute of Antoninus of about the year A.D. 160 regulates the appointment of these physicians. 'The smallest towns may have five physicians who may enjoy immunity from taxation. . . . The more important towns may have seven. . . . The towns of larger grade may have ten. . . . It is suitable for the largest number to be allowed to the capital cities, the second to cities with a court of

Fig. 11.—A ROMAN LATRINE AT TIMGAD IN ALGERIA
Flushed with water from a constant fountain.  See page 27.

Fig. 12.—ADVANCED DRESSING STATION
From Trajan's Column.

Left : a wounded legionary is aided by two comrades.
Right : a surgeon bandages the thigh of an auxiliary.
See page 30.

justice. . . . These numbers may not be surpassed either by an ordinance of the curia or by any other means soever, but it is lawful to diminish them if this is done in view of the civil charges.' The main duty of these physicians was to attend to the needs of the poor. In the code of Justinian (A.D. 533) there is an article urging them to give this service cheerfully rather than the more subservient attendance on the wealthy. Their salaries were fixed by the *decuriones* or municipal councillors. They were encouraged to undertake the training of pupils. Inscriptions prove the existence of such municipal *archiatri* in many towns, and attest the respect in which they were held.

It is in connexion with the army that we see the Roman medical system at its best. The actual medical organization of the Roman army is, however, a very debatable topic, and information concerning it has to be gathered from very scattered sources. The matter may be thus summed up. ' Each of the 25-30 legions of 10 cohorts (numbering 6,500-7,000 men in all) had a legionary physician (*medicus legionis*) ; each of the 9 pretorian cohorts, the 4 urban cohorts, and the 7 cohorts of *vigiles* (who acted as police and firemen in the city) had four cohort surgeons (*medici cohortis*). Every body of auxiliary troops and every ship of the pretorian fleet had also its physician. All these physicians, as part of the military establishment, were regarded as *immunes*, exempt from guard and combat-duty or day-labour, and ranked among the *principales* (non-commissioned officers). In the pretorian and city cohorts, they were required to be Roman citizens, while the physicians of the *vigiles* and auxiliary troops, serving in Italy and the provinces, could be freedmen or foreigners. For this reason, the staff surgeons of these latter organizations were called *medici ordinarii*. The legionary physicians were all of equal rank, had no other medical superiors, and were subordinated only to the camp commander (*praefectus castrorum*) or, in his absence, to the tribunes of the legion.

The social status of the medical staff in this military hier-
archy was that of the innumerable grades of non-commissioned personnel and of the highly elaborated bureaucracy
attached to the army, which included accountants, notaries,
registrars, secretaries, and civilian functionaries of all kinds '
(F. H. Garrison). The actual administration of first-aid
by Roman military surgeons is represented on Trajan's
column [Fig. 12].

The great contribution of Rome to medicine—and it is
a very great one—is the hospital system. It is a scheme that
naturally arose out of the Roman genius for organization
and is connected with the Roman military system. Among
the Greeks *iatreia*, ' surgeries,' were well known ; they
were, however, the private property of the medical man.
Larger institutions were connected with the Aesculapian
temples, but there is no evidence of scientific medical treatment in these places. In Republican times the Romans
were no better off, and the work of Cato shows that there
was no provision for sick slaves. A temple to Aesculapius
had been established on an island of the Tiber in Republican
times. The island was ship-like in form. Part of it had
been hewn to the shape of a ship's poop whereon the staff
and serpent of Aesculapius and the head of the god were
carved ; remains of these symbols can be seen there to this
day [Fig. 13]. ' On this island of Aesculapius,' Suetonius
tells us, ' certain men exposed their sick and worn-out slaves
because of the trouble of treating them. The Emperor
Claudius (A.D. 41–54), however, decreed that such slaves
were free, and, if they recovered, they should not return to
the control of their masters.' Thus the island became a
place of refuge for the sick poor. We may regard it as an
early form of public hospital.

Columella (first century A.D.) speaks of *valetudinaria*,
' infirmaries,' for such persons, and gives humane directions
for their management. Seneca tells us that *valetudinaria*
were in use even by free Romans. The excavations at

FIG. 13.—SITE OF TEMPLE OF AESCULAPIUS, THE FIRST ROMAN HOSPITAL

On the ship-like island of S. Bartolommeo. From an engraving by Piranesi. See page 30.

Pompeii show that a physician's house might even be built somewhat on the lines of a modern ' nursing home.' There are passages in Galen (A.D. 130–200) which seem to imply that it was in the provinces that private institutions first developed into subventioned public hospitals.

This development of public hospitals naturally early affected military life. At first sick soldiers had been sent home for treatment. As the Roman frontiers spread ever wider this became impossible and military hospitals were

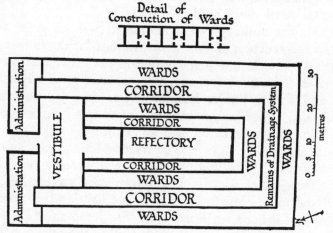

FIG. 14.—General Plan of Roman Military Hospital at Novaesium near Düsseldorf. The assigning of the uses to the different parts of the building is conjectural.

founded at important strategic points. The sites of several such military hospitals have been excavated. The earliest that has come to light is of the first century and is at Carnuntum, about twenty miles from Vienna. The best explored is at Novaesium [Fig. 14] on the lower Rhine near Düsseldorf. The military hospital at Novaesium was founded about 100 A.D., but has later elements. It is built on the corridor system. Entering from the north between the administrative offices we come on a large hall on which succeeds a long narrow room placed along the axis of the building. This room was probably used as a refectory.

It is surrounded on three sides by a corridor out of which open chambers for the sick. Around this series of chambers runs another corridor also along three sides of the building, and around this outer corridor again is another series of chambers. These outer chambers are peculiarly arranged so that they do not open directly into the corridor, but each pair is reached through a small vestibule. (See detail in Fig. 14.) The arrangement must be related to sanitation, and traces of the drainage system have been uncovered. The general scheme is much in advance of any military hospital until quite modern times.

From the military *valetudinarium* it was no great step to the construction of similar institutions for the numerous imperial officials and their families in the provincial towns. Motives of benevolence, too, seem to have gradually come in, and finally public hospitals were founded in many localities. The idea naturally passed on to Christian times, and the pious foundation of hospitals for the sick and out-cast in the Middle Ages is to be traced back to these Roman *valetudinaria*. The first charitable institution of this kind concerning which we have clear information was established at Rome in the fourth century by a Christian lady named Fabiola of whom we learn from St. Jerome. The plan of such a hospital projected at St. Gall in the early years of the ninth century has survived. It reminds us in many respects of the early Roman military hospitals. These mediaeval hospitals for the sick must naturally be distin-guished from the even more numerous ' spitals ' for travellers and pilgrims, the idea of which may perhaps be traced back to the rest-houses along the strategic roads of the Empire.

## § 5. *Mathematics and Physical Sciences*

As with all other peoples, the first system of numeration adopted by the Romans was based on finger counting. From it was developed a method of mechanical reckoning on a counting board. The simplest form was a board covered with sand divided into columns by the finger or by the stylus, counters being used in calculation. Cicero, referring to this method, speaks of an expert calculator as *eruditum attigisse pulverem*, 'clever at handling the sand.' The counters employed had graven upon them figures of the hand in various positions to represent different numbers. Many such counters have survived [Fig. 15] and their symbols are identical with those which remained in vogue till late mediaeval times.

FIG. 15.—Carved Bone Counters employed in calculation, found in Pompeii and now in the British Museum. The positions of the hand indicate numbers, and are identical with symbols still used in England in the sixteenth century.

A more complicated apparatus was the true *abacus*. This began as a board with a series of grooves in which pebbles or *calculi* could be moved up and down, hence the verb *calculo* and the modern use of *calculate*. The actual form of the Roman abacus is well known, and several excellently preserved specimens have been recovered. In its more developed form the abacus consisted of an upper row of short and a lower row of long rods [Fig. 16]. Each of the short rods had a single perforated bead running on it and each of the longer ones four such beads.

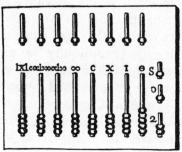

FIG. 16.—A late form of Roman Abacus.

The first rod on the right was marked for units, the next on its left for tens, and so on up to a million. Its mode of application was very much more complicated than might be imagined. Persius had both forms of calculating board in mind when he derides the zany *qui abaco numeros et secto in pulvere metas scit risisse*, ' who sniggers at the figures on the abacus or the ridges of furrowed sand.'

The whole mathematical system of antiquity was handicapped by its inadequate notation. The Roman numerals were, it is believed, derived from Etruscan sources. The decimal system with which we are nowadays familiar is of Indian origin, and reached Europe through Arabic channels in the Middle Ages. The Greeks often used geometrical methods where we should invoke the aid of algebra, and their mathematical developments made little impression on the Romans. How slight was the mathematical knowledge absorbed by Latin scientific authors may be gathered from *Geometrica* and *Arithmetica* bearing the name of Boethius (A.D. 480–524). Those elementary works ascribed to ' the last of the ancients ' represent the mathematical legacy of antiquity to the earlier Middle Ages. Even when Rome had world dominion, Cicero bemoaned that ' the Greek mathematicians lead the field in pure geometry while we limit ourselves to the practice of reckoning and measuring.'

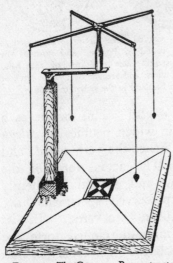

FIG. 17.—The Groma. Reconstructed from descriptions, remains, and ancient representations.

The Romans held that the art of mensuration was at least as old as their city, and it was said to have been first practised by the priests for ecclesiastical purposes at a very early date. The knowledge of the subject advanced in Imperial times and a regular school for the teaching of surveying was established. The chief instrument in general use was known as the *groma*. It consisted of two lineals fixed at

right angles and arranged to turn horizontally about a
vertical pivot. From the end of each lineal a plummet was
suspended. One of the lineals was used for sighting and
the other to determine the direction in the field at right
angles to the first. As both agricultural and town-planning
were mainly on rectangular lines this instrument was of
wide application. A figure of it has been found on the grave
of a Roman surveyor, and an actual specimen has been
recovered from Pompeii [Fig. 17].

That site has also yielded a number of compasses and other
apparatus employed in mensuration [Fig. 18]. The in-
accuracy of some Roman measurements is strange when
we consider the exactness of these Pompeiian instruments.
Thus $3\frac{1}{8}$ is given as the ratio of the circumference of the
circle to the diameter by Vi-
truvius, a competent architect
who must often have had occasion
to examine the drums of columns.
A better result might have been
expected from any schoolboy
provided with a compass and
tape measure.

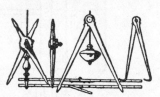

FIG. 18.—Mathematical instruments.
From Pompeii, after Oberbeck.

An interesting description of the method of estimation
of the distance from the observer of an inaccessible point
on the same level as himself, e.g. the opposite bank of a
river, has come down to us. A line is traced along the near
bank, and is measured off by rolling along it a *hodometer*,
an instrument consisting of a wheel the length of the circumference of which is known and whose revolutions can
be counted. Vitruvius has preserved for us a description
of this apparatus which is in effect a ' taxicab ' [Fig. 19].
From each end of this measured line a sight is taken by means
of the dioptra—the Roman form of which was inferior to
that described by Hero of Alexandria (*c.* 1st cent. A.D.).
The angles and the base being thus available a triangle
congruent to that formed by joining the point on the far
bank to the extremities of the measured line, is constructed

on the near bank. The vertical height of this triangle can now be measured by the hodometer and this will give the distance of the point from the observer, or the breadth of the river. We may here note that the work of Vitruvius

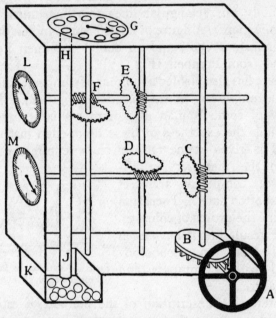

FIG. 19.—'Taxicab' or hodometer as described by Vitruvius. The wheel A runs along the ground. It has, eccentrically attached to its axle, a peg which fits into the cogs of wheel B. At every rotation of wheel A the wheel B therefore turns one peg. The rotation of B is transmitted to a vertical shaft and the rotation of this shaft is transmitted and reduced by passage through the series of joints C, D, E, and F. Finally the rotation at F is transmitted to a vertical shaft which is fastened to the disk G. This disk G is perforated with holes. As disk G rotates these holes come in turn opposite to the open end of the tube H J which leads into the reservoir K. Pebbles are placed on each of the holes in G and the machine is so geared that for every mile traversed one falls into the reservoir K. The distance traversed may be checked by counting these pebbles. Dials may be fitted to the horizontal shafts as at L and M.

was first printed in 1486 at Rome and was early circulating in an Italian translation. It was perhaps from such a version that Leonardo da Vinci (1452–1519) obtained hints which enabled him to design his ' taxicab.'

Mechanical knowledge among the Romans was very

evident in certain departments ; it had always a practical direction and was not cultivated for its own sake.   Among the inventions that the Romans may have made independently is the steelyard.   This instrument is a device of considerable antiquity among them, and may be traced back at least as far as the third century B.C. .Its use was widely understood and many specimens have been recovered [Fig. 20]. The principle of the pulley, too, was well known.   Thus on one of the monuments we can follow the mechanism of a crane.   It is worked by a treadmill and raises blocks of stone by acting through a whole system of pulleys [Fig. 21].

The inadequate *theoretical* basis of the physical conceptions of Latin writers is shown in various directions.   Thus Pliny recounts a fable of the Remora, a fish of the Mediterranean which has a sucker on its head.   ' This tiny fish can restrain all the forces of the ocean. Winds may rage and storms may roar, yet the fish restrains their might and fury, and causes ships to stand still . . . by simply adhering to them.'   Centuries before, Archimedes (287–212 B.C.) had demanded ' a *fixed* place on which to stand that he might move the world.'   The full understanding of the works of Archimedes failed for the next

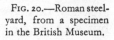

FIG. 20.—Roman steelyard, from a specimen in the British Museum.

millennium and a half.   Yet his simpler practical devices, such as the water screw, were familiar enough to the Romans.

Seneca is superior, scientifically, to Pliny.   This in itself is no great distinction, but there are several passages in the *Quaestiones naturales* which suggest that Seneca did occasionally take the trouble to verify some of the statements that he makes.   He has a clear idea too of the value of astronomical observations.  Thus he tells us that ' it is essential to have a record of all former appearances of comets.  These bodies appear seldom and therefore we do not yet know . . . if they follow periodic laws and whether some definite cause is responsible for their reappearance at the appointed day.  Such a development of astronomy is but recent.'  In spite of this statement of Seneca there is a passage in the *Meteorologica* of Aristotle which seems to ascribe the knowledge of the periodic return of comets to the Pythagoreans and to Hippocrates of Chios (*c.* 425 B.C.), five hundred years before the days of Seneca.

Seneca's statement concerning the magnifying powers of glass globes is peculiarly noteworthy.  Fallacious attempts have been made to show that the ancients knew of the effect of refraction of light at curved surfaces.  That they knew of the burning-glass is clear from references in Pliny and elsewhere, and many glass or crystal spheres, probably used as fire-makers, have been recovered from Roman sites.  These burning glasses do not, however, seem to have been used for magnifying purposes, and Seneca has bequeathed to us one of the very few passages in ancient writings that suggest that this power of transparent spheres had even been noticed.  He records that ' letters however small and dim appear large and clear when viewed through a glass globe filled with water.'  It has been claimed that globes of this type were used by the gem cutters of antiquity, but such suggestions are unsupported by evidence.  The oft-repeated statement that Nero used a cut emerald as a lens to aid his defective vision has arisen from a mistranslation of a passage in Pliny.

Applied mathematics underwent some development at the end of the Republican period.  Julius Caesar himself was an astronomical author and Pliny used a book of his as a source.  Caesar had planned two undertakings of great scientific import.  He wished to improve the Roman

FIG. 21.—CRANE
Worked with human labour by treadmill.
Lateran Museum.   See page 37.

calendar which had fallen into great confusion, and to organize a general survey of the Empire. Both of these projects were ultimately realized.

The early history of the Roman calendar is obscure. We learn from Censorinus (*fl.* A.D. 238) and Macrobius (*fl.* A.D. 400) that the Roman year consisted at first of ten months and 304 days. Livy (59 B.C.–A.D. 17) and Plutarch (A.D. 46–120) give contradictory accounts of the reforms of Numa, who is said to have introduced a year of twelve months. It is clear that at an early date there emerged a lunar year of 355 days which is almost exactly twelve lunations. Of this calendar Martius (the month of Mars) was the first month, Aprilis (probably for *aperilis* from *aperire*, 'to open '), Maius (perhaps related to *major*), and Junius (which may be related to *junior* and *juvenis*) were named in connexion with the opening, growth, and ripening of vegetation. The following six months, Quinctilis, Sextilis, September, October, November, and December, were given merely the numerical names which most of them still bear. Januarius was perhaps named from the god Janus, and Februarius, the last month, was the season of ritual purification (*februare*, ' to purify ' or ' expiate '). To obtain some relation of this lunar reckoning to the solar year a cycle of four years had been invented of which the first year contained 355 days, the second 377, the third 355, and the fourth 378. The cycle thus covered 1,465 days and the average year was of $\frac{1465}{4} = 366\frac{1}{4}$ days. It is obvious that so variable a year was useless for agricultural purposes. The farmer had thus still to rely on the rising and setting of certain constellations, such as Arcturus and the Pleiades, for timing his operations. The year was variously modified at different periods, but until the reforms of Julius Caesar no adequate correspondence to solar events was attained.

In place of this system Julius Caesar, acting under the advice of the Alexandrian mathematician Sosigenes, substituted a solar year of 365 days and abandoned any attempt to adapt the years or months to the lengths of the lunations.

In every fourth year one day called the *bis-sextus* was interpolated before the 24th February (*i.e.* before ' dies *sextus*
ante calendas Martis '). These fourth or leap years became
known as ' bissextile ' years. It is believed that this reform
was a reproduction of the Egyptian calendar that had been
enacted in 238 B.C. and had been perhaps designed at a
yet earlier date by the Greek astronomer Eudoxus (*fl. c.*
350 B.C.). In 44 B.C., the second year of the Julian Calendar,
one of the months was named *Iulius* in honour of its founder.
In 8 B.C. another month was called *Augustus* after his
successor.

## § 6.  *Geography*

Geography in the limited sense as distinct from cosmography was a topic that might be expected to appeal to the
practical and imperialistically minded Roman. We learn
of the existence of maps from a variety of Latin authors—
Cicero, Pliny, Seneca, Suetonius, and Vitruvius. From
Varro we gain a hint of the early religious associations of
land-surveying, for he tells us that a map of Italy engraved
on marble had a place in the temple of Tellus.

The survey of the Empire planned by Caesar may have
been suggested, like his calendarial reform, by ideas culled
from Alexandria. The division of the provinces, the demands of trade, the distribution of the fleet, all made the
need of this work evident. In the event the execution
of the scheme fell to Augustus. The survey was super-
intended by his son-in-law M. Vipsanius Agrippa (died
12 B.C.), and was finally carried through in 20 B.C. after
nearly 30 years' work. Agrippa wrote a commentary
illustrating this map, quotations from which have survived
in the writings of Ammianus Marcellinus (*c.* A.D. 325–92)
and Pliny. It was fairly accurate for the provinces of Italy,
Greece, and Egypt, whereas other countries were only
roughly surveyed.

The survey was rendered possible by the fact that the

Empire was well furnished with roads marked out with milestones. There was a regular service of skilled *agrimensores* or surveyors whose work, incorporated in the reports of provincial governors and generals, would be available at head-quarters. From this mass of material a huge map was prepared which was exhibited in a building erected for the purpose. This was the prototype of later strategical maps, a copy of one of which has survived to this day and is known as the *Peutinger table* after the sixteenth-century scholar who first published it. It was originally drawn in the year A.D. 366, but the copy we have, which is now at Vienna, was prepared in 1265. On it are shown the routes for armies throughout the Empire. These routes are indicated by lines which are notched at intervals that correspond to a day's journey. The whole map is greatly distorted by being enormously prolonged in the east-west direction [Fig. 22 and Fig. 23]. It is evident that, in its construction, cartographical accuracy was less considered than the purely practical aim of a convenient view of the itineraries. It may thus be compared to the distorted maps issued by some of our railway companies. The unit is usually a Roman mile (a thousand steps = *mille passuum* = 1,651 yards). Distances are sometimes indicated by figures.

Some idea of the manner in which the main routes of the Empire were surveyed and marked out may be gained from certain monuments, notably the inscribed marble pillars of Autun (Augustodunum). The monument gives—or gave, for most of it is now lost—the distances of a number of places on the road from Autun to Rome such as Autessio-durum (Auxerre), Bononia (Bologna), and Mutina (Modena). Somewhat similar inscriptions—sometimes of the nature of simple milestones—have been found at Tongres in Belgium, in Luxembourg, at Valencia, near the Roman wall in Northumberland, and in other places. Very remarkable are four silver bowls from Vicarello which give the route between Gades (Cadiz) and Rome. Of especial interest to English readers is a round bronze dish found in 1725

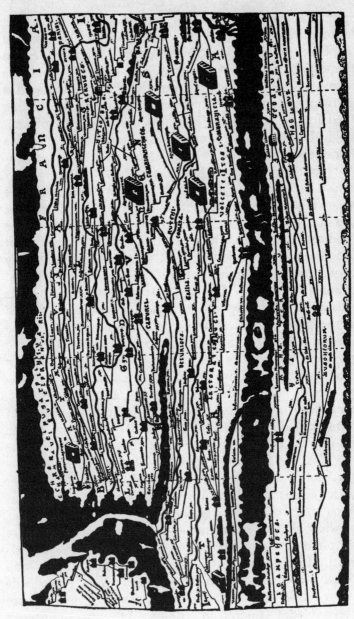

FIG. 22.—Section of Peutinger map showing France and Belgium and parts of Britain and Spain.    See Fig. 23 and page 41.

at Rudge Coppice in Wiltshire. Around its edge are written in second-century script the names of a number of places in the northern part of the country.

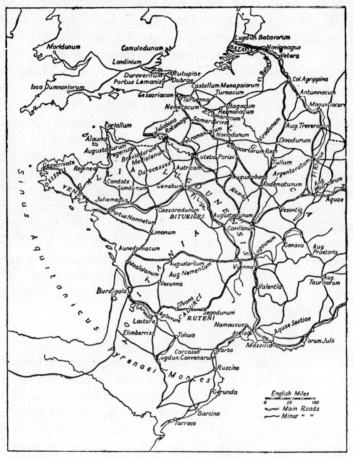

FIG. 23.—Roman Gaul, showing the area covered by the section of the Peutinger map on the opposite page and exhibiting the Roman roads included in that section.

In addition to inscribed stones and vessels and besides maps or *itineraria picta* such as the Peutinger table, we have true route-books or *itineraria adnotata*. One of these, the *Itinerarium Antonini*, a remarkably complete register of

the roads of the whole Empire, was probably put together
in its present form about A.D. 300, though its original goes
back at least to the beginning of the third century.  Both
principal and cross roads are indicated by lists of the
towns and stations upon them, the distance from place to
place being given in Roman miles.  Of more limited scope
are the pilgrim-books such as the *Itinerarium Burdigalense*
of 333 from Bordeaux to Jerusalem and back to Milan and
the journey-book to Palestine of the lady-pilgrim called
Silvia of Aquitania of about 380.  Rutilius Namatianus of
Toulouse wrote in 417 a versified *Itinerarium de reditu suo*
which gave an account of a journey from Rome to Gaul.
He was a pagan who fiercely attacked the monks—men who
dread the evils without being able to support the blessings
of the human condition.  His work naturally delighted the
heart of Gibbon, and is of interest as still exhibiting the
faith that Rome is immortal.  The anonymous *Geographus
Ravennas*, though put together as late as the end of the
seventh century, contains, in a corrupt form, much valuable
information concerning Roman roads and towns.  The
Ravenna geographer seems to have used sources employed
by Ptolemy.

To general geography and cosmography as distinct from
the limited subject of military and imperial surveys the
Romans paid less attention.  The only Latin writer of any
importance who deals with the subject is Pomponius Mela.
He was a Spaniard, and his date may be gleaned from his
reference to Britain as about to be more fully explored by
an expedition then in progress.  This must refer to the visit
of the Emperor Claudius in A.D. 43.
Pomponius Mela clearly meant his work to be an easy
account of his subject.  Beginning with a general description of the earth he avoids mathematical topics and does
not give distances or measurements.  The world is a sphere,
and the land upon it is surrounded on all sides by sea
[Fig. 24].  Five zones may be distinguished on the earth's

surface ; that in the middle is burnt up by heat and is as
uninhabitable as are the two extreme zones by reason of
cold. Between the torrid and frigid zones lie the two
habitable temperate zones. In one of these we live, while

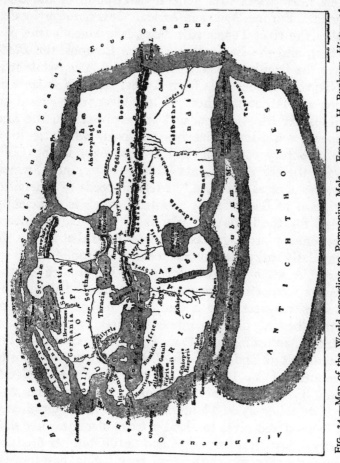

FIG. 24.—Map of the World according to Pomponius Mela. From E. H. Bunbury, *History of Ancient Geography*, ii. 368 ; by permission of Messrs. John Murray.

in the other dwell the *Antichthones*. Our own hemisphere
is completely surrounded by ocean, from which it receives
four seas or gulfs, one at the north, the Caspian, two in
the south, the Persian Gulf and the Red Sea, and the fourth
to the west, the Mediterranean. The scheme as a whole

is taken from Eratosthenes (275–c. 194 B.C.), whose geographical ideas governed the world until the time of Ptolemy (*fl.* A.D. 150), and it is clear that Pomponius Mela is here borrowing mainly from Greek sources.

Mela next passes to a general description of the three continents, Europe, Asia, and Africa. It is noteworthy that he takes the river Tanais (the *Don*), lake Maeotis (the *Sea of Azov*), and the Euxine Sea (Pontus Euxinus, the *Black Sea*) as the frontiers between Europe and Asia, while it is the Nile that divides Asia from Africa. Asia is as large as Europe and Africa together. These ideas were passed on to the earlier Middle Ages and are expressed in the first European world-map that has survived, which is in a seventh-century codex of Isidore (560–636) at St. Gall. Between the three continents is the Mediterranean, which Mela speaks of as ' our sea.' Mela proceeds to a detailed description of the different countries which is sufficiently detailed for the lands and islands of the Mediterranean, but becomes more vague as he passes from that area. He is singularly hazy as regards central Europe, which is remarkable when one considers the importance of the military operations in progress in that area. His account of Britain may serve as a sample of his descriptions of countries beyond his own immediate area.

' Britain, according to present knowledge, extends in the directions North and East. It offers a wide angle opposite the mouths of the Rhine. One arm of this angle looks towards Gaul, the other towards Germany. The two sides abut obliquely on a long straight line which terminates them behind and gives the land a triangular form like that of Sicily. Britain is flat, large, and fertile, but her produce is more suitable for cattle than men. She has forests, lakes, and considerable rivers which flow with alternating motion into the sea and towards their sources (according to the alternate movements of the tide) ; some of them produce pearls and precious stones. The inhabitants . . . are all savage and rich only in flocks. They paint the body either by way of ornament or from some other motive. They make pretexts of war and often attack each other, impelled solely by the ambition to command and to extend their borders. Armed like the Gauls, they fight not only on foot and on horseback but also in chariots which they call *covini* and which have scythes attached to their axles.

'Beyond Britain is Ireland, stretching nearly as far and of an oblong form. Its climate is unfavourable for ripening cereals, but it abounds in herbs of pleasant appearance and so sweet that the flocks fill themselves to repletion in a short part of the day, so that if not prevented from eating they would burst with fatness. The natives are rude and more ignorant of the virtues and devoid of piety than any other people.'

The haziness of the geographical ideas even of a very intelligent Roman of Imperial times may be gathered from the pages of Tacitus (c. A.D. 55–120). He tells how, under Agricola, the Roman fleet rounded Britain and proved it to be an island, discovering at the same time the Orcades (Orkney Islands) and coming in sight of Thule, by which the Shetlands are perhaps meant. Yet Tacitus, like Caesar and the elder Pliny, believes that Spain lies to the west of Britain [Fig. 25]. He describes the Pyrenees as running north and south. He goes on to explain the phenomenon of the midnight sun—which he brings as far south as the North of Scotland—by telling us that 'the flat extremities of the earth, casting a low shadow, do not throw the darkness up high, and the night does not reach to the sky and stars.' This statement implies the view that the earth is a disk with flattened edges.

The final geographical synthesis of antiquity was made by Claudius Ptolemaeus, who worked and observed at Alexandria during the reigns of Hadrian (117–38) and Antoninus Pius (138–161), whom he survived. Ptolemy, who was no less important as a geographer than as an astronomer, wrote in Greek but worked on itineraries of Roman officials and merchants. Thus he may be said to preserve for us a summary of Roman knowledge of the earth's surface, presented, however, in a way in which no Latin writer was capable. Ptolemy is generally thought to have used the map prepared by M. Vipsanius Agrippa which was placed in the porch of Pollux at Rome.

Ptolemy developed his own manner of representing the

curved surface of the earth on a plane surface. In his scheme of projection the parallels of latitude are arcs of concentric circles, the centres of which are at the North Pole. Chief among the parallels are the Equator and circles passing respectively through Thule, through Rhodes, and through Meroe. The meridians of longitude are represented by straight lines which converge to the Pole. He delineates in this manner the whole of the then known world, and the limits that he sets give a clear idea of the range of geographical vision in Imperial Roman times. The boundaries of Ptolemy's world are : on the north, the Ocean which sur-

FIG. 25.—Map of Western Europe reconstructed from the descriptions of Tacitus. From *Tacitus*, vol. i, translated by W. Peterson, by permission of Messrs. William Heinemann.

rounds the British Isles, the northern parts of Europe, and the unknown land in the northern region of Asia ; on the south, the unknown land which encloses the Indian Sea, and the unknown land to the south of Libya and Aethiopia ; on the east, the unknown land which adjoins the eastern nations of Asia, the Sinae (Chinese) and the people of Serica, the silk-producing land ; on the west, the great Western Ocean and unknown parts of Libya.

The portion of the earth thus surveyed covers in length
a hemisphere and in breadth between 63° north latitude
and $16\frac{3}{12}$° south latitude.

The Γεωγραφικὴ Ὑφήγησις, *Geographical Outline*, of
Ptolemy is the only complete scientific ancient geography
that we have. As originally written it was furnished with
maps. These have long since disappeared, but as Ptolemy
gives the latitude and longitude of the places that he men-

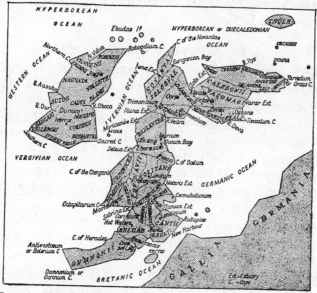

FIG. 26.—Map of British Isles reconstructed by plotting out the fixed
points given by Ptolemy and joining them together by straight lines.

tions his charts can be reconstructed. A peculiar interest
attaches to the map of Britain which can be thus put together
[Fig. 26]. It would seem that Scotland was bent eastward
with its axis at a right angle to that of England. This is
an unusual degree of error for Ptolemy. It has therefore
been suggested that he was here working not on records
brought back by travellers, but on actual maps of the
island, and that he made the mistake of fitting the map of
Scotland on to that of England along the wrong side.

Ptolemy's *Geographical Outline* was not available in Latin until a translation was made by the Italian Giacomo Angelo, who was Chancellor of the University of Montpellier early in the fifteenth century. That translation was printed at Bologna, perhaps as early as 1472, and deeply influenced Renaissance geographical ideas. Many editions of it appeared adorned with reconstructed charts in the early years of printing. It was to errors in the work of Ptolemy that Columbus owed his belief in the practicability of a western passage to the Indies.

## § 7. *Astronomy and Cosmology*

The Romans did not deal with astronomical matters until fairly late and then mostly for practical purposes. They never developed a mathematical astronomy such as that which formed the basis of Greek cosmological speculations. A bronze plaque has, however, been found at Salzburg which is engraved with the names and figures of constellations. Pliny tells us that in his time there were 1,600 named stars. These bodies, he considered, were composed of fire and filled with air.

Popular astronomy and geography are represented in Latin by certain poetical works bearing the name of Avienus (*c*. A.D. 380). The geographical poems of Avienus are adapted from Greek works by Dionysius Periegetes (*c*. A.D. 100), which were rendered again into Latin by Priscian in the sixth century. For his astronomical works Avienus draws upon Greek treatises of Aratus of Soli (271–213 B.C.). To one of these known as the *Aratea Phaenomena* quite peculiar interest is attached. St. Jerome tells us that when, in the Acts, St. Paul is reported as saying 'In him we live, and move, and have our being; as certain even of your own poets have said, *For we are also his offspring*' (Acts xvii. 28), he is quoting the *Aratea Phaenomena*. The words τοῦ γὰρ καὶ γένος ἐσμέν, *for we are also his offspring*, are in fact to be found in the opening invocation to Zeus in Aratus, and in a slightly different form in a work of the poet Cleanthes (3rd cent. B.C.) and in an expanded form in Avienus. Aratus was a native of Cilicia, St. Paul's native province. Both Aratus and Cleanthes were claimed by the Stoics, who, with the Epicureans, were opposing the apostle at Athens (Acts xvii. 18).

St. Jerome gives us also the approximate date of Avienus, for he speaks of the *Phaenomena* '*Arati, quem Cicero in Latinum sermonem transtulit et Germanicus Caesar et nuper Avienus,*' 'which Cicero and Germanicus Caesar translated into the Latin tongue and lately also Avienus.' These three versions all still exist in whole or in part. That of Cicero is found in a certain very peculiar early manuscript. It is written with the words arranged to form figures representing the signs of the constellations. The figures resemble those engraved on the Salzburg plaque. They are important as exhibiting the passage of late Imperial into early mediaeval book illustration.

FIG. 27.—Sundial found in the Stabian Baths at Pompeii in 1854. On the base are carved three lines in the Oscan script and language written from right to left, which may be read as follows :—

MR ATINIĬS MR KVAĬSSTUR EĬTIUVAD | MŬLTASĬKAD KŬMBEN-NIEĬS TANG(INUD)|AAMAN (A)FFED

The Latin equivalent of this would probably be :

MARAS ATINIUS MARAS QUAE-STOR PECUNIA | MULTATITIA CON-VENTUS DECRETO | AEDIFICAVIT, and it may be translated :

'Maras son of Maras of the gens Atinia, the Quaestor, built (this) by order of the Corporation out of fine-money.'

Though backward in astronomy the Romans had early developed a good knowledge of such elementary developments as the sundial, which was known to them in the third century B.C. and the results of which were early applied to calendarial reckoning. Several sundials have been recovered from Pompeii, one bearing an inscription in the old Oscan dialect [Fig. 27]. Full directions for the construction of sundials are given by Vitruvius, who tells of a number of different forms in use in his time. These he says were invented by Berosus the Chaldaean (*fl.* 250 B.C.)

and by various Greeks of whom Aristarchus of Samos
(*c.* 220–143 B.C.) and Eudoxus (*fl. c.* 350 B.C.) are the best
known.   The construction of these various forms implies
command of considerable mechanical skill and some
efficiency in the making and recording of elementary
astronomical observations.   Sundials suitable for use by
travellers have been recovered from several sites [Fig. 28].
Vitruvius describes another form of time-measurer.   It
is a water clock working on an extremely simple and effec-

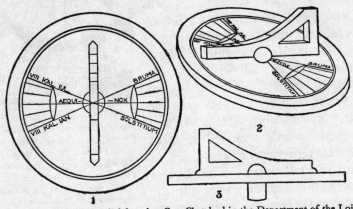

FIG. 28.—Portable sundial found at Cret-Chatelard in the Department of the Loire.
The winter solstice (*bruma*) is given as the eighth day before the Kalends of January,
i.e. December 23, and the summer solstice (*solstitium*) as the eighth day before the
Kalends of July, i.e. June 22.   The dates now given are one day earlier.   The ground
plan of the sundial is shown at 1, the complete sundial in perspective at 2, and in
elevation at 3.

tive principle [Fig. 29].   He says he borrowed the idea
from Ctesibius (*c.* 120 B.C.), an ingenius barber of Alexandria.
   The difference in the length of day in different latitudes
was well known to the Romans.   From the fact that the
longest day in Alexandria was 14 hours, in Italy 15, and in
Britain 17 hours, Pliny deduces that lands close to the pole
must have a 24-hours day around the summer solstice,
and a 24-hours night in winter.

   Many passages in Pliny reflect a contest concerning
the form of the earth, reminding us of the similar

dispute of the seventeenth century that turned around the name of Copernicus and the views of Galileo.  Pliny opens his work with a description of the general structure of the universe.  With the theory of the spherical form of the earth had come the view that man was much more widely distributed than had been thought. The general character of ancient mathematical geography had been fixed by Eratosthenes, who presided over the school of Alexandria for more than forty years, till about 194 B.C.  Geographical theory had altered by little since his time, but, with the dissemination of his sphericist view of the earth, the belief in the existence of antipodean races became not un-usual among educated Romans.

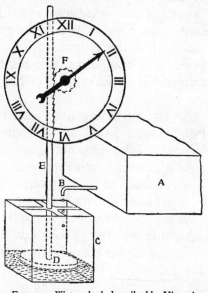

Fig. 29.—Water clock described by Vitruvius. From the tank A water drips at a uniform rate through the small pipe B into the reservoir C in which is the float D. From the upper surface of D rises the shaft E, the teeth of which, by their movement as the shaft rises, rotate the cog-wheel F. To this cog-wheel is attached a hand the position of which, on the surface of the dial, indicates the hour.

'Science and the opinion of the mob,' says Pliny, 'are in direct opposition. According to the former the whole sphere of the earth is inhabited by men whose feet point towards each other while all have the heavens above their heads.  But the mob ask how men on the antipodes do not fall off ; as though that did not present the opposite query why they should not wonder at *our* not falling off.  Usually, however, the crowd objects if one urges that water also tends to be spherical.  Yet nothing is more obvious, since hanging drops always form little spheres.' Among his proofs of the curved surface of the earth is the gradual appearance of ships, mast first, then hull, as they approach the shore.

The teaching of the spherical form of the earth thus became the common belief of the educated during Imperial times. There were also individuals by whom the heliocentric teaching, of which the germ was among the Greeks, was not entirely ignored. Copernicus fifteen hundred years later sought to link his teaching to antiquity and quoted Cicero in support of his views.

To the moon and fixed stars the Romans had already in Pliny's time began to attribute an influence on human affairs. ' Who does not know,' he asks, ' that when Sirius rises it exercises influence on the widest stretch of earth ? ' The influence of the dog-star is an idea that may be traced back in Greek literature at least as far as Hesiod (8th century B.C.) and has given us our modern superstition of the ' dog days.' It was recognized that the moon had influence on tides and it was thought that influencing the outer world, the macrocosm, it had influence also on the body of man, the microcosm. With the waxing of the moon it was believed that the muscles became bigger and blood increased. This theory gave rise to the practice of periodical bloodletting.

The supposed influence of the heavenly bodies on the earth and on the life of man is a topic that leads on to judicial astrology. A knowledge of that subject became under the Empire a professional possession illegal and prohibited but often tolerated and resorted to even by emperors. Astrology was beginning to spread in Rome in the first century of the Christian era. ' There are those,' Pliny tells us, ' who assign [all human events] to the influence of the stars, and to the laws of their nativity. They suppose that God, once for all, issues his decrees and never after interferes. This opinion begins to gain ground and both the learned and the vulgar are falling in with it.' The art was of foreign origin. The credit of its invention is always ascribed to the 'Chaldaeans.' Orientals were certainly practising astrology in Rome from an early date, but the main channel of transmission was Greek. 'As for the branch of astronomy which concerns the influences of the twelve signs of the zodiac, the five planets and the sun and moon on man's life,' says Vitruvius, ' we must leave it to the calculations of the Chaldaeans to whom belongs the art of casting nativities, which enables them to declare the past and future.'

It is largely against these Chaldaeans that Cicero directs his dialogue *On divination*. He misunderstands the basis of astrology and marshals ancient and fallacious arguments against it. Yet even Cicero accepted some astrological doctrine, and in his *Dream of Scipio* he spoke of the planet Jupiter as helpful and Mars as harmful. To the early Christian writers astrology was even more abhorrent, for it seemed to them to be the negation of that doctrine of free-will that was so dear to them. Tertullian (*c.* 155–*c.* 222), Lactantius (*c.* 260–*c.* 340), and Augustine (354–430) all inveigh against it. With the spread of Christianity in the West and the disappearance of the Stoic philosophy, astrology passed into the background to return with the Arabian revival and the rise of the Universities.

A large literature arose on the subject, of which we have remains in the works of Manilius (1st century A.D.), Censorius (3rd century A.D.), and Firmicus Maternus (4th century A.D.). Nevertheless, astrology seems on the whole to have been rather less cultivated in Rome itself than the general state of society and the wide spread of the Stoic philosophy might perhaps suggest. Lovers sought to learn of astrologers a lucky day for a wedding, travellers inquired what was the best day for starting on a journey, and builders asked the correct date for laying a foundation stone. All these may easily be paralleled by instances among the empty-headed in our own time and country. But Galen

(A.D. 130–200), who practised among the well-to-do and educated, assures us that they only bothered about astrology for forecasting legacies—and again a parallel might be drawn. The new astrology introduced by Greeks and ' Chaldaeans ' tended, however, to replace the native magical system. The process can be observed in action in the work of Censorinus, *De die natali*.

But astrology must not be considered only as a super-stition and an occupation for empty heads and idle hands. The astrological system of antiquity was, after all, only a formal statement of the beliefs concerning the nature and working of our mundane sphere which the ideas of a scientific astronomy and cosmology had fostered.    Faith in it was almost part of the Stoic creed.    In the presentment of the world which science thus made, there was no room for those anthropomorphic gods, the belief in whom was still fostered by the priests and held by the multitude.    The spread of science had led at last to a complete breach between the official faith and the opinions of the educated classes. The idea of ' universal solidarity,' of the interdependence on one another of all parts of the universe, produced a new form of religion.    The world itself must be divine. ' Deity,' says Pliny, ' only means nature.'    From such a view to the monotheism of Virgil, in which the world as a whole is regarded as the artistic product of an external god, is perhaps no great step.

On the whole, however, science, linked with Stoicism, failed to take that step, and assumed among later Latin writers a fatalistic and pessimistic mood. ' God, if God there be, was outside the world and could not be expected to care for it,' says Pliny.    The idea of immortality seems to him but the ' childish babble ' of those who are possessed by the fear of death, as Lucretius had once maintained.    After death, so Pliny would have us believe, man is as he was before he was born—and this he tells us as he plunges into his magic-ridden pages !

Once and once only in these Latin scientific writings have

we a clear note of real hope. It is significant that that note is sounded in connexion with a statement of a belief in the *progress* of knowledge, an echo of the Greek thought of the fifth and fourth centuries B.C. It is significant too that the note is sounded by one who approached, nearer perhaps than any other pagan Latin philosopher, to the idea of the divine immanence. In his *Quaestiones naturales* Seneca wrote :

There are many things akin to highest deity that are still obscure. Some may be too subtle for our powers of comprehension, others imperceptible to us because such exalted majesty conceals itself in the holiest part of its sanctuary, forbidding access to any power save that of the spirit. How many heavenly bodies revolve unseen by human eye ! . . . How many discoveries are reserved for the ages to come when our memory shall be no more, for this world of ours contains matter for investigation for all generations . . . God has not revealed all things to man and has entrusted us with but a fragment of His mighty work. But He who directs all things, who has established and laid the foundation of the world, who has clothed Himself with Creation, He is greater and better than that which He has wrought. Hidden from our eyes, He can only be reached by the spirit . . . On entering a temple we assume all signs of reverence. How much more reverent then should we be before the heavenly bodies, the stars, the very nature of God !

But the science of antiquity as exhibited elsewhere in Latin writings contains very little of this belief in man's destiny, this hope for human knowledge. The world in which the Imperial Roman lived was a finite world bound by the firmament and limited by a flaming rampart (*Frontispiece*). His fathers had thought that great space peopled by *numina*, ' divinities,' that needed to be propitiated. The new dispensation—that *lex naturae* of the world that had so many parallels with the *jus gentium* of the Empire—had now taken the place of those awesome beings.

In the inevitableness of the action of that law Lucretius the Epicurean might find comfort from the unknown terror. Yet for the Stoic it must have remained a limited, fixed, rigid, and cruel law. His vision, we must remember, was very different from that given by the spacious claim of modern science which explores into ever wider and wider regions of space and time and thought. It was an iron, nerveless, tyrannical universe which science had raised and in which the Roman thinker must have felt himself fettered, imprisoned, crushed. The Roman had forsaken his early gods, that crowd of strangely vague yet personal beings whose ceremonial propitiation in every event and circumstance had filled his fathers' lives. He had had before him an alternative of the oriental cults whose gods were but mad magicians—a religion unworthy of a philosopher—and the new religion of science whose god, he now saw, worked by a mechanical rule. He had abandoned the faith of his fathers and had flung himself into the arms of what he believed to be a lovelier god, and lo ! he found himself embracing a machine ! His soul recoiled and he fled into Christianity. Science had induced that essential pessimism which clouds much of the thought of later antiquity. It was reaction against this pessimism which led to the great spiritual changes in the midst of which antiquity went up in flames and smoke.

PLATE II

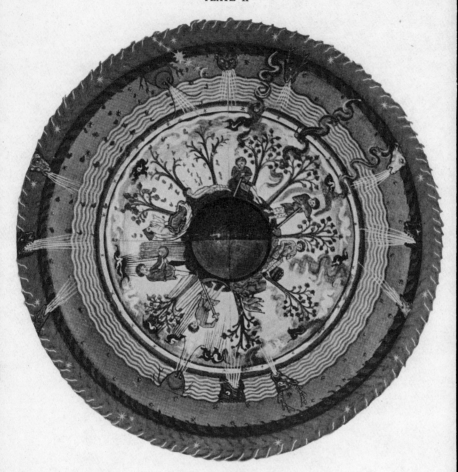

CELESTIAL INFLUENCES ON MEN, ANIMALS, AND PLANTS

From a MS. at Lucca of the *Liber Divinorum Operum Simplicis Hominis* of Hildegard, written about 1200.
See pp. 58 and 218–21.

# II

## THE DARK AGES AND THE DAWN OF SCIENCE

### § 1. *The Limits of the Middle Ages of Science*

THE Middle Ages, by general admission, present us with a set-back in the development of scientific ideas. Between the fall of the Empire and the revolution in physics carried through by Galileo in the seventeenth century, the conception as to the nature of the world in which they lived that prevailed among educated men was not conducive to the first-hand study of nature. It is because these views were finally shattered by Galileo and his successors that many of the authors whose works we shall have to discuss may seem insignificant. Yet some of these men, who are now well-nigh forgotten, have had their share in determining the current of human thought and with it the course of human destiny. The test of importance that we must apply is not our assent to their opinions but the influence their works have had on the period we are considering. We must remember, too, that the period has the intense interest of presenting us with the *beginning* of something, the birth— or rather the rebirth—of the scientific idea.

We cannot, then, pass over in silence the millennium that intervenes between antiquity and modernity. There is a continuity in the history of the human intellect. Looking back on the hundreds of thousands of years during which man has inhabited the surface of this planet, we cannot fail to be struck by the fact that only during the last few thousand years have civilizations appeared. We must, therefore, suppose that these civilizations developed with some sort of dependence on each other, that, in fact, they are versions of one movement in the development of humanity. To understand our own version of civilization we must trace it back to its origin, and this we can do only *through* the Middle Ages. It is beside the point to urge that the Middle Ages contributed little to the actual sum of knowledge of the external world. What we want to know is *why* they contributed so little, and *how*, contributing so little, they yet succeeded in passing on to our time the basic ideas from which science has grown.

These Middle Ages, after all, were not a thousand years of cataclysm. They represent doubtless a deterioration of the human mind, but the nature and causes of that deterioration are themselves the subject of intense scientific interest. The Middle Ages can no more be disregarded in considering the general course of science than can a degenerate or parasitic series of plants or animals be passed over when considering the larger group to which they belong and from which they have sprung. The very degeneracy of such a series has an interest of its own, and may, by helping us to exclude accidental elements, enable us to detect essential traits which we might otherwise overlook.

We begin our task with some attempt to delimit the period with which we are concerned. Without attempting to define science, we may describe it as *the process of making knowledge*. Being a *process* it must also involve the idea of progress or at least of movement. The world of science is a dynamic world with its own stores of ever-acting energy. The world of the mediaeval thinker, on the other hand, was a static one, a world in which such forces as were acting were impressed from without. When and how was this static element introduced ?

We may first consider the *terminus a quo* of the mediaeval attitude toward the external world. The Middle Ages begin, for science, at that period when the ancients ceased to make knowledge. Now, ancient science can be traced clearly as an active process up to the end of the second century of the Christian era. Galen, one of the very greatest and most creative biologists of all time, died A.D. 200. Ptolemy, one of the greatest of the cosmographers, was his older contemporary (p. 47). After Galen and Ptolemy, Greek science flags and scientific inspiration dwindles.

Mathematics holds out the longest, but with the mathematician Theon of Alexandria, who died about 400, we part altogether with the impulse of the science of antiquity. Stoicism and Neoplatonism too, the chief systems of thought of the late Empire, are dying and are giving place to that great philosophical and religious movement, the repercussion of which is felt right through the Middle Ages and down to our own time. The standpoint of its great protagonists, Tertullian (155–222), Lactantius (260–340), and, above all, St. Jerome (340–420) and St. Augustine (354–430), is outside the department with which we have here to deal, but it was assuredly not conducive to the exact study and record of phenomena. We may fix the end of Antiquity and the beginning of the Middle Ages for science at the end of the fourth or the beginning of the fifth century [chart, p. 66].

The *terminus ad quem* of mediaeval science is, perhaps, less easy to determine. Mediaevalization, in our view, was a slow process under the action of which the human mind, failing to increase the stock of phenomenal knowledge, sank slowly into an increasing ineptitude. At a certain point the nadir of mental deterioration was reached and intellectual competence tended again upward. The time of lowest degradation of the human intellect varied according

to the state of civilization in different parts of Europe. It
was probably most general about the tenth century. After
this may be discerned a slow ascent. Later, in the thirteenth
and fourteenth centuries, we encounter considerable extension of natural knowledge. There is still, however, no
widespread acceptance of the ancient view that had been
voiced by the philosopher Seneca (3 B.C.–A.D. 65) that
knowledge may be indefinitely extended (p. 57). That view
appears to be an essential element in any effective doctrine
of progress. In the scholastic period, however, there
do at last appear a very few forward-looking minds, such
as that of Roger Bacon (1214–94), but they are as yet very
rare and exceptional. When we reach the fifteenth century
and the full influence of Humanism we encounter a larger
number of forward-looking thinkers, but they are still
isolated. Not until the sixteenth century is there any
effort, at once organized and conscious, to translate into
action this new-born hope in the future. It is only in the
early years of the seventeenth century that the hope obtains
formal philosophical expression once more, with Francis
Bacon (1561–1626) and René Descartes (1596–1650). By
that time, however, not only are the Middle Ages past but
they are so much forgotten that the reading public needs
skilled interpreters to explain the mediaeval point of view.

If we have to name a year for the end-point of mediaeval
science we would select 1543. In that year appeared two
fundamental modern works based on the experimental
method, the *De fabrica corporis humani* of the Belgian Andreas
Vesalius (1514–64) [Fig. 46] and the *De revolutionibus orbium
caelestium* of the Pole Nicholas Copernicus (1473–1543)
[Fig. 45]. It is true that for generations before 1543 there
was a dawning consciousness of the inadequacy of the
mediaeval cosmic system. That discontent, however, was
vague and ill-expressed, and of the nature rather of mental
discomfort than of intellectual revolt. It is also true that for
some generations after the time of Vesalius and Copernicus
the characteristic doctrines of the science of the Middle

Ages were almost universally taught in the schools. Such doctrines, too, were still diffused by literature, and are, for instance, displayed in the writings of Shakespeare. But the ideas on which the works of Vesalius and Copernicus had been based gain, from this time onward, an ever wider hearing. The year 1543 saw for the first time two published authoritative works that formally rejected the old views. These works, though produced by men who had steeped themselves in the old system, yet provided a new standpoint. For science, then, 1543 is the natural *terminus ad quem* of the Middle Ages.

Now, since the human mind turned on its upward course after the tenth century, and since the process was accelerated during the great scholastic period of the thirteenth century and again at the Revival of Learning of the fifteenth century, it may be asked why should we not choose one or other of these dates as the end-point of the scientific Middle Ages ? The thirteenth century, the epoch of consolidation of Catholic philosophy, has been selected as one of exceptional enlightenment, and has been specially exalted by those who lay great emphasis on the continuing rôle of the Church in the development of the intellectual system of our modern world. There are, therefore, some who would place the division in the thirteenth rather than in the sixteenth century. There are yet others, biased perhaps by the literary training of the classics, who would place the cleavage about the year 1400. They would make the Revival of Learning, and especially of Greek letters, the basis of the differentiation between mediaeval and modern. There are even those who are so steeped in pessimism concerning our own time and have such a yearning for the ' Ages of Faith ' that they have found much to exalt in the spiritual life of the earlier Middle Ages and little to appreciate in the rationalism of the thirteenth and later centuries.

Yet to make the great division at any such date as 1000, 1200, or 1400 would be an error, because, with very few exceptions, the point of view of the eleventh-century encyclopaedist, of the thirteenth-century scholastic, and of the fifteenth-century scholar was formally and essentially an effort to return to the past. It was the literature and language of antiquity, the antiquity of the fathers, of the philosophers, or of the poets, that these men sought more or less vainly to revive.

In an encyclopaedia of the eleventh century nothing can be found that is not derived from patristic sources.

The great Catholic scholastics of the thirteenth century believed that they were reconstructing the philosophy of Aristotle. Few first-hand students of that great man of science will now be found to agree with the interpretation supplied by them. It is true that, despite the errors of philosophical interpretation, scientific elements are not wholly wanting in scholastic writings. Yet in that age the infinity of the knowable universe was passionately denied, originality of view was furtively hidden under the cloak of authority, and knowledge—so the knowers claimed—was always based on the wisdom of antiquity.

Imitation rather than origination was the characteristic mental attitude also of the most enthusiastic scholars of the fifteenth century. The Revival of Learning, even the process by which the ancient texts were recovered, though it may rightly be regarded as containing scientific elements, had for its motive the imitation of the past by the present, rather than the modern archaeological aim of the mental reconstruction of the past with the object of understanding the present. The ablest writers of the time sought to become the ' apes of Cicero.' What is true of the literary studies of the Renaissance is just as true of the scientific studies of the period. The rescue of the Greek texts enormously enlarged the mental horizon, it is true, but it kept vision ever on one plane. It chained men's minds more closely than ever to the past, though it was a newly discovered past. Even the revolt against the ' Arabists,' led with such enthusiasm by the classical scholars, had for its object a yet closer return to antiquity.

FIG. 30.—TENTH-CENTURY FIGURE SHOWING ZODIACAL SCHEME

In the centre is the figure of Christ in the attitude of benediction. Around him are the signs of the
Zodiac assigned each to a part of the body. Thus we read *Aries d(ominatu)r frons hominis, Taurus
d(ominatu)r nares,* and so through the body to *Pisces d(ominatu)r tibie.* Above the scribe has written
*Secundum philosophorum deliramenta notantur duodecima signa ita ab arietem incipiamus,* "According to the
ravings of the philosophers the twelve signs are thus assigned. We begin with the Ram"; and
below, *Hec omnia signa sunt corporis hominis et signa sunt solis in celo apparentis.* At the four corners are
four figures representing the four seasons.

There is a point, however, at which those interested in phenomena—the physicists, and especially the physicians, —show a general willingness to turn their gaze from the past and toward the future. We may at least say of the two great works that appeared in 1543 that they present a new thing in that their authors are looking to the future for the development and vindication of their views.

The work of the aged Copernicus, though not published till 1543, had been prepared many years before. It is therefore much the more conservative of the two, and still bears marks of the Middle Ages on every page [Fig. 45]. Vesalius, on the other hand, when he published his magnificently printed and illustrated *Fabrica* was a vigorous young man of but twenty-eight [Fig. 46]. Only four years earlier he had produced a treatise which, while rejecting the anatomical views of the Arabists, had expressed full faith in the complete reliability of Galen. His conversion had been rapid, and now he parts definitely with the Middle Ages. As an anatomical observer he has become independent. His physiological theory, however, is still based on Galen just as surely as the circular orbits ascribed by Copernicus to the planets are derived from Aristotle.

With Copernicus and Vesalius, however, organized and systematic *observation* had found her place. Fabricius ab Aquapendente (1537–1619) in Anatomy and Tycho Brahe (1546–1601) in Astronomy did but practise a method which their two great predecessors had formally initiated. But for the process of free generalization on such observation and for the effective wielding of the new weapon of *experiment* the world had still to wait for the generation of Galileo (1564–1642), Kepler (1571–1630), and Harvey (1576–1657).

## § 2. *The Dark Age*

Thus for effective purposes we may place the limits of the mediaeval attitude towards nature between the years 400 and 1543, with a debatable period of another half-century up to 1600. This vast stretch of time is divided

## THE CLASSICAL TWILIGHT

| Latins | Greeks | Fathers | |
|---|---|---|---|
| | Ptolemy | | |
| | Soranus | | |
| | Galen | | |
| **200** | | | **200** |
| Apuleius | | Tertullian | |
| Porphyry | | | |
| Chalcidius | | Lactantius | |
| **300** | | | **300** |
| Pseudo { -Dioscorides / -Hippocrates / -Apuleius | Oribasius | [Baptism of Constantine] | |
| | Nemesius | St. Ambrose | |
| Firmicus  Avienus | | | |
| Vindician | Theon | St. Jerome | |
| **400** Martianus Capella | **THE DARK AGE** | St. Augustine | **400** |
| Macrobius | | | |
| Sextus Placitus | | | |
| Marcellus Empiricus | | | |
| **500** Moschion | Alexander of Tralles | | **500** |
| Boethius | | | |
| Cassiodorus | | | |
| | | Gregory the Great | |
| **600** Isidore | Paul of Aegina | | **600** |
| | | | |
| **700** Bede | | | **700** |
| Alcuin | | | |
| **800** Raban | | | **800** |
| Erigena | | | |
| **900** | **AGE OF ARABIAN INFILTRATION** | | **900** |
| | *First Arabian Impact* | | |
| | Donnolo | | |
| | ' Alchandrus ' | | |
| Byrhtferth | Gerbert | | |
| **1000** Gariopontus and other | Herman the Cripple | | **1000** |
| early Salernitans | | | |
| *Translators* | | | |
| Constantine | Later Salernitans | | |
| Adelard | | *Transmuters* | |
| **1100** | Marbod | Hugh of St. Victor | **1100** |
| | Odo of Meune | Bernard Sylvestris | |
| Avendeath.  Gonzalez | | Hildegard | |
| Robert of Chester | | | |
| Gerard of Cremona | **SCHOLASTIC AGE** | Alexander of Neckam | |
| Michael Scot | *Experimenters* | | |
| **1200** | Witelo.  Adam Marsh | Alexander of Hales | **1200** |
| | Roger Bacon.  Pecham | Albert | |
| Alfred the Englishman | William of Saliceto | St. Thomas Aquinas | |
| Farragut | Theodoric | Grosseteste.  Vincent of | |
| | | Beauvais  [lishman | |
| | | Bartholomew the Eng- | |
| **1300** | Arnald.  Mondino | | **1300** |
| | Peter of Abano | | |
| | Levi ben Gerson | | |
| | Guy de Chauliac | | |
| **1400** | Nicholas of Cusa  [nus | | **1400** |
| | Purbach.  Regiomonta- | | |
| | Pomponazzi | | |
| | Leonardo | | |
| **1500** | Paracelsus | | **1500** |
| | Copernicus | | |
| | Vesalius | | |

FIG. 31.—See page 67.

by an event of the highest importance for the history of the human intellect. Between the beginning of the tenth and the end of the twelfth century there was a remarkable outburst of intellectual activity in Western Islam. This movement reacted with great effect on Latin Europe, and especially on its views of nature, by means of works which gradually reached Christendom in translations from the Arabic. In the light of this great intellectual event we may divide our vast mediaeval period into three parts, an earlier *Dark Age*, an intermediate *Age of Arabian Infiltration*, and a later *Scholastic Age*. The *Age of Arabian Infiltration* may itself be conveniently subdivided into an earlier period of *First Arabian Impact* and a later one of *Arabian Translation* [Fig. 31]. During all these periods the general beliefs as to the nature of the external world hardly change, but the difference in presentment of the material is such that the mediaevalist need seldom be in doubt into which category to place any document from these centuries treating of a scientific topic.

The task of the first mediaeval period was the conveyance of the remains of the ancient wisdom to later ages. During the closing centuries of the classical decline, the literature that was to be conveyed had been delimited and translated into Latin, the only language common to the learned West. We may briefly discuss this classical heritage.

The work of Plato that is least attractive and most obscure to the modern mind fitted in well with the prevalent views of the Neoplatonists. The commentary on the *Timaeus*, prepared by Chalcidius in the third century from a translation by Apuleius in the second, presents the basis of views held throughout the entire Middle Ages on the nature of the universe and of man. Thus the *Timaeus* became one of the most influential of all the works of antiquity, and especially it carried the central dogma of mediaeval science, the doctrine of the macrocosm and microcosm.

Of Aristotle there probably survived only the *Categories* and the *De interpretatione*, translated in the sixth century by

Boethius (480–524). A Greek introduction to the *Categories* had been prepared by Porphyry in the second century, and this also was rendered into Latin by Boethius. Thus the only Aristotelian writings known to the Dark Age of science were the logical works, and these determined the main extra-theological interest for many centuries. It is a world-misfortune that Boethius did not see his way to prepare versions of those works of the Peripatetic school that display powers of observation. Had a translation of Aristotle's *Historia animalium* or *De generatione animalium* survived, or had a Latin version of the works of Theophrastus on plants reached the earlier Middle Ages, the whole mental history of the race might have been different. Boethius repaired the omission, to some small extent, by handing on certain mathematical treatises of his own compilation, the *De institutione arithmetica*, the *De institutione musica*, and the (doubtful) *Geometrica*. These works preserved throughout the darkest centuries some fragment of mathematical knowledge. Thanks to them we can at least say that during the long degradation of the human intellect, mathematics, the science last to sink with the fall of the Greek intellect, was not dragged down quite so low as the other departments of knowledge. The main gift of Boethius to the world, his *De consolatione philosophiae*, which preserved some classical taste and feeling, lies outside our field.

A somewhat similar service to that of Boethius was rendered by Macrobius (395–423) and by Martianus Capella (*c.* 500). The latter, especially in his *Satyricon*, provided the Dark Age with a complete encyclopaedia. The work is divided into nine books. The first two contain an allegory, in heavy and clumsy style, of the marriage of the god Mercury to the nymph Philology. Of the last seven books of the work, each contains an account of one of the ' Liberal Arts,' grammar, dialectic, rhetoric, geometry, arithmetic, astronomy, and music, a classification of studies that dates back to Varro (116–27 B.C., p. 10) and was retained throughout the Middle Ages. The section on Astronomy has a passage containing a heliocentric view of the universe, a view that had been familiar to certain earlier Greek astronomers. The cosmology of Capella, like that of Chalcidlus, is Neoplatonic, as is also the work of Macrobius, whose commentary on the *Somnium Scipionis* of Cicero gave rise to some of the most prevalent cosmological conceptions of the first mediaeval period.

In addition to the little cosmography, mathematics, and astronomy that could be gleaned from such writings as these, the Dark Age inherited a group of scientific and medical works from the period of classical decline. By far the most important was the *Natural History* of Pliny the elder (A.D. 23–79, p. 12), which deeply influenced the early encyclopaedists. Somewhat akin to it are the *Quaestiones naturales* of the moralist Seneca (3 B.C.–A.D. 65, p. 14), whose ethical attitude toward phenomena delighted many mediaeval writers by whom he was taken for a Christian.

Very curious and characteristic is a group of later medical pseudepigrapha bearing the names of Dioscorides, Hippocrates, and Apuleius. These extremely popular works were probably all prepared or at least translated between the fourth and sixth centuries. They provided much of the medical equipment of the Dark Age and reappear in the early Anglo-Saxon vernacular literature (see page 141).

Such material, then, was the basis of the mediaeval scientific heritage. Traces of it are encountered in *De Institutionibus divinarum et humanarum literarum* of Cassiodorus (490–585), perhaps the earliest general writer whose works bear the authentic mediaeval stamp. The scientific heritage is, however, much more fully displayed in the *Origines* of Isidore of Seville, a late sixth-century work which formed a cyclopaedia of all the sciences in the form of an explanation of the terms proper to each. For many centuries Isidore was very widely read, and the series Isidore (560–636), Bede (673–735), Alcuin (735–804), Rabanus Maurus (776–856), who borrow from one another

successively and all from Pliny, may be said to contain the
natural knowledge of the Dark Age.  These writers are
summarized by the early eleventh-century English writer

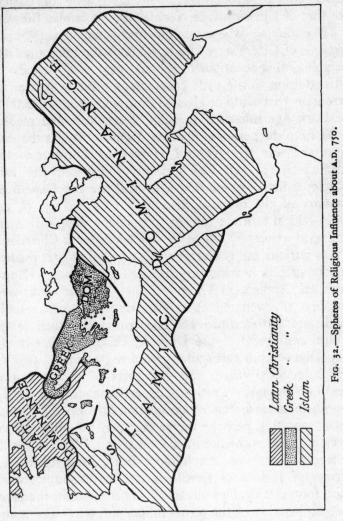

FIG. 32.—Spheres of Religious Influence about A.D. 750.

Byrhtferth (died *c.* 1020, see page 143), whose copious
commentary on Bede may be regarded as the final product
of the nature-knowledge of the Dark Age.  With this some-

what belated author we part company with the Dark Age, and enter upon a new period, with new forces and new movements at work.

### § 3. *The Age of Arabian Infiltration*

The tenth century and those that follow bring us into relation with the wisdom of the East. In these centuries the relation of East and West with which we are nowadays familiar is reversed. In our time most Oriental peoples recognize the value of Western culture, and give it the sincerest form of flattery. The Oriental recognizes that with the Occident are science and learning, power and organization and public spirit. But the admitted superiority of the West does not extend to the sphere of religion. The Oriental who nowadays gladly accepts the Occidental as his judge, his physician, or his teacher, wholly repudiates, and perhaps despises, his religion. In the Europe of the tenth, eleventh, and twelfth centuries it was far other. The Westerner knew full well that Islam held the learning and science of antiquity. His proficiency in arms and administration had been more than sufficiently proved— the Occidental belief in them is enshrined in our Semitic words ' arsenal ' and ' admiral.' There was a longing, too, for the intellectual treasures of the East, but the same fear and repugnance to its religion that the East now feels for Western religion. And the Western experienced obstacles in obtaining the desired Oriental learning analogous to those now encountered by the Eastern in the Occident.

The earliest definitely Oriental influence that we can discern as affecting ideas about nature is of the character of infiltration rather than direct translation. The first literary agents of this process appear to have been mainly Jews who had been under Saracen rule. Such influence can be traced in two works in the Hebrew language by Sabbatai ben Abraham ben Joel (913–82), better known as Donnolo, a Jew of Otranto who practised medicine at Rossano in Southern Italy. Donnolo learnt Arabic while a prisoner in Saracen hands ; he was taught the language by a native of Baghdad, and, like Constantine the African in the next century, claimed to have studied ' the sciences of the Greeks, Arabs, Babylonians, and Indians.' He travelled in the Italian peninsula in search of learning, and must thus have spread some of his Arabic science. His most important work, known as the *Book of Creation*, is dated to the year 946. It is a mystical treatise of great historical and philological interest and involves a knowledge of astrology. It unquestionably draws on Arabic sources, and sets forth fully the ancient doctrine encountered in the *Timaeus* of the macrocosm and microcosm or parallelism between the external world of nature and the internal world of man's body (see page 215). This idea was very popular among the Arabian writers.

The earliest Latin document exhibiting Oriental influence is a treatise on astrology to which the name ' Alchandrus ' (Alexander ?) is attached. This work has come down to us in a manuscript written about 950 probably in Southern France. The repeated use of Hebrew and Arabic equivalents for the names of constellations and planets, and the occasional use of Hebrew script, leave no doubt that it also is of Jewish origin.

The existence of these works enables us to understand the Oriental influence in the mathematical writings of the learned Pope Silvester II (Gerbert, d. 1003), who spent some years in Northern Spain, where Jews are known to have acted as intermediaries between Moslems and Christians. Gerbert was, perhaps, among the earliest to introduce the so-called ' Arabic system '—really the Indian system—of numbering, which slowly replaced the much clumsier Roman system, with its tiresome use of the abacus for simple mathematical processes. He is also believed to have instigated a translation from the Arabic of a work on the Astrolabe.

Herman the Cripple (1013–54) spent his life at the Benedictine abbey of Reichenau in Switzerland. He wrote certain mathematical and astrological works which were extensively used in the following century. Herman was

FIG. 33.—Spheres of Religious Influence about 1150.

unable to read Arabic, and could not travel by reason of his infirmity. Yet his writings display much Oriental influence,

FIG. 34.—Spheres of Religious Influence about 1500.

which was almost certainly conveyed to him by wandering scholars of the type of Donnolo and ' Alchandrus.' Similar though somewhat belated evidence of the influence of what we have called the process of Arabic infiltration is exhibited

in the lapidary of Marbod of Anjou, Bishop of Rennes
(1035–1123), and in the extremely widely read work on the
medicinal use of herbs, probably composed by Odo of
Meune, Abbot of Beauprai (Macer Floridus, d. 1161).

The Arabic learning thus beginning to trickle through
to the West in a much corrupted form was, however, by
no means an entirely native Saracen product; it was derived
ultimately from Greek sources. There was, indeed, yet
one channel by which the original Greek wisdom might
still reach Europe. Communication between the West
and the Byzantine East was very little in evidence in the
centuries with which we are now concerned, but a Greek
tradition still lingered in certain Southern Italian centres,
and especially in Sicily. South Italy and Sicily remained
for centuries under the nominal suzerainty of Byzantium,
and the dialects of the ' many-tongued isle ' bear traces to
this very day of the Greek spoken there and in Calabria and
Apulia, until late mediaeval times. But the Saracens had
begun their attacks on Sicily as early as the eighth century,
and their rule did not cease until the Norman conquest of
the eleventh century. The Semitic language of the Saracens
left the same impress on the island as did their art and
architecture, so that between the tenth and thirteenth centuries Sicily is a source of Greek and Arabic learning for
Western Europe.

One seat of learning in the Southern Italian area felt
especially early the influence of the Graeco-Arabic culture.
Salerno, on the Gulf of Naples, had been a medical centre
as far back as the ninth century (see p. 240). It is
clear from surviving manuscripts that, even apart from the
Greek language, some traces of ancient Greek medicine
lingered in Latin translation widely diffused in Magna
Graecia during the centuries that succeeded the downfall
of the Western Empire. Such learning as remained was
galvanized into life by Saracenic energy and, with what we
know of the carrying agents of Arabic culture, it is easy
to understand the tradition that attributes the founding of

the great medical school of Salerno to the co-operation of a Greek, an Arab, a Latin, and a Jew (see p. 241). From the latter part of the eleventh century Salernitan material is full of Semitic words, a few of which, such as the anatomical term ' nucha ' and the names of some drugs, linger in medical nomenclature to this day.

## § 4. *Translation from the Arabic*

A very important agent of the Arabic revival was Constantine the African (d. 1087), a native of Carthage, who came to Italy about the middle of the eleventh century. He became a monk at Montecassino, and spent the rest of his life turning current Arabic medical and scientific works into Latin. His sources are mainly Jewish writers of North African origin. In his desire for self-exultation Constantine often conceals the names of the authors from whom he borrows, or he gives them inaccurately. His knowledge of both the languages which he was treating was far from thorough and his translations are wretched. But these versions were very influential, and they remained current in the West long after they had been replaced by the better workmanship of Toledo students of the type of Gerard of Cremona (1114–87). It is interesting to note that one of Constantine's works is dedicated to Alphanus, Archbishop of Salerno (d. 1085), who was perhaps the first medical translator direct from the Greek.

The earliest Oriental influences that reached the West had thus been brought by foreign agents or carriers, but the desire for knowledge could not be satisfied thus. The movement that was soon to give rise to the universities was shaping itself, and the Western student was beginning to become more curious and more desirous of going to the well-springs of Eastern wisdom.

His main difficulty was one of language. Arabic was the language of Eastern science and letters, and its idiom was utterly different from the speech of the peoples of Europe. Moreover, its grammar had not yet been reduced to rule in any Latin work, nor could teachers be easily procured. Even in the thirteenth century we find that Roger Bacon, though he clearly perceived the importance of linguistic study and eagerly sought to unlock the literature of foreign tongues, had still not found the key. He had only time to commence laboriously the grammatical apparatus of the Greek and Hebrew languages. The only way to learn Arabic was to go to an Arabic-speaking country. Yet this

FIG. 35.—Map to illustrate the recession of Islam in the Spanish peninsula. The figures after the names of the towns are the dates of their conquest by Christendom.

was a dangerous and difficult adventure, involving hardship, secrecy, and perhaps abjuration of faith. Moreover, to learn the language at all adequately for rendering scientific treatises into Latin meant a stay of years, while the work of translation demanded also some understanding of the subject-matter to be translated. There is good evidence that an effective knowledge of this kind was very rarely attained by Westerns, and probably never until the later twelfth century.

At the period during which Western science began to

draw from Moslem sources there were only two areas of
contact of the two cultures : these were respectively Spain
and ' the Sicilies.' The conditions in the two were somewhat similar. In the tenth century the Iberian peninsula
was Moslem save for the small kingdoms of the French
march, Leon, Navarre, and Aragon. Here the grip of

FIG. 36.—Italy at the beginning of the thirteenth century.

Islam had soon relaxed and this territory remained historically, religiously, racially, and linguistically a part of
the Latin West. The Moslem South was ruled from Cordova, which became increasingly Mohammedanized, but
at the more northern Toledo the subject population, though
speaking an Arabic patois, remained in the main Christian,
though with a very large Jewish element. In 1085 Alphonso
VI of Leon (Alphonso I of Castille), aided by the Cid,
conquered Toledo, and there most of the work of transmission took place.

The schools of Southern Italy and Sicily were on the whole less influential, though their work of translation continued to a somewhat later date. They are, however, important in another respect, for from them went forth the first renderings of scientific works made direct from the Greek. These translations of scientific works direct from the Greek began to appear as early as the eleventh century, when Alphanus, Archbishop of Salerno (d. 1085), produced a Latin version of a work by Nemesius (fourth century). Such translations increased in number and importance gradually and very slowly. A most interesting worker in Sicily was Burgundio of Pisa (d. 1194), who made translations both from the Arabic and the Greek.

It is evident that the process of translation from Arabic, especially in Spain, was frequently carried on by the intervention of Jewish students, and many of the translated works were themselves by Jews. The tenth, eleventh, and twelfth centuries, a time of low degradation of the Latin intellect, was the best period of Jewish learning in Spain. Arabic was the natural linguistic medium of these learned Jews. Among them were the Egyptian physician Isaac Israeli ben Solomon (d. c. 1000), called in the West Isaac Judaeus, Solomon ibn Gabirol (1021–58 ?) of Saragossa, who was disguised in scholastic writings as Avicebron, and Moses ben Maimon (1135–1204) of Cordova, more familiarly known as Maimonides. These three authors were among the more important and influential that were rendered into Latin from Arabic during the Middle Ages, and their works form part of the Eastern heritage won by the translators during these centuries. All three deeply influenced Western scholasticism.

In the twelfth, thirteenth, and fourteenth centuries, when the tide had turned and Islam was in retreat, it was occasionally possible for a scholar with a gift for languages, such as Gerard of Cremona (1114–87), to find a skilled native Christian teacher. But in the tenth or eleventh century Christian learning and Christian society in Spain were subject and depressed. Like many modern peoples similarly placed, these native Christians were attached with the more fanaticism to the religion which held them together and to the language of their Church. The student of an earlier time could find no effective Christian teacher of literary Arabic, while the very sciences which he sought to acquire were suspect as the mark of the infidel and the oppressor.

It thus comes about that there is some obscurity— much of it doubtless intentional—as to the circumstances under which the best translations from the Arabic were made. It is apparent, however, that these earlier versions were sometimes prepared by a group of three or more who would interpret one to the other. One would turn the Arabic text, sentence by sentence, into the vernacular or into Hebrew, another would then render it into Latin, and perhaps a third would turn it into literary form. Naturally, in this process many words would be encountered that could not be rendered either into the vernacular or into thè barbarous Latin of the time. Especial difficulty would be encountered with technical terms. The meaning of some of these might well be imperfectly known to the translators themselves. Such words were therefore often simply carried over, transliterated, in their Arabic or Hebrew form, and the early versions are full of Semitic expressions. The Latin mediaeval astronomical and mathematical vocabularies especially abound in these Semitic words, many of which, such as ' azure,' ' zero,' ' zenith,' ' cipher,' ' azimuth,' ' algebra,' ' nadir,' and names of stars, as ' Aldebaran ' and ' Altair,' are still in use. Most of the Latin medical literature of the Middle Ages was also of Arabian origin and contained a whole host of Semitic words which, however, were almost all displaced by equivalents of Greek origin during the sixteenth and seventeenth centuries.

The sort of translation which emerged from the process that we have described may well be imagined. When it is also remembered that to reach the Arabic from the original Greek the text had sometimes already passed through similar stages with Syriac or Hebrew as intermediaries, it will be understood that the first scientific books that reached the West were often but travesties of the Greek originals from which they were ultimately derived.

Men who may be supposed to have worked in such a way as we have pictured are Adelard of Bath (c. 1100), who journeyed both to Spain and to Sicily, and published a compendium of Arabic science, and the wizard Michael Scot (1175 ?–1234 ?), who visited the court of Frederick II at Naples and produced versions or abridgements of the biological works of Aristotle. Such men, like Gerbert before them and Peter of Abano after them, were frequently accused of magical practices. More scientific in their methods and probably better equipped linguistically were Robert of Chester (c. 1144), who rendered the Koran into Latin and translated the valuable arithmetic of Al Khowarizmi (fl. 830) as well as works on alchemy and astronomy, and Alfred the Englishman (c. 1180), who translated from Arabic a corrupted work of the Aristotelian school on plants that would otherwise be lost. Robert and Alfred worked in Spain.

But the greatest and most typical of all the translators from the Arabic was Gerard of Cremona (1114–87), who spent many years at Toledo and obtained a thorough knowledge of Arabic from a native Christian teacher. He is credited with having translated into Latin no less than ninety-two complete Arabic works. Many of them are of very great length, among them being the *Almagest* of Ptolemy, on which Regiomontanus (p. 101) began his work in the fifteenth century, and the enormous *Canon* of Avicenna (980–1037), perhaps the most widely read medical treatise ever penned, editions of which continued to be issued right down to the middle of the seventeenth century. The *Canon* of Avicenna is still in current use in the East.

Contemporary with Gerard of Cremona, and perhaps stimulated by him, were certain native translators. One of these was Domenico Gonzalez (Gundissalinus, *fl.* 1140), a Christian who rendered into Latin the *Physica* and the *De caelo et mundo* of Aristotle. Another Spaniard, Johannes Hispalensis or Ibn Daud, known to the Latins as Avendeath (*fl.* 1130–55), was a converted Jew. Avendeath translated, among many other works, the pseudo-Aristotelian treatise *Secretum secretorum philosophorum* which greatly influenced Roger Bacon, as well as the astronomical works of the Baghdad Jewish writer Messahalah (Ma scha'a Allah = ' What God will,' 770–820). This Latin translation of Messahalah long formed the staple popular account of the system of the world under the name of the Englishman John Holywood (' Sacrobosco,' d. 1256). Gonzalez and Avendeath, like Gerard, worked at Toledo.

The Sicilian group was less active. The *Optics* of Ptolemy was translated about 1150 by the Sicilian admiral Eugenius of Palermo. He rendered it from the Arabic, though he had an effective knowledge of Greek. The great astronomical and mathematical system of Ptolemy known to the Middle Ages as the *Almagest* was also first translated into Latin from the Arabic in Sicily in 1163 (some twelve years before it was rendered by Gerard at Toledo), and Arabian versions only of the work were available until the fifteenth century. The last important translator of Sicilian origin, the Jew Farragut (Farradj ben Selim, Moses Farachi, d. 1285), was a student at Salerno, and his works were among the latest of any influence that issued from that ancient seat of learning. Such later translators were, however, usually less influential, and at the end of the thirteenth century we may say that the period of important translations was rapidly closing.

## § 5. *Content of Mediaeval Science. The Astrological Clue*

We have now to turn to the actual material thus conveyed to Latin Christendom. It differed rather in degree than in kind from that of the earlier Dark Age and from that of the age of Arabian infiltration. The systems differed in the extent to which certain logical conclusions from the premises provided were pushed, and in the amount of which each was influenced by certain theological conceptions.

In the late classical age there had developed the Stoic system of thought, which divided with Neoplatonism and Epicureanism all the more philosophical minds of the ancient world. This Stoic philosophy assumed that man's fate was determined by an interplay of forces, the nature and character of which were, in theory at least, completely knowable. The microcosm, man, reflected the macrocosm, the great world, that lay around him. But how and to what extent did the one reflect the other? In seeking to determine these points Stoicism, like Neoplatonism and the other philosophical systems of the classical twilight, gleaned, from many sources, material which it passed on in a corrupted state to the Latin West. In a somewhat less imperfect form such material lingered for centuries in the Byzantine East, until, with the great outburst of Islam, it was caught up and elaborated by the Arabic culture. Thus elaborated, it was sent forth a second time to Latin Europe by the process of infiltration and translation.

The astrological conceptions of the Stoics and of the later Christian ages had drawn both on Plato and on Aristotle. The hylozoism of the *Timaeus*, the doctrine that the universe itself and the matter of which it is composed is living, gave a suggestive outline to the hypothesis of the parallelism of the outer and inner universe. But the main details, on which the hypothesis was based, were drawn from Aristotle, whose views or supposed views as to the structure of the universe formed the framework on which the whole of mediaeval science from the thirteenth century onward was built. Especially Aristotle's conception of the stars as living things, of a nature higher and nobler than that of any substance or being in the spheres below, was a point of departure from which the influence of the heavenly bodies over human destinies might be developed. Changes undergone by bodies on the earth below—all phenomena in

FIG. 37.—FROM A MANUSCRIPT, WRITTEN 1282, OF A LATIN TRANSLATION BY FARRAGUT

On the left Farragut delivers his translation to Charles of Anjou. On the right he receives the Arabic original from an Eastern potentate. See page 81.

fact—were held to be controlled by parallel movements in the heavens above [Figs. 30, 38, 42 ; especially Plate II, see page 219].

The theory carried the matter farther. Taking its clue from the Aristotelian conception of the ' perfection ' of the circle among geometrical figures, it distinguished the perfect, regular, circular motion of the fixed stars from the imperfect, irregular, linear motion of the planets. The fixed stars, moving regularly in a circle, controlled the ordered course of nature, the events that proceeded in recurring, manifest, and unalterable rounds, such as winter and summer, night and day, growth and decay. The planets, on the other hand, erratic or at least errant in their movements, governed the more variable and less easily ascertainable events in the world around and within us, the happenings that make life the uncertain, hopeful, dangerous, happy thing it is. It was to the ascertainment of the factors governing this kaleidoscope of life that astrology set itself. The general outline was fixed, death in the end was sure, and, to the believing Christian, life after it. But there was a great uncertain zone between the sure and the unsure that might be predicted and perhaps avoided, or, if not avoided, its worst consequences abated. It was to this process of insurance that the astrologer set himself, and his task remained the same throughout the Middle Ages. In this hope, *savoir afin de prévoir*, the mediaeval astrologer was at one with the modern scientist. The matter is summarized for us by Chaucer (1340?–1400) :

> Paraventure in thilke large book,
> Which that men clipe the hevene, y-writen was
> With sterres, whan that he his birthe took,
> That he for love sholde han his deeth, allas !
> For in the sterres, clerer than is glas,
> Is written, God woot, whoso koude it rede,
> The deeth of every man, withouten drede.

> . . . But mennes wittes ben so dulle
> That no wight kan wel rede it atte fulle.
> *The Man of Lawes Tale.*

In the earlier Middle Ages, however, as in the earliest
Christian centuries, the world was but God's footstool
and all its phenomena were far less worthy of study than
were the things of religion. In the view of many patristic
writers the study of the stars was likely to lead to indifference to Him that sitteth above the heavens. This is
the general attitude of the fourth and fifth centuries, set
forth for instance by Augustine, who speaks of ' those
impostors the mathematicians (i.e. astrologers) . . . who
use no sacrifice, nor pray to any spirit for their divinations,
which arts Christian and true piety consistently rejects and
condemns.'

By the sixth and seventh centuries, however, the Church
had come to some sort of terms with astrology, and Isidore
regards it as, in part at least, a legitimate science. He
distinguishes, however, between *natural* and *superstitious*
astrology. The latter is ' the science practised by the
*mathematici* who read prophecies in the heavens, and place
the twelve constellations [of the Zodiac] as rulers over the
members of man's body and soul, and predict the nativities
and dispositions of men by the courses of the stars.' Nevertheless Isidore accepts many of the conclusions of astrology.
He advises physicians to study it, and he ascribes to the
moon an influence over plant and animal life and control
over the humours of man, while he accepts without
question the influence of the dog-star and of comets.
He is followed by the other Dark Age writers on natural
knowledge, who accept successively more and more
astrological doctrine.

With the advent of the Arabian learning the matter was
carried further, and astrology became the central interest.
It retained this position until the triumph of the experimental method in the seventeenth century. We cannot here
follow the details of the developed astrological scheme.
It is enough for our purposes to have observed that the
general material law which it implies had become widely
accepted in the Middle Ages, and to have traced its passage

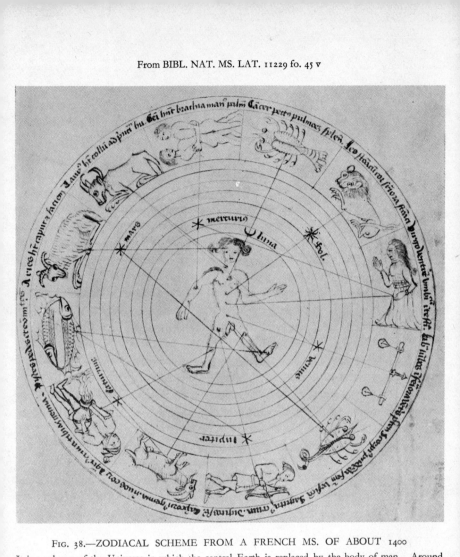

FIG. 38.—ZODIACAL SCHEME FROM A FRENCH MS. OF ABOUT 1400

It is a scheme of the Universe in which the central Earth is replaced by the body of man. Around him circle the seven planets in the order, from within outwards, of Moon, Mercury, Venus, Sun, Mars, Jupiter, Saturn. Each planet is connected with one or with two signs in the outermost sphere, that of the signs of the Zodiac. These signs act through the planets on the various parts of the body. Against each of these signs is written the part of the body which it controls. Thus, *Aries h(abe)t caput et faciem, Taurus h(abe)t collu(m) ad p(ri)nci(pium) hu(meri)* down to *Pisces pedes et ex(tre)mi(ta)tes.*

from antiquity and from the Orient into the thought of the West and of the period of which we are treating.

Especial attention was always paid to the zodiacal signs and to the planets. Each zodiacal sign was held to govern or to have special influence on some region of the body, and each of the planets was held to influence a special organ. The supposed relations of zodiacal signs, planets, and bodily parts and organs, together with their power to produce disease, had been set forth in such late Latin writers as Firmicus Maternus (c. 330) and Avienus (c. 380) and in innumerable Greek texts. This belief, conveyed to the Dark Age, but much corrupted and attenuated during its course, was brought back again to the West, reinforced and developed, in translations from the Arabic during the scholastic period which followed [Figs. 30, 38, 42].

## § 6. *Scholasticism and Science*

Doctrine of this type received into Europe was stamped with the special form of Western thought. Now, it was characteristic of the mediaeval Western thinker that, like the early Greek thinker, he sought always a complete scheme of things. He was not content to separate, as we do, one department of knowledge or one class of phenomena, and consider it in and by itself. Still less would he have held it a virtue to become a specialist, to limit his outlook to one department with the object of increasing the sum of knowledge in it, and in it alone.

His universe, it must be remembered, so far as it was material, was limited. The outer limit was the *primum mobile*, the outermost of the concentric spheres of which the Aristotelian world was composed. Of the structure and nature of all within the sphere of the *primum mobile* he had been provided with a definite scheme. The self-appointed task of mediaeval science was to elaborate that scheme in connexion with the moral world. This was first especially undertaken by mystical writers working under the stimulus of the new Arabian influence. Such authors as Hugh of St. Victor (1095–1141), who drew on the earlier and more vague Arabian rumours, Bernard Sylvestris (c. 1150), who relied on Herman the Cripple (1013–54), and Hildegard (1099–1180), who was influenced by Bernard Sylvestris and by other Arabicized writings, all produced most elaborate mystical schemes based on the doctrine of the macrocosm and microcosm. One of these schemes we discuss elsewhere in this volume (Essay VI, p. 215). These schemes took into account the form of the world and of man as derived from Arabian sources, and read into each relationship a spiritual meaning. For such an attitude of mind there could be no ultimate distinction between physical events, moral truths, and spiritual experiences. In their fusion of the internal and external universe these mystics have much in common with the mystics of all ages. The culmination of the process, so far as our period is concerned, is reached with Dante (1265–1321). [See Fig. 39.]

But with the thirteenth century new currents of thought set in. Arabian science had at last been won, the scientific works of Aristotle were becoming accessible and gradually entering the curriculum, the universities were firmly established, and there were the beginnings of a knowledge of Greek. A contemporary religious movement of vast importance was the foundation of the mendicant religious orders, the activities of which largely replaced those of the monastic Benedictines. Among these new orders were two that specially influenced the Universities, the Dominicans or Black Friars founded at Toulouse in 1215 by the austere and orthodox Dominic (1170–1221) and the Franciscans or Grey Friars founded in 1209 by the gentle and loving Francis of Assisi. The contributions of the Carmelites or White Friars and the Hermits or Austin (Augustinian) Friars were less weighty. The name of Dominic is associated with the terrible extermination of the Albigenses, and the Dominicans, whose name was paraphrased as *Domini canes*, ' hounds of the Lord,' set themselves to the

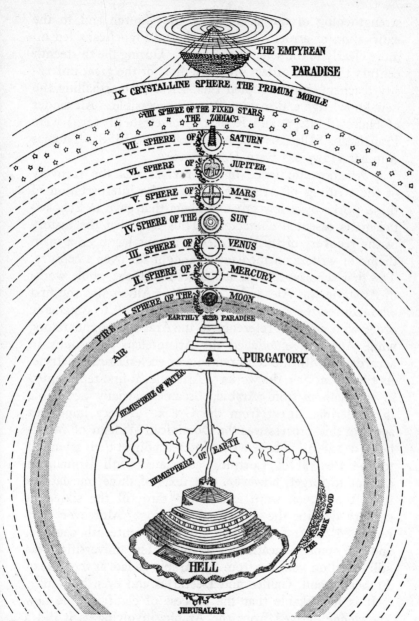

FIG. 39.—Dante's Scheme of the Universe modified from Michelangelo Caetani, Duca di Sermoneta, *La materia della Divina Commedia di Dante Alighieri*, Monte Cassino, 1855.

strengthening of the doctrine of the Church and to the
extirpation of error. The work of the Franciscans led up
more clearly to the scientific revival. During the thirteenth
century these two orders provided most of the great university teachers, who occupied themselves in marshalling the
new knowledge and making it more accessible. Alexander
of Hales (d. 1245) and Robert Grosseteste (d. 1253) were
Franciscans, Albertus Magnus (1206–80) and St. Thomas
Aquinas (1227–74) were Dominicans.

A foremost influence in the revival was the recovery
of the writings of Aristotle. It was the interpretation of
these works by a few great thinkers that gave to Scholasticism its essential character. Thus it is that the history
of the recovery of the Aristotelian corpus has been a main
theme of writers on mediaeval thought for over a century.
The first scholastic to be acquainted with the whole works
of Aristotle was Alexander of Hales. Albert was the first
who reduced the whole philosophy of Aristotle to systematic
order with constant reference to the Arabian commentators,
while Aquinas remodelled the Aristotelian philosophy in
accordance with the requirements of ecclesiastical doctrine.
As time went one, the works of Aristotle, at first represented
in translations from Arabic, became partially accessible
in renderings direct from the Greek. A very important
agent in this process was the Dominican William of Moer-
beke (d. 1286). Those whose interests direct their attention
to the Revival of Learning associated with Humanism
are apt to forget, however, that texts of these translations
from the Greek were excessively rare till the sixteenth
century despite the advent of printing. Moreover they
remained far from common till the seventeenth century,
and the staple education of all but a few universities was
still based on versions from the Arabic as late as the time of
Francis Bacon, Galileo and Descartes and even beyond.

It is remarkable that the process of codifying the new
knowledge derived from the Arabic, involving as it did a
rapid development in the whole mental life, did not early

give rise to a more passionate and more conscious faith in the reality and value of progress in knowledge. The test of such faith, so far as nature is concerned, must be the direct appeal to nature. Yet there is very little evidence of direct observation of nature in the great physical encyclopaedias of the thirteenth century, such as those of the Augustinian Alexander of Neckam (1157–1217), the Dominican Vincent de Beauvais (1190–1264), or the Franciscan Bartholomew of England (c. 1260). The fact is that the mediaeval mind was obsessed with the idea of the world as mortal, destructible, finite, and therefore completely knowable both in space and in time. Thus the motive for detailed *research*, in our modern sense of the word, was hardly present. One great Islamic philosopher there was, Averroes (Ibn Roschd, d. 1198), who took an opposite view. His works were available in Latin, but the great ecclesiastics set their face against him, though he was widely and illicitly read. Moreover his theories were adopted by Jews and Latins with heretical leanings, tacit or expressed.

The mediaeval world thus knew nothing of that infinite sea of experience on which the man of science nowadays launches his bark in adventurous exploration. The task of the writers of these encyclopaedias was rather to give a general outline of knowledge, to set forth such a survey of the universe as would be in accord with spiritual truth. The framework on which this encyclopaedic scheme was built was Aristotle, largely as conveyed by his Arabic commentator Averroes, the philosopher whom the heads of the Church had condemned. Yet it is an amusing reflection on the incompleteness of all philosophical systems that Albert (1206–80), who perhaps more than any man was responsible for the scholastic world-system, was among the very few mediaeval writers who were real observers of nature. It is, after all, in the very essence of the human animal to love the world around it and to watch its creatures. *Naturam expellas furca tamen usque recurret.* Albert, scholastic of the scholastics, drowned in erudition and the most learned man of his time, has left us evidence in his great works on natural history that the scientific spirit was beginning to awake. As an independent observer he is not altogether contemptible, and this element in him marks the new dawn which we trace more clearly in his successors.

### § 7.  *The Dawn of Modern Science.  Roger Bacon*

Thus the best of the systematizers among the schoolmen were leading on to the direct observation of nature. Contemporary with Albert (1206–80) and Aquinas (1227–74) were several remarkable scholastic writers who form the earliest group with whom the conscious advancement of knowledge was a permanent interest. These men were the first consciously forward-looking scientific thinkers since the fourth century. Perhaps the most arresting of them was Robert Grosseteste (*c.* 1175–1253), Bishop of Lincoln. Grosseteste determined the main direction of physical investigation in the thirteenth century by his work on *Optics*. He knows something of the action of mirrors and of the nature of lenses. It would appear that he had actually experimented with lenses, and many of the optical ideas of Roger Bacon were taken straight from his master. The main Arabian source of Grosseteste was a Latin translation of the mathematical work of Alhazen of Basra (965–1038). Another important optical writer whom Alhazen deeply influenced was the Pole Witelo (*fl.* 1270), an acute mathematical investigator who worked in northern Italy. Roger Bacon was largely dependent on Witelo.

The opposition between the followers of Dominic and of Francis was paralleled by certain very remarkable developments among the Franciscans themselves. There is no stranger and more impressive chapter in the whole history of thought than that of the early history of the Franciscans. Within the memory of men who had known the saintly founder of the order (1181–1226), the ' penitents of Assisi,' the ' friars minor,' sworn as ' *jongleurs* of God ' to bring Christ cheerfully to the humblest and the meanest, sworn

to possess nothing, to earn their bread from day to day by
the work of their own hands or at need by begging, forbidden to lay by store or to accumulate capital, this order
of humble servants of Christ had produced a series of
monumental and scholarly intellects. These men not
only initiated what bid fair to be a renaissance of science
and letters, but also aided in the formation of the bulwark
which long resisted the very movement that thus emanated
from the order itself. To both parties the English Franciscan houses contributed an overwhelming share. To
the former, or scientific party, as we may call it, belonged
Robert Grosseteste, Bishop of Lincoln (c. 1175-1253), John
Pecham, Archbishop of Canterbury (d. 1292), the elusive
Adam Marsh (d. 1257), and above all Roger Bacon (1214-
94). To the latter or theological party are attached the
names of Alexander of Hales (d. 1245), Duns Scotus
(1265 ?-1308 ?), and William of Ockham (d. 1349).

The primary inspirer of the scientific movement was
the great Bishop of Lincoln himself, as we learn from his
pupil Roger. ' Nobody,' says Bacon, ' can attain to proficiency in the science of mathematics by the method
hitherto known unless he devotes to its study thirty or
forty years . . . and that is the reason why so few study
that science. . . . Yet there were found some famous men,
as Robert [Grosseteste] Bishop of Lincoln, and Adam Marsh,
and some others, who knew how by the power of mathematics to unfold the causes of all things and to give a sufficient explanation of human and divine phenomena. The
assurance of this fact is to be found in the writings of those
great men, as, for instance, in their works on the impression
[of the elements], on the rainbow and the comets, on the
sphere, and on other questions appertaining both to theology
and to natural philosophy.' The work of this remarkable
group of Franciscans at Oxford extended beyond the sciences
to language and literature. There was thus the beginning
of a real renaissance of Greek letters which died an early
death. After Roger Bacon's death the scientific revival

also languished until recalled to life by a second revival of a later century.

It may be convenient to give a summary of the scientific achievements of Roger Bacon, the greatest of the Franciscan group and the first man of science in the modern sense.

1. He attempted to set forth a system of natural knowledge. This system was far in advance of his time, and its basis was observation and experiment. He was clearly the first man in modern Europe of whom this can be said.

2. He was the first to see the need for the accurate study of foreign and ancient languages. He attempted grammars of Greek and Hebrew along definite scientific lines. He also projected a grammar of Arabic. Moreover, he laid down those lines of textual criticism which have only been developed within the last century.

3. He not only discussed the nature of the experimental method, but was himself an experimenter. His writings are important for the development of the following sciences :

(a) *Optics*. His work on this subject was a textbook for the next two centuries. He saw the importance of lenses and concave mirrors, and showed a grasp of the mathematical principles of optics. He described a system equivalent to a two-lens apparatus, and there is trustworthy evidence that he actually used a compound system of lenses equivalent to a telescope.

(b) *Astronomy* was Bacon's perpetual interest. He spent the best part of twenty years in the construction of astronomical tables. His letter to the Pope in favour of the correction of the calendar, though unsuccessful in his own day, was borrowed and reborrowed, and finally, at third-hand, produced the Gregorian correction.

(c) *Geography*. He was the first systematic geographer of the Middle Ages. He gave a systematic description of Europe, Asia, and part of Africa. He collected first-hand evidence from travellers in all these continents. His arguments as to the size and sphericity of the earth were among those that influenced Columbus.

(*d*) *Mechanical Science*. Suggestions by him include the automatic propulsion of vehicles and vessels. He records a plan for a flying machine.

(*e*) *Chemistry*. The chemical knowledge of his time was systematized in his tracts. His description of the composition and manufacture of gunpowder is the earliest that has reached us. It is clear that he had worked out for himself some of the chemistry of the subject.

(*f*) *Mathematics*. His insistence on the supreme value of mathematics as a foundation for education recalls the attitude of Plato. It was an insistence that the method of thought was at least as important as its content.

Summed up, his legacy to thought may be regarded as accuracy of method, criticism of authority, and reliance on experiment—the pillars of modern science.

Bacon was not an isolated phenomenon, but an important link in the chain of scientific development. But during the century after Bacon, though his mathematical and philosophical works were still studied in the schools, the greatest advances were to be found among the physicians. Of medical men the last half of the thirteenth and the first half of the fourteenth century exhibit an especially brilliant group. Bologna had possessed a medical school since the twelfth century, and had inherited the learning of Salerno. At Bologna had worked Hugh of Lucca (d. 1252 ?) and his son or pupil Theodoric (1206–98). Here surgery may be said to have been born again with the practice of Roland of Parma (*c*. 1250), the successor and faithful follower of Roger of Salerno (*c*. 1220). At Bologna, above all, William of Saliceto (1215–80), backed by the authority of Thaddeus of Florence (1223–1303), established a practical method of anatomization which was inherited by Mondino da Luzzi (1276–1328), whose work based on translations from the Arabic text of Avicenna became the general anatomical textbook of the later Middle Ages. By the

fourteenth century the practice of dissection of the human
body had become well recognized [Fig. 40].

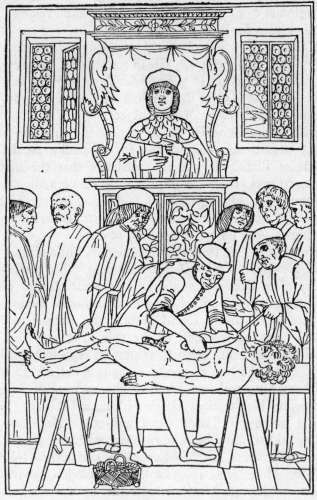

FIG. 40.—Mondino directing a dissection.   From a fifteenth-century
woodcut.

At the end of the thirteenth century the ancient foundation of the medical school of Montpellier was coming to the
fore.   The Catalan Arnald of Villanova (1235–1311), one

of the most remarkable personalities of mediaeval medicine, taught there. Arnald was not only one of the earliest exponents of the Hippocratic method of observing and carefully recording symptoms of actual cases of disease, but he also deeply influenced alchemy. That study was effectively of Arabian origin so far as the western world is concerned. It begins in 1144 with the translation into Latin from Arabic by Robert of Chester of the *De compositione alchemiae* which Morienus Romanus, a contemporary hermit of Jerusalem, had ' edited for Kalid, king of the Egyptians.' Alchemy had taken its rise with a real effort to understand the properties of metals, prompted by the hope of transmuting the baser into the more precious. Like other mediaeval studies, it became linked with astrology, and the ' seven metals ' were each of them controlled or influenced by the ' seven planets ' much in the same way as were the organs of the human body. Of such ideas Arnald was a prolific exponent. He had direct access to both Arabic and Hebrew. A student at Naples and Salerno, a traveller in Italy, Sicily, France, and Spain, he served as medical adviser to the Papal Curia both at Rome and Avignon and was employed as ambassador on more than one special mission. Arnald influenced politics no less than learning and ended his adventurous life at sea. A character very different from Arnald was the Majorcan Raymond Lull (1235–1313), who was also learned in oriental languages. The numerous alchemical works bearing Lull's name are, however, falsely ascribed to him. Lull was a visionary who perished as he desired, in his attempt to convert the Mohammedan world.

§ 8. *Humanism*

In outlook no less remarkable than Arnald was the heretical Peter of Abano (1250–c. 1318). He earned a reputation as a magician, and his natural death saved him from the hands of the Inquisition. His body is said to have been exhumed and burned. Peter—who was a most voluminous writer—had a knowledge of Greek, acquired at Constantinople, and he translated works from that language. He was a professor at the University of Paris and later at Padua in the generation which followed that in which the newly won Aristotelian works on physics had entered the curriculum.  His greatest and best-known work, the *Conciliator*, expresses his mediation between the now commencing humanistic Greek school and the Arabists, though it appears that he had no knowledge of the Arabic language.  From the *Conciliator* we may learn that he had come into contact with the great traveller Marco Polo (*c.* 1254–1324).  Among the views of Peter of Abano that are most worth record may be mentioned his statements that the air has weight, that the brain is the source of the nerves and the heart of the vessels—all ideas that were novel in his time.  He made a remarkably accurate measure of the length of the year as 365 days 6 hours 4 minutes.

The second half of the fourteenth century, perhaps owing to social disturbance and notably to the effects of the Black Death (1347–9), shows a distinct falling off in the intellectual advance.  In medicine the most noteworthy name is that of Guy de Chauliac of Montpellier (1300–70), the most influential of all the mediaeval surgeons.  Outside the ranks of the physicians the most striking figure in fourteenth-century science is probably the French Jewish philosopher Levi ben Gerson (1288–1344). His work on astronomy was important as illustrating the consciousness of a growing discontent with the Ptolemaic system of the universe.

With the fourteenth century appeared, too, a great movement the hand of which is still heavy on our own day. Humanism was born.  Historians have perhaps linked the humanistic movement too intimately with a knowledge of the Greek language.  Instances of knowledge of that language in the West can, however, be adduced far back into the Dark Ages (e.g. John Scot Erigena, *c.* 850), while many of the greatest of the humanists, including Petrarch himself (1304–74), were without such knowledge. It is worth noting too, as linking humanism with the Middle Ages, that Petrarch's epistolary style was still moulded on St. Augustine rather than on Cicero.

The backward-looking habit, strong in man from his nature and strengthened by the teaching of the Christian religion, was yet further enforced by the humanists. From Petrarch onward they were ever brooding on the past that had been Greece and Rome. Yet even from the first, the humanists had the sensation too of being *builders*, so that their glance was at times turned away from the past and towards what was to come, nay, what was in the act of becoming. Roger Bacon and a few isolated souls had had this double vision, but for a whole school to possess it was something new. In his *Book of memorable things* Petrarch says outright, ' Here stand I as though on a frontier that divides two peoples, looking both to the past and to the future.' While studying the classics some of these very men were indeed visibly forging new intellectual weapons, those national vernaculars that have made modern literature and thought possible. It is no mere coincidence that Boccaccio (1313–75), friend and contemporary of Petrarch, should have been at once the first modern literary man to study Greek and the first great master of Italian prose.

We must note, however, that save for reference for the one supreme poet in their own tongue, Dante (1265–1321), the backward gaze of the Italian humanist is always fixed on the more distant classical past, not on the nearer period that came to be regarded as a yawning chasm, an abyss across which he sought to reach back to the thought of antiquity. To him the Middle Ages seemed real enough and dark enough. It stood for the period during which the sweet Greek literature had been ignored. Even in this new age it could be understood by few except in Latin dress, and the work of translation remained somewhat of a specialist's occupation. To the end of the fifteenth century an effective knowledge of Greek continued to be a rarity even among scholars, and we may point to some of the most important teachers of the sixteenth century who were still without it.

The great influence of the masterpieces of Greece, therefore, was then as now something indirect, often conveyed through translators and special interpreters, something esoteric, the full beauty of which was shared only by a few adepts, a subtle thing that influenced men's way of thinking rather than the actual content of their minds. The mere capacity for translation from the Greek goes back, as we have seen, to the eleventh century, the ninth century, or even beyond. It can therefore hardly have been simply the discovery of the actual Greek language which brought about the revival of letters. But if the knowledge of Greek goes back so far, can we speak of a real Renaissance at all ? How can we account for the change of heart that came over the world when humanism was born ? Or is that change of heart but an illusion, a difference of degree rather than of kind in a world where everything is in a state of becoming ?

Some answer to this absorbing question we may glean by comparing the earlier Greek works which came to the West to those of later advent. The general character of the earlier translations was determined by the outlook of a world becoming ever more deeply Arabicized. Islam, the inheritor of antiquity, entered into the enjoyment of its legacy with great spirit, but with a taste already fixed. The literary and artistic works were debarred by a definite theological standpoint. Homer and Hesiod, Sophocles and Euripides, Greek Art and Greek Architecture were chapters as closed and forbidden to Islam as to early Christian Europe. It was the philosophical, the scientific, the mathematical, the medical works that made an appeal. These gave an illusory impression of completeness to life with which Islam long rested content. It was these very works that were the first to be rendered into Latin from the Arabic, and the Latin taste being thus determined it was similar works that were the first to be turned into Latin direct from the Greek.

Such material—and it is bulky and intricate enough—represents the Western access to Greek wisdom before the fourteenth century. It does not lack variety, but it lacks life. They err who think the discovery of the humanists was the Greek language—here the humanists were but followers where others had been pioneers. It is something much deeper and more fundamental which they have handed on to us, something the nature of which they hardly knew and the meaning of which they missed—which perhaps they still miss—in their enthusiasm. The humanists discovered the literary works of antiquity. In them they became absorbed to the exclusion of all else. The humanist eagerness passed into a literary vogue, and long cast the blight of a purely literary education on the modern world. The barren striving after form as distinct from substance, the miserable and slavish imitativeness that is no flattery but an insult to its model, these features exhibited typically in the literature of the late Empire, were repeated by the humanists as they have been often repeated in modern times and as they still remain a curse to the so-called ' classical education.'

The humanist then did not give us the knowledge of a language nor did he even give an insight into the life of antiquity. What the humanist really gave was a something which, added to the heritage already there, made possible a completer reconstruction of the Greek spirit. That reconstruction, indeed, he was himself never able to make ; it was the succeeding generations that made it for themselves. With that reconstruction Greece lived again, the modern world was ushered in, and modern science, art, literature, and philosophy were born. It is an illuminating reflection and one not without bearing on our present state that both the mediaeval heritage of Greek science and the Renaissance heritage of Greek literature proved barren by themselves. It was not until the one fertilized the other that there was real and vital growth. Modern thought, modern science, modern art, and modern letters are the offspring of that union. Let us put from our minds the time-worn fallacy that they are the parthenogenetically produced offspring of one of these elements alone.

§ 9.  *The Science of the Renaissance*

The humanists as a class did not exhibit great sympathy with the scientific outlook. Their interests were literary and their peculiar aversion was the Arabist tendency of the Middle Ages that they were leaving behind. That Arabist tendency was very largely expressed in the ancient scientific and philosophical themes, some of which we have discussed in outline. In the movement initiated by Roger Bacon in the thirteenth century a new element had been introduced. That movement had fallen into the background after Roger's death. It had not entirely died, but it had become ' quietist '—if the expression may be used in this connexion—a part of the seldom expressed faith of a small band of philosophically-minded recluses. Faith in the appeal to nature was at last to find more open expression. With the fifteenth century, discontent with the entire mediaeval scientific scheme becomes more generally obvious, and we perceive a first hint of the idea that it may be possible to adjust theory by means of experiment.

The earliest suggestion is made by a man of high genius and scholarship, the Rhinelander Nicholas of Cues (1401–64), who became a cardinal and made a fruitless attempt to reform the calendar. A groping towards a philosophical basis for the experimental method is exhibited in his book *De docta ignorantia*, which has nothing to do with the absurdity of erudition, as its name might be thought to imply, but concerns itself with acknowledged ignorance, i.e. with the inability of the human mind to conceive the infinite. The theoretical views of Nicholas led him to a belief that the earth is moving, though he attained to no genuine heliocentric theory. He records a careful experiment of a growing plant—afterward pirated by the seventeenth-century writer van Helmont (1577–1644)—proving that it absorbs something of weight from the air. This is the first biological experiment of modern times, and incidentally the first formal proof that the air has weight. In another work, *De staticis experimentis*, Nicholas shows that he knew how to apply the experimental method in detail, and he suggests in outline many investigations which were not taken in hand until the time of Galileo 150 years later.

The tradition of the combination of scholarship and observation that Nicholas had started was carried on by several astronomers in the second half of the fifteenth century. For part of this work we are indebted to the far-sightedness of another cardinal, Johannes Bessarion (1389–1472), a Greek by birth, who was equally anxious to aid the progress of astronomical knowledge and to diffuse Greek literature in the West. Bessarion's friendship, extended to the two German astronomers Purbach and Regiomontanus, made possible their work which formed the foundation of that of Copernicus.

George Purbach (1423–61) followed with great avidity the study of Ptolemy. He died prematurely and had only translations from the Arabic on which to base his work. He improved on his original, however, by calculating a table for every 10 minutes, using sines instead of chords.

Johannes Müller (1436–76) of Königsberg (= *King's mountain*), usually known from his birthplace as Regiomontanus, though his life was hardly longer than that of Purbach, had the good fortune to work on Greek originals. He produced the first systematic treatise on trigonometry and a table of sines for every minute and of tangents for every degree. He edited too the *Epitome of Ptolemy* which Purbach had left behind him in an imperfect state. He died at Rome, whither he had been summoned by the Pope to aid in the long contemplated reform of the Calendar. The important works of Regiomontanus were only published after his death [Fig. 42]. His name has become associated with an ill-founded legend that he taught the heliocentric view of the solar system before Copernicus. The statement has been made of several other contemporaries, Leonardo da Vinci (1452–1519) among them. It has been verified, however, for only one of them (Celio Calcagnini, 1479–1541), who perhaps borrowed the idea from Copernicus.

The Renaissance of Letters was contemporary with the Renaissance of Art, and the artists had also their reaction

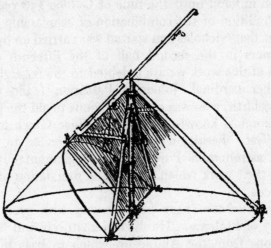

FIG. 41.—Leonardo's Parabolic compass. The pen which is shown above and to the left moves freely in its fitting. It is held by its own weight to the surface of the plane on which it is writing. The character of the curve traced by it is determined by the angle with the horizontal which this plane is made to assume. When fixed parallel to the limb of the compass shown to the right, a parabola will be traced.

upon scientific thought. The great painters had begun to study nature more closely. Antonio Pollaiuolo (1429–98) and Andrea del Verrocchio (1435–88), among others, had made careful investigations of surface anatomy, while the exquisite figures of plants in the pictures of Sandro Botticelli (1444–1510) mark him out as a very accurate observer. There was, however, one artist of the time who takes a quite peculiar place among students of nature. Leonardo da Vinci (1452–1519) stands for many as the turning-point of the Renaissance into modern times.

FIG. 42.—FRONTISPIECE TO THE *EPITOME OF PTOLEMY'S ALMAGEST*
By Johannes Müller (Regiomontanus), Venice, 1496

It would be impossible to give in a paragraph the titles to fame of one of the very greatest geniuses that the human race has produced. The marvellous rapidity of his insight, the sureness of his intuitions, and his extreme versatility made earlier students place Leonardo in an isolated and almost non-human position. His very limitations, more-over, while they have increased the apparent gulf which separates him from other men, have hampered us in our comprehension of his mind. Isolated he remains by the loftiness of his genius, but more prolonged study has revealed many of the sources of his knowledge and some of his methods of work.

To understand anything of Leonardo's scientific work and of its fate we must however recognize his defects. Leonardo's great limitation was on the literary and linguistic side. He had no gift for language and did not acquire even an elementary knowledge of Latin till well on in life. He had no power of literary expression. The language that he employs is that of a Florentine shopkeeper of the lower class. He created no great phrase or saying. In his notebooks his sentences are usually ungrammatical and often unfinished. Even allowing for the purely private nature of these memoranda, it is yet fairly evident that in a literary sense he was incoherent. The very rush of his ideas seems to have obstructed the natural channels of their expression. Of him his biographer Vasari quotes with admirable point the lines of Petrarch :

> E l'amor di saper che m'ha si acceso
> Che l'opera e retardato dal desio.

> My love of knowledge so inflamed me
> That my work was retarded by my very desire.

With what we now know of Leonardo the question may reasonably be raised whether his art did, in fact, consume the major part of his energy and his thoughts. Among the great artists he was notorious for the smallness of his output and for the extreme slowness with which he worked. On the other hand, he left behind him a vast mass of papers, about 5,000 leaves of which have survived. These contain evidence not only of a unique scientific insight but of a tireless industry which is almost incredible. He covers the whole field of science from mathematics to physiology, and there is nothing that he touches which he does not illuminate. To give but a few scattered instances : he presents us not only with a model of a flying machine but with an invention of a helicopter, and he analyses the nature of the flight of birds in a way that has only been surpassed during the last few years ; he has a design for a parabolic compass on a principle that was not adopted till late in the seventeenth century [Fig. 41] ; he hints at a heliocentric view of the world ; he has admirable drawings of quick-firing and breech-loading guns ; he was an ingenious inventor of engineering apparatus [Fig. 44]; he has mastered the theoretical principles of perspective ; he sets forth the homologies of the vertebrate skeleton ; he has passages which suggest the laws of motion ; and his anatomical and embryological standpoint was not passed in certain respects for hundreds of years [Fig. 43].

Leonardo may be linked with his time by tracing some of his scientific ideas back to his predecessors. The break in continuity is much more marked if we seek to trace them forwards. He had indeed very little influence on the science of the age which immediately followed him. Save in certain ideas and drawings of a few sixteenth-century anatomists leading on to Vesalius, the scientific work of Leonardo was without effect until modern times. If Leonardo be regarded as the topmost peak of the Renaissance, that peak, continuous with a long range of mighty mountains on one side, terminates in an almost sheer precipice on the other.

Before we quite part with the Renaissance we must consider another remarkable character whose life-course was almost as isolated and aberrant as that of Leonardo.

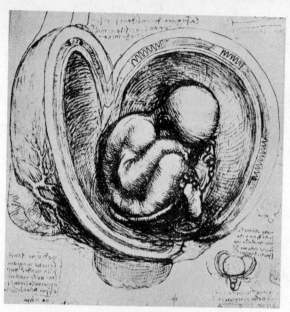

FIG. 43.—CHILD IN ITS MOTHER'S WOMB
Drawn from the object by Leonardo.   Windsor Library.

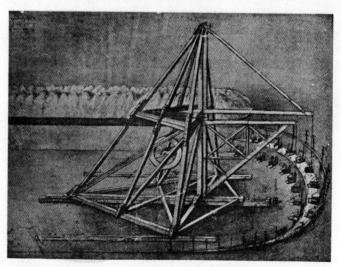

FIG. 44.—DRAWING BY LEONARDO OF A DREDGE FOR A CANAL

It can be made to move forward in the excavated bed.   The engine works on
two levels, at each of which is placed a semicircular series of buckets.   The
buckets are filled with earth, through wooden shoots.   When filled, they are
carried by the cranes right and left to the line of advance.   When the bucket
reaches the bank it is emptied and the resulting bank of accumulated debris can
be seen behind the crane.   From a drawing in the *Codex Atlanticus* at Milan.

The Swiss writer Aureolus Philippus Theophrastus Bombastus von Hohenheim, commonly known as Paracelsus (1493–1541), was a person of violent, dramatic, and repellent temper, a born rebel whose iconoclasm doubtless did something to deter men from the worship of the old idols. His symbolic act of burning the works both of the Greek Galen and of the Arab Avicenna, as an introduction to his lecture course at Basel, typified the position of the independent investigators of the generation that immediately followed him. A writer of excessive obscurity, an obscurity of language, of form, and of thought, very few have claimed the privilege of penetrating to his full meaning, and those few have nearly all been infected with some of the defect of expression from which the master suffered. There is, however, a general agreement among the learned and nebulous band of Paracelsists that their hero did indeed foreshadow the ' new instauration.' His aim was to see the world in the ' Light of Nature.' That light of his is dimmed for us because of his extreme gullibility in some matters, his violence and self-contradiction in others, and the involved and mystical presentment in all. ' Nature ' contained for him the influence of the stars upon the lives of men and many other mysterious phenomena then generally credited. He believed still in a relation of microcosm and macrocosm—as in a residual sense we all do—but his free modification of that theory paved the way for its rejection in the generation which followed.

## § 10. *The Great Instauration*

Francis Bacon (1561–1620), coming at the very end of our period, grasped the nature of the truth that had been struggling to birth since the days of his great namesake. He called it the *Instauratio Magna*, the great restoration. Of him a modern enthusiast for research (Mark Pattison) has written, ' the great instaurator of all knowledge, in preaching the necessity of altering the whole method of knowing included the method of "teaching to know." ' Of the reformers of the method of teaching to know, two stand at the very threshold of the new era, Nicholas Copernicus and Andreas Vesalius.

The Pole, Nicholas Copernicus (1473–1543), despite the vast change that was introduced in his name into men's ideas, was himself more in the line of such comparatively conservative scholars as Nicholas of Cues and Regiomontanus than the more revolutionary Leonardo or Paracelsus. No man was ever more ' academic,' and he continued to attend university courses until over thirty years of age. He studied at several Italian universities, giving attention to classics, mathematics, astronomy, medicine, law, and theology. His skill in painting suggests that he had that type of visualizing imagination frequently associated with scientific power.

Copernicus was not, however, a first-hand observer on any large scale. He had, it is true, taken a number of observations of eclipses and oppositions of planets, but for the most part his results were obtained in the study. He tells us that he was induced to seek a new theory of the heavenly bodies by finding that mathematicians differed among themselves on this subject. He had counted up the various motions of the heavenly bodies involved in the old system and concluded that some essential factor had been missed. He therefore turned to antiquity and learned from Cicero—who quotes Hiketas—and Plutarch that some among the ancients were of the same opinion.

' Occasioned by this,' he says, ' I decided to try whether, on the assumption of some motion of the earth, better explanations of the revolutions of the heavenly spheres might not be found. Thus assuming the motions which I attribute to the earth . . . I have found that when the motions of the other planets are referred to the circulation of the earth and are computed for the revolution of each star, not only do the phenomena necessarily follow therefrom, but that also the order and magnitude of the stars and of all their orbits and the heaven itself are so connected that in no part can anything be transposed without confusion to the rest and to the whole universe.'

In this new scheme the ancient theory of the uniform circular motion of the heavenly bodies was still retained. Since it involved the retention of the theory of epicycles as well as the displacement of the sun from the true centre of the planetary orbs, the simplicity of the scheme was only apparent and comparative [Fig. 45].

Vesalius (1514–64) was in almost every respect a contrast to Copernicus. Young, ardent, and combative, his

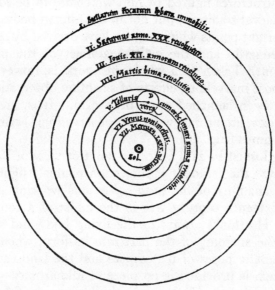

FIG. 45.—Diagram by Copernicus to show his heliocentric system. The planets, Earth among them, circle round the sun. The fixed stars are all at a fixed distance from the earth in a *sphaera immobilis*.

life's work was well-nigh complete at twenty-five, and its effective and creative part was crowded into the four years that preceded the publication of the *Fabrica* in 1543. The contents of that great work were delivered in the form of lecture-demonstrations to crowded audiences. It contains an enormous number of first-hand observations which must have been accumulated while working under the most extreme pressure. Vigorous and fearless in the demonstration of observed fact, Vesalius becomes more timid and less effective in the discussion of theory, and he leaves the Galenic physiology practically intact. He was a man of the laboratory and lecture-room rather than of the study [Fig. 46], and reflection was not the source of his power. Yet even his observations are by no means completely free from traditional bias. Thus some of the poses of the figures and the treatment of the skeletons in his book have been shown to be derived from scholastic sources, and there are anatomical structures figured by him which are to be found in the mediaeval tradition, but not in the human body. There are important points which he may have derived by tradition from Leonardo and the artist-anatomist of the previous generation. Taken as a whole, his work is, however, one of the most marvellous efforts of scientific observation that has ever been launched upon the world. It is, moreover, the earliest important work of observational science in modern times [Fig. 46].

A word must be said as to the point of view of Vesalius. Nowadays the student's dissection-manual figures for him the anatomy of the dead. Vesalius working in Italy in the sixteenth century was in the midst of a country of artists. He thinks always of the living body and seeks to restore the anatomy of the part into its form when living. The dramatic poses of his corpses and the landscape with which each is provided is no piece of idle artistry. It is a part of his scheme. Nor does he think so much of the actual body he is dissecting as of the idea towards which God is tending in us all. Each body is, as it were, one of that supreme artist's 'studies' for an ideal and final work of art. It is the anatomist's duty to attain as near as he can to that ideal.

The work of Vesalius was carried farther by a number of investigators in the latter part of the sixteenth century, but by none with greater skill and intensity than Hieronymus Fabricius ab Aquapendente (1537-1619), a successor of Vesalius in the Chair at Padua, where he taught for over sixty years and where William Harvey (1578-1657) was his pupil. Fabricius was one of the most successful and stimulating of medical teachers, and he added an enormous number of facts to the sum of anatomical and physiological knowledge. As an investigator, however, he lacked, like all his contemporaries, complete speculative freedom. For that the time was still hardly ripe, and his physiology was still largely Galenic. While he provided many of the observations on which the view of the circulation of the blood was built, his vision remained obscured by the traditional outlook. It was left to his great English pupil to enunciate the basic doctrine of modern physiology in the next century. The grasp of Galen was weakening, but it had not yet wholly relaxed.

The mentality of Tycho Brahe (1546–1601), the greatest astronomer of the second half of the sixteenth century, was not dissimilar to that of Fabricius, its greatest anatomist. Tycho, like Fabricius, was a first-class observer, but, like him, weak and timid in drawing conclusions. By means of newly designed but simple apparatus employed with exquisite skill, Tycho attained an unprecedented degree of accuracy in astronomical observation. His records were employed later by his colleague Johann Kepler (1571–1630). These observations aided Kepler to purge the Copernican hypothesis of the traditional notions concerning the movements of the heavenly bodies in circles. The circles were replaced by ellipses and modern astronomy was born.

The year 1600 is associated with two important events in the history of science, which mark it out as the final parting of the ways. In that year Giordano Bruno (1548–1600), a profound student of the works of Nicholas of Cues and an ardent follower of Copernicus, suffered martyrdom at the stake. In that year William Gilbert (1540–1603) produced his work *On the magnet, on magnetic bodies, and on the earth as a great magnet, a new physiography,*[1] *demonstrated by many arguments and experiments.* The work is the first great

---

[1] The word he uses is *physiologia*, which is best translated by our word *physiography*.

scientific treatise published in England, but it is much more. It is a landmark in the history of science as a whole. Gilbert accepts fully the Copernican view of a heliocentric world, and he speculates fearlessly on observed conclusions. Above all, as the title of the work tells, his views are demonstrated by *arguments* and *experiments*. It is a distinction of which he never loses sight, and he is careful to record exactly and by a special device his own personal experiences. These are clearly separated from his arguments and from the experiences of others. The book has the form and spirit of a modern scientific treatise.

We have now left utterly behind the Middle Ages and all their works and ways. The old hypothesis of the macrocosm and microcosm was no longer possible to those who had studied and understood the works of Copernicus and Vesalius. Men no longer studied macrocosm and microcosm as such, but they became physicists or physiologists, taking each of them a separated portion of the universe for special study. This disposition to base opinion on observation, involving separation of nature into departments, characterizes the modern method and distinguishes it from the mediaeval. The early morning twilight is over, the dawn is upon us and it was the risen sun that Harvey and Galileo saluted, and in the light of which Francis Bacon and Descartes did their prophesying.

FIG. 46.—VESALIUS DISSECTING AT PADUA AMONG HIS
STUDENTS

From his *De fabrica corporis humani* of 1543.

# III

## THE LORICA OF GILDAS THE BRITON.
## A MAGICAL TEXT OF THE SIXTH CENTURY.

### § 1.  *Title, Author, and Date*

The word *Lorica* meant primarily a *leather coat* or *cuirass* and was used in this sense as early as Plautus (d. 184 B.C.). In later classical writings the term came to describe a hauberk or byrnie of linked mail.  A *Lorica* of this kind is described by Virgil :—

> Loricam consertam hamis auroque trilicem.
> A hauberk of linked mail and triple tissue of gold.

AENEID, iii. 467.

Mail coats of this kind were well known to the Celtic and Teutonic tribes.  Such a mail coat is carved, together with Runic writing, on a whalebone box of about A.D. 700 in the British Museum, known as the ' Franks Casket ' [Fig. 49], and a *hringde byrnan* is described in Beowulf (*c.* A.D. 700), where we read :—

> Bēowulf madhelode—on him byrne scān,
> Searo-net seowed smithes or-thancum.

> Bēowulf spake, the byrnie on him shone,
> The armour-net linked by the skill of the smith.

BEOWULF, 405, 406.

Loricae of this type have been recovered by excavation from Teutonic sites from Switzerland to Sweden, and it is evident that such armour was widely known in barbarian Europe [Figs. 47 and 48].

The special liturgical use of the word *lorica* is probably derived from passages in the Vulgate where St. Paul speaks of those who have ' put on the lorica of righteousness,' *induti loricam justitiae* (Ephesians, vi, 14), or are ' covered with the lorica of faith and love,' *induti loricam fidei et caritatis* (I Thess. v. 8).[1] In connexion with the later development of the idea of a lorica of prayer, the former of these passages may be considered in its context.

*Ephesians VI.*

| Vulgate Version | English Translation |
|---|---|
| 10. . . . Fratres confortamini in Domino, et in potentia virtutis ejus. | 10. . . . Brethren, be ye strong in the Lord and in the power of His might. |
| 11. Induti vos armaturam Dei, ut possitis stare adversus insidias diaboli. | 11. *Put on yourselves the armour of God* that ye may be able to stand against the wiles of the devil. |
| 12. Quoniam non est nobis colluctatio adversus carnem et sanguinem, sed adversus principes, et potestates, adversus mundi rectores tenebrarum harum, contra spiritualia nequitiae, in caelestibus. | 12. Since for us the struggle is not against flesh and blood but against principalities and powers, against the rulers of the world of this darkness, against the Church (*spiritualia*) of wickedness in the heavens. |
| 13. Propterea accipite armaturam Dei, ut possitis resistere in die malo, et in omnibus perfecti stare. | 13. Wherefore *take up the armour of God*, that ye may be able to withstand in the evil day and, being perfected in all things, to stand. |
| 14. State ergo succincti lumbos vestros in veritate, et induti loricam justitiae ; | 14. Stand therefore *having girded your loins with truth and having put on the lorica of righteousness ;* |
| 15. Et calceati pedes in praeparatione Evangelii pacis ; | 15. And *having feet shod with preparation of the gospel* of peace ; |

[1] In the original Greek the word translated lorica is θώραξ in both cases.

FIG. 47.—Corslet or byrnie of iron rings.
Vimose, Funen, Denmark

FIG. 48.—Detail of Fig. 47, showing arrangement of rings.

FIG. 49.—ONE OF THE FACES OF THE SO-CALLED *FRANKS CASKET*

This important relic is Northumbrian carving in whalebone of about A.D. 700.
It was presented to the British Museum in 1857 by its Director, Sir A. Wollaston
Franks (1826–97). The scene represents an attack on a walled house defended
by a hero whose name ÆGILI is inscribed above him in Runic letters. Arrows
hurtle through the air and dead and dying lie about. Two of the attackers wear
*Loricae* of chain mail.

16. In omnibus sumentes scutum fidei, in quo possitis omnia tela nequissimi ignea exstinguere.

16. Above all *taking up the shield of faith* with which ye may be able to extinguish all the fiery darts of the most evil one.

17. Et galeam salutis assumite, et gladium spiritus, quod est verbum Dei.

17. And *take the helmet of salvation, and the sword of the spirit,* which is the word of God.

A similar range of ideas is encountered in Isaiah lix. 17, and in Psalm xci. In the former we read of one who ' has put on righteousness as a lorica and a helmet of salvation on his head,' *indutus est justitia ut lorica, et galea salutis in capite ejus.* It is interesting also to observe that Psalm xci is treated in Rabbinic literature as a protection against demoniac foes and against disease, and is used in much the same way as the lorica that we here describe.

In early Christian Europe the devotee regarded himself as surrounded constantly by devils who were always thrusting at him and endeavouring to pierce his breast-plate of good deeds and Christian observance. It became an ecclesiastical commonplace to speak of those protected from such attacks by a life of devotion, chastity, and asceticism as *loricati.* Thus the demon- and sin-repelling apparatus of prayer and mortification was conventionally looked upon as itself a lorica.

This feature is well brought out in the Irish hymn attributed to Bishop Sanctan, an early saint of Welsh origin, which begs that :—

> To my soul for every black sin
> Let never demons' godlessness visit me.
>
> .       .       .       .       .
>
> I shall utter the praises of Mary's Son
> Who fights for good deeds.
> And God of the elements will reply,
> For MY TONGUE IS A LORICA for battle.
> In beseeching God from the heavens
> May my body be incessantly laborious
> That I may not come to horrible Hell.[1]

---

[1] Printed and translated by J. H. Bernard and R. Atkinson, *The Irish Liber Hymnorum,* London, 1898, i, p. 129, and ii, p. 47.

Certain prayers regarded as of special efficacy, to which the name of some well-known and much tried saint was sometimes attached, came thus to be called *loricae*. In Ireland a special lorical value was attached to the prayers of St. Patrick ; thus in an early Irish poem in praise of him we read that ' a hymn which thou hast chosen in thy life-time shall be a LORICA of protection to all.'

The most famous of all the loricae is indeed that which claims to have been written by St. Patrick himself. Whether the claim is just or no, the composition is certainly very ancient and perhaps dates back to the fifth or sixth century, since it was written in a period when paganism had still considerable influence. The ' Lorica of St. Patrick,' the *fáeth fiada* or ' cry of the deer ' as it is called,[1] betrays its early origin by the call for protection ' against incantations of false prophets ; against black laws of paganism . . . against deceit of idolatry and against spells of women, smiths and druids.' In the first lines of this text we read how ' Patrick made this hymn . . . for the protection of himself and his monks against the enemies that lay in ambush for the clerics. And it is a LORICA of faith for the protection of body and soul against demons and men and vices. When any person shall recite it daily with pious meditation on God, demons shall not dare to face him, it shall be a protection to him against all poison and envy, it shall be a guard to him against sudden death ; it shall be a LORICA for his soul after his decease.' The Lorica which bears the name of Gillus or Gildas, which we here discuss, is of a somewhat similar type and designed for a like purpose to that of Patrick, which it closely resembles in tone and style.

---

[1] Bernard and Atkinson, *loc. cit.*, i. p. 133, and ii, p. 49. The interpretation of the term *fáeth fiada* is disputed. Some would read it *feth fiada* and consider that it was a spell peculiar to Druids and poets who by pronouncing certain verses of the hymn could make themselves invisible. The point is one that only Celtic scholars can decide. See Hugh Williams, *Gildae de excidio Britanniae (Hon. Soc. of Cymmrodorion)*, 2 vols., London, 1899, ii, p. 292.

The earliest copy of the Gildan Lorica that can be dated with any accuracy is a Cambridge manuscript of Anglo-Saxon workmanship. This manuscript has been recognized on palaeographical grounds as a product of the ninth century, while its date can be more narrowly determined by its acrostic containing the name *Aedeluald Episcopus*.[1] This Aedeluald or Aethelwald was Bishop of Lichfield between 818 and 830. But the composition of the Lorica is anterior to the earlier of these dates, since it is clearly Celtic in origin and character, and there was no direct Celtic influence on the liturgy of the English Church during the ninth century. The Welsh frontier had been flung back across the Severn fifty miles and more from the seat of his bishopric well-nigh two centuries before Aethelwald occupied it, so that by the eighth century Mercia was politically cut off from Wales. To separative political elements must be added the odium resulting from the schismatic character of the British Church after the Council of Whitby (664), reflected even in the writings of so gentle a soul as Bede (672-735). Thus to explain the Celtic source of the Lorica and to reach a point when a Mercian would have adopted a prayer of British origin, we must certainly look further back than the days of Aethelwald, and at least to the seventh century.

There is, moreover, external literary evidence that the composition of the Lorica was anterior to the eighth century. Aldhelm of Malmesbury (died 709) appears to have known of it, and his peculiar expression *tuta pelta protegente* is a reminiscence of stanza 16.[2] Further, all the MSS., except that at Vienna, associate the Lorica with one Laidcend, Loding, or Lodgen. The *Leabhar Breac* or *Speckled Book*, a work of the fourteenth century, speaks of the prayer as introduced into Ireland by *Laidcend, son of Baeth the Victorious*. This Laidcend, according to the Irish annals,

---

[1] The entire document is printed by A. B. Kuypers, *The Book of Cerne*, Cambridge, 1902.

[2] F. J. H. Jenkinson, *The Hisperica Famina*, Cambridge, 1908, p. xxii.

died in 661, and if the Laidcend of the *Leabhar Breac* is the same as Lodgen or Loding the prayer must be earlier than this date.

The opening sentence of the *Leabhar Breac* tells us that ' Gillus composed this Lorica to expel the demons who beset him.' It has been suggested that this Gillus is identical with Gildas the ' British Jeremiah.' Gildas Badonicus, the earliest British historian, was born in 516, the year of the battle of Mount Badon, and died about 570. Gillus or Gillas is known to be a common form of Gildas, especially in Irish documents. His well-known history, *De excidio Britanniae*, was written about 560, and a date about the middle of the sixth century must be ascribed to the Lorica if it is from his hand. The evidence that the work is by this Gildas is however by no means conclusive. It may well be that it dates from the century in which he lived, to which period other specimens of Hibernian Latin have been attributed,[1] though it is probable that most of them are at least a century later. If Gildas Badonicus were really the author we could regard the *mortalitas huius anni*, referred to in the text, as the *yellow plague*, which is said to have ravaged Britain about 547, at which date the composition of the Lorica would then be approximately fixed.[2] A more likely date for our document is perhaps about 600, and it is probably the work of a British Gildas other than he of Badon.

[1] The view that the Lorica is of the sixth century, and the work of Gildas, is upheld by H. Zimmer, *Nennius Vindicatus*, Berlin, 1893. It is regarded as of the seventh century (*circ.* 660) by R. Thurneysen in *Zeit. f. deutsch Philologie*, xxviii. p. 111, and by Hugh Williams, *Gildas*, London, 1889–1901, p. 295, and *Christianity in Early Britain*, Oxford, 1912. There is general consent that it is not later than the seventh century.

[2] The dates of this plague lie between 543 and 548. The occurrence of this plague is doubted by C. Creighton, *A History of Epidemics in Britain*, Cambridge, 1912, 2 vols., i. p. 4. It is thought that the story may have arisen as a rumour of the great plague at Byzantium and elsewhere in 543 and subsequent years. Cf. O'Donovan, *Annals of the Four Masters*, Dublin, 1851, i. p. 183.

## § 2. *Language*.

The language of the Lorica of Gildas has attracted a great deal of attention. The difficulty presented by mediaeval Latin is usually in the vocabulary, and is seldom constructional. To this rule the Lorica is no exception, for, with a very simple structure, it presents a most extraordinary collection of out-of-the-way and exotic words. The language of the Lorica has been much studied in connexion with the *Hisperica Famina,* a curious document of the seventh century in the Vienna Library, which the Lorica in many ways resembles.[1]

A similar specimen of the so-called 'Hibernian' or 'Hisperic' Latin is encountered in a hymn attributed to St. Columba (died 597), known from its opening words as *Altus prosator*.[2] The earliest manuscript of this composition is of the eleventh century, but there can be no doubt that it was composed at a far earlier date.

The *Altus prosator* also, we are assured, renders the reciter thereof secure from all manner of spiritual destruction, and further ' protects against every death save death on the pillow.'

Another early fragment of Celtic origin, the ' Leyden

---

[1] The text of the *Hisperica Famina* is accessible in Migne's *Patrologia Latina*, xc, p. 1186. Important discussions containing the bibliography of the text will be found in H. Bradshaw, *Collected Papers*, Cambridge, 1889, p. 453 (reprinted from a publication of 1872), and by H. Zimmer, *Nennius Vindicatus, Über Entstehung, Geschichte und Quellen der Historia Brittonum*, Berlin, 1893, and in the *Nachrichten von d. Konigl. Ges. der Wissenschaften zu Göttingen*, 1895, Heft ii. Another curious specimen containing many of the ' Hisperic ' words of the Lorica is encountered in the Luxemburg folio transcribed by J. Rhys, *Revue celtique*, i, p. 346, Paris, 1871. An excellent review of Hisperic or Hibernian Latin texts is given by H. Williams, *loc. cit.*, pp. 298 ff. Lastly, the text of the *Hisperica Famina* has been critically edited and compared with other specimens of Hibernian Latin by F. J. H. Jenkinson, *The Hisperica Famina*, Cambridge, 1908.

[2] Reprinted by Bernard and Atkinson, *loc. cit.*, i. p. 62 ; ii. pp. 23 and 140.

Lorica,' enumerates the parts of the body in great detail, in the same way as does the Lorica of Gildas, and uses much of the same obscure vocabulary. The Leyden Lorica is, on the whole, however, much simpler and less interesting than is the Gildan document.[1]

Modern research shows that the earlier stages of the process by which the Anglo-Saxon replaced the British tribes was one of infiltration and penetration rather than of invasion, conquest, and extermination, although doubtless both elements were present.  On this view we should expect to find connecting links between the Anglo-Saxon and the Celtic languages, yet such links are extraordinarily difficult to trace, and the classical Anglo-Saxon tongue— early literary English—contains even fewer Celtic words than does modern English.  Such Celtic remains as are to be discovered in Anglo-Saxon documents must be sought either in Hisperic texts and their glosses or in other magical formulae.  To find any real connexion between the two languages, if any such ever existed, we should probably need to look much further back than the formed literary English of which the best examples are of the tenth century, beyond the Danish devastation of the ninth century, beyond the racial bitterness of the eighth, beyond the schism of the seventh century, perhaps even beyond the Roman missionary effort of the sixth century under Augustine of Canterbury.  Documentary material of this order is, however, wholly lacking.

Now although the race and language movement was always westward, yet the cultural advantage for centuries was, as is well known, on the side of the receding peoples. The Celtic and English idioms are so vastly different that then, as now, little mixture of the two can have taken place, but there was a cultural diffusion in an eastward direction which is traceable in written documents.  A small amount of Celtic magic and folklore spread among men of English

[1] V. H. Friedel, ' La Lorica de Leyde,' in the *Zeit. f. celtische Philologie*, 1898, ii. p. 64.

speech, carrying its characteristic ideas with it. Of this influence the 'Leechdoms' give evidence in several places. To the Anglo-Saxon clerics, who shared a knowledge of Latin with their Celtic colleagues, there was, however, an easy and natural means of communication, and of this interchange the Lorica of Gildas is a very early monument. It is written in that very characteristic form of Latin, known as 'Hisperic' or 'Hibernian,' that was affected in south-west Britain and Ireland in the sixth and seventh centuries. Considerable remnants of what must have been an extensive Hisperic literature have now been recovered.[1] In this surviving Hisperic literature the Lorica of Gildas stands almost alone in that, while thoroughly Celtic in tone and style, and in use moreover by both the Irish and Welsh, it was yet popular with the English. This curious fact is sufficiently proved by the existence of three copies of the Lorica of Anglo-Saxon workmanship, two of them fully glossed in the Anglo-Saxon language. The Gildan Lorica is thus perhaps the earliest surviving literary link between the two rival cultures and rival tongues.

That the Lorica of Gildas was not the only specimen of Hisperic Latin that had reached the Saxon monasteries we learn from the occurrence of difficult words from other Hisperic documents in Anglo-Saxon vocabularies from the eighth to the eleventh centuries, and occasionally in the writings of Aldhelm (died 709). Through the medium of these glosses and vocabularies the combined efforts of mediaevalists, and Greek, Semitic, Celtic, and Anglo-Saxon scholars have now extracted the meaning and source of a great number of these obscure terms. There are also several passages in the Leechdoms which must have been written

---

[1] A readable account of the literature of Hibernian Latin is contained in the article on the Celtic Church, by H. Zimmer, in the *Realencyclopädie f. prot. Theologie und Kunst*, and has been conveniently translated into English by A. Meyer as *The Celtic Church in Britain Ireland, and* London, 1902.

under Hisperic influence.[1]   One of the most surprising
things about the Hisperic vocabulary is the occurrence of
Semitic elements.

It is not easy to understand how a knowledge of
Hebrew sufficient to suggest to its author some of the
out-of-the-way words included in the Lorica of Gildas can
have reached Britain in the sixth or seventh century.[2]
Modern study of the Hisperic Latin literature has reduced
the number of words to which a Semitic source was
ascribed by the earlier investigators.   There still remains,
however, a small group which appear to be truly of Semitic
origin, and cannot be otherwise explained.   Prominent
among these are *iduma* = יָדַיִם = hands ;  *gibrae* = גֶּבֶר =
man ; and *senas* = שֵׁן = tooth.   While the source of such
words cannot yet be fully explained, there are certain
points in connexion with this peculiar Semitic relationship
that may be borne in mind.

(*a*) From an early date interest in the works of Jerome
attracted attention to the words of Hebrew origin used by
him, and information as to the meaning of these and,
perhaps, of other Hebrew words thus reached these shores.
Two very early vocabularies of Anglo-Saxon origin contain
a considerable proportion of Hebrew words.[3]   Bede had a
vestigial knowledge of Hebrew.

[1] These are to be found in vol. i. p. 386 and pp. 388–90 ; vol. ii.
p. 112 and pp. 348–50 ; vol. iii. p. 26, p. 78, pp. 288–90, and p. 294 of
O. Cockayne's *Leechdoms, Wortcunning and Starcraft of Early England*,
3 vols., London, 1864–6.

[2] A Gallican psalter with Hebrew equivalents dating from the tenth
century has also been described, F. E. Warren, ' Un Monument inédit de
la Liturgie Celtique,' Paris, 1888, *Revue Celtique*, ix. p. 88.   It may have
been from some source such as this that Bede derived his slight
knowledge of Hebrew.   The question of Hebrew alphabets in early
Latin manuscripts is discussed by the author in *The Legacy of Israel*, Oxford,
1927, p. 290.

[3] J. H. Hessels, ' An Eighth Century Latin-Anglo-Saxon Glossary '
(*The Corpus Glossary*), Cambridge, 1890, p. 3 ; and ' A Late Eighth
Century Latin-Anglo-Saxon Glossary ' (*The Leyden Glossary*), Cambridge,
1906, pp. 27 and 221.

(b) It is possible that writers of Hibernian Latin may have had direct access to Jewish sources. No evidence is forthcoming that there were Jews in England before the Conquest, but there are ample records of their presence in Gaul.[1]

(c) Recent research has demonstrated unexpectedly early Arabian influence in southern Gaul beginning not later than the early part of the eighth century.[2]

(d) Syriac influence has been traced also in the Lorican vocabulary. From an early date Syrian wanderers, travelling for trade purpose, had reached the West. Thus a Spanish work on Technology of about the year 700 contains many Syriac terms. Again, Gregory of Tours (538–94), who was contemporary with the supposed date of our Lorica, tells that he learned the story of the Seven Sleepers of Ephesus from the mouth of a Syrian.[3] The same writer preserves also the Syrian legend of Cosmas and Damian.[4] Syrian influence in art was also prominent.

Such knowledge of Greek, on the other hand, as the Lorica displays, in common with other specimens of Hisperic Latin, was no very unusual accomplishment in Ireland from a date as far back as the fifth century.[5] This knowledge,

---

[1] S. A. Hirsch, *Trans. Jewish Historical Soc. Eng.*, London, 1915, vii. pp. 3 and 4. Gregory of Tours has many references to Jews in his *History of the Franks*. References to Jews in France have been collected by H. Gross, *Gallia Judaica*, Paris, 1897.

[2] Leo Wiener, *History of the Arabico-Gothic Culture*, New York, 2 vols., 1917. The conclusions in this work are generally unsound, but the important chapter on Virgilius Maro contains valuable material that has been commented on by H. Bradley in the *English Historical Review*, London, 1918, xxxiii. p. 252.

[3] Gregory of Tours, *De gloria martyrum*, ch. xcv.

[4] Charles and Dorothea Singer, ' Miniature of an Operation of Cosmas and Damian,' *Osler Presentation Volume*, New York, 1919.

[5] Ludwig Traube, ' O Roma nobilis ' (*Philologische Untersuchungen aus den Mittelalter*, Munich, 1891). See also K. Meyer, *Learning in Ireland in the Fifth Century and the Transmission of Letters*, Dublin, 1913. A popular account of the part played by Irishmen in the spread of learning during the Middle Ages is given in *The Irish Element in Mediaeval Culture*, by H. Zimmer, translated by J. E. Edmunds, New York, 1891.

the extent of which has been often exaggerated, may have reached the island from southern Gaul, where, as we know from Apollinaris Sidonius (430–87), Greek was well-known in the fifth century. The special magic value attached to the Lorica of Gildas, alike by the Celtic and English speaking peoples, arose perhaps from this mysterious and exotic character of its phraseology.

### § 3. *Text and Translation*

The text of the Lorica is found in six manuscripts of which the earliest is of the eighth century. These manuscripts we designate by the latters of the alphabet A to F. They are enumerated in the appendix to this essay. Our version is taken mainly from B with readings from other manuscripts. One of the manuscripts has been glossed in the Kentish dialect of Anglo-Saxon, a second in West Saxon, and a third in Irish. These glosses help greatly in the interpretation of the numerous very peculiar words. The text combines its magical elements with a sort of anatomical list. This list betrays, in places, contact with classical science in the last stage of degeneration.

Gillus hanc loricam fecit ad demones expellendos, eos qui aduersauerunt illi.

Peruenit angelus ad illum, et dixit illi angelus : Si quis homo frequentauerit illam addetur ei seculum septim annis et tertia pars peccatorum delebitur. In quacumque die cantauerit hanc orationem . . . es, homines uel demones, et inimici non possunt nocere ; et mors in illo die non tengit. Laidcend mac Búith Bannaig uenit ab eo in insolam Hiberniam ; transtulit et portauit super altare sancti Patricii episcopi, saluos nos facere, amen.

Gildas made this lorica to drive out those demons who pestered him.

An angel came to him, and the angel said to him, ' If any man should recite it constantly, a period of seven years would be added to his life and a third part of his sins blotted out. On whatsoever day he should chant this prayer . . . men, demons, or enemies cannot harm him, nor death touch him on that day.' Laidcend, son of Baeth the Victorious, came from him to the island of Ireland ; he brought it over and placed it upon the altar of Saint Patrick the Bishop, to make us whole. Amen.

Metrum undecassillabum quod et bracicatelecticon dicitur quod undecem sillabis constant ; sic scanditur.[1]

The metre is hendecasyllabic and is also called brachycatalectic because it consists of eleven syllables. It is scanned thus :—

1. Suffragare trinitatis[2] unitas
unitatis miserere trinitas

Help, O oneness of Trinity,
have pity, O threeness of unity,

2. Suffragare quaeso mihi posito

maris magni uelut in periculo

I beseech thee to help me who am placed
in peril as of a mighty sea,

3. Ut non secum trahat me mortalitas
huius anni neque mundi uanitas

So that neither the pestilence of this year
nor the vanity of the world may suck me under.

4. Et hoc idem peto a sublimibus
celestis militiae uirtutibus

And this I beg from the might
of the power of the high heavens ;

5. Ne me linquant lacerandum hostibus
sed defendant me iam armis fortibus

that they may not leave me to be torn by foes,
but may defend me with their mighty arms ;

6. Ut me illi praecedant in acie

caelestis exercitus militiae

that they may stand before me in battle array
as the army of heaven's levy.

7. Cherubinn et seraphinn cum milibus
Michael et Gabrihel similibus

Cherubim and Seraphim with their thousands,
Michael and Gabriel and their like,

8. Opto tronos uirtutes[3] archangelos
principatus potestates angelos

I conjure the thrones, the virtues, the archangels,
the principalities, powers and angels

9. Ut me denso defendentes agmine
inimicos ualeam prosternere

that, shielding me in dense formation,
I may stand strong to strike down the enemy.

10. Tum deinde ceteros agonithetas
patriarchas quattuor quater prophetas

(I beg) then the other chieftains,
the patriarchs and the four times four prophets,

---

[1] This introduction is inserted from E ; B has Hanc luricam lodgen in anno periculoso constituit. Et alii dicunt magna sit uirtus eius. Si ter in die cantatur. A has only Hanc luricam loding cantauit ter in omne die.

[2] B reads trinitas. Our reading is inserted from E.

[3] A reads inuentes. B reads uiuentes. Uirtutes is inserted from E.

11. Et apostolos nauis Christi pro-retas
et martyres omnes peto anthletas

and I beg the Apostles, the pilots of the ship of Christ,
the martyrs, yea, all of them captains,

12. Atque adiuro et uirgines omnes uiduas fideles et confessores[1]

and I adjure also all virgins, faithful widows and confessors,

13. Ut me per illos salus sepiat

atque omne malum a me pereat

that for their sake salvation may circle me

and all evil may perish from before me,

14. Christus mecum pactum firmum fereat
timor tremor tetras turbas terreat.

that Christ may make a strong alliance with me
that terror and fear may affright the foul host.

Finit primus prologus graduum angelorum et patriarchum apostolorum et martirum cum Christo.

Here ends the first prologue of the degrees of angels and patriarchs, of apostles and martyrs with Christ.

Incipit prologus secundus de cunctis membris corporis usque ad genua.[2]

Here begins the second prologue concerning all the members of the body as far as the knees.

15. Deus inpenetrabili tutella undique me defende potentia

O God, with thy inscrutable saving power defend all my parts,

16. Meae gibrae pernas omnes libera
tuta[3] pelta protegente singula

deliver the whole trunk of my body with thine own protecting shield

17. Ut non tetri demones in latera mea librent ut soleant iacula

that foul demons may not hurl, as is their wont, their darts at my flanks,

18. Gigram cephale cum iaris et conas

pattham liganam sennas atque michinas

skull, head with hair and eyes,

forehead, tongue, teeth and nose,

19. Cladum crassum madianum talias

bathma exugiam atque binas idumas

neck, breast, side and reins,

thighs, under-rump and two hands.

20. Meo ergo cum capillis uertice[4] galea salutis esto capite

To my head, with hairs on top of it, be a helmet of protection,

---

[1] The whole stanza 12 is omitted by A and B but found in E.

[2] The two clauses between stanzas 14 and 15 are omitted by A and B and inserted from E.

[3] A and E read tuta, B tua.

[4] A reads capiti, as also E.

21. Fronti oculis et cerebro triformi rostro labie facie timpore

to forehead, eyes and triformed brain,

22. Mento barbae superciliis auribus

to nose, lip, face and temple,

genis buccis internaso naribus

to chin, beard, eyebrows, ears, cheeks, lips, internasal septum and nares,

23. Pupillis rotis palpebris tautonibus

to the round pupils, eyelids and eyelashes,

gingis anile [1] maxillis faucibus

gums, breath, jaws, fauces,

24. Dentibus linguae ori uuae[2] guttori

to the teeth, tongue, mouth and throat,

gurgulioni et sublinguae ceruici

uvula, larynx and frenum of the tongue,

25. Capitali ceotro cartilagini

to head-pan, brain and gristle,

collo clemens adesto tutamini

and to my neck be thou a protection in thy mercy ;

[Obsecro te domine Iesu Christe propter nouem ordines sanctorum angelorum.[3]]

[I beseech thee, O Lord Jesus Christ, for the nine orders of holy angels,

26. Deinde esto LORICA tutissima

Be thou a secure lorica

ergo membra ergo mea uiscera[4]

both to my members and to my viscera.

27. Ut retrudas a me inuisibiles

So that thou turn back from me the invisible

sudum clauos quos fingunt odibiles

points of the shafts which transfix the abhorred.

28. Tege ergo Deus fortis lurica

Cover (me) then, O God, Thou strong lorica,

cum scapulis humeros et brachia

as to my shoulders, arms and forearms ;

29. Tege ulnas cum cubis et manibus

Cover arms with elbows and hands,

pugnos palmas digitos cum ungibus

fists, palms, fingers with nails.

30. Tege spinam atque costas cum arctibus

Cover the spine and ribs with their joints,

terga dorsumque neruos cum ossibus

the rear and back with nerves and bones.

---

[1] B reads Anale. The reading anile is inserted from A.

[2] B reads ubae only. The reading ori uuae is inserted from A.

[3] This invocation is absent in A and B and is inserted from E.

[4] The order of membra and uiscera is inverted in B.

31. Tege cutem sanguinem cum renibus

Cover skin, blood with kidneys,

cata crines nates cum femoribus

haunches and rump with thighs.

32. Tege cambas surras femoralia cum genuclis po(p)lites et genua

Cover hams, calves and thigh parts with knuckle-bones, poplites and knees.

33. Tege ramos con crescentes decies

Cover the tenfold branches (of the fingers)

cum mentagris ungues[1] binos quinquies

with toes and their twice five nails.

34. Tege talos cum tibiis et calcibus

Cover ankles with shanks and heels,

crura pedes plantarum cum bassibus.

legs, feet, soles with insteps.

35. Tege pectus iugulam pectusculum

Cover breast, peritoneum and breast bone,

mamillas[2] stomachum et umbilicum

mammae, stomach and navel.

36. Tege uentrem lumbos genetalia et aluum et cordis uitalia

Cover belly, groins, genital parts and paunch and vital parts of the heart.

37. Tege trifidum iecor et ilia

Cover the trifid liver and ilia,

marsem reniculos fithrem cum obligio

scrotum, kidneys, intestines and rete mirabile.

38. Tege toliam toracem cum pulmone

Cover tonsils, thorax with lung,

uenas fibras fel cum bucliamini

vessels, sinews, gall with pericardium.

39. Tege carnem inginem[3] cum medullis

Cover flesh, groin with marrow,

splenem tortuosis intestinis

spleen with tortuous intestines.

40. Tege uesicam adipem et pantes[4]

Cover bladder fat and all

compaginum innumeros ordines

the innumerable sorts of structures.

41. Tege pilos atque membra reliqua

Cover hairs and the other members

quorum forte praeteribi nomina

the names of which I have perchance omitted.

---

[1] B has iunges.   The reading ungues is from A.
[2] B has mamellum.   The reading mamillas is from A and E.
[3] B has iunginam, as also A.   The reading inginem is from E.
[4] B has partes.   The reading pantes is from A and E.

42. Tege totum me cum quinque sensibus

Cover all of me with my five senses,

et cum decim fabrefactis foribus

and with the ten doors that were contrived (for their use,)

43. Ut a plantis usque ad verticem

that from the soles to the top of the head

nullo membro foris intus egrotem

in no member, without or within, may I be sick ;

44 Ne de meo possit uitam trudere

that there may not thrust the life from my body

pestis febris languor dolor corpore

neither pest nor fever nor languor nor pain,

45. Donec iam Deo dante seneam

while by God's grace I may reach old age

et peccata mea bonis deleam

and may wipe out my sins with good deeds,

46. Et de carne iens imis caream

And leaving the flesh I may be blameless

et ad alta euolare ualeam

and may be worthy to pass on high

47. Et miserto[1] Deo ad etheria

And by God's pity I may rise happy

laetus regni uechar refrigeria

to the refreshing ether of His Kingdom.

Amen. Amen.

Amen. Amen.

## § 4. *Vocabulary*

The chief interest of the Lorica of Gildas is the very extraordinary vocabulary of foreign words. The origin of many of these is still very obscure. In the following notes we give interpretations of most of them. There are still some on which scholars are by no means agreed. The capital letters refer to the manuscripts enumerated in the list at the end of this essay. A glance at the notes which follow here will give an idea of how, at certain cultural stages, any phrase or idea that is foreign or strange can be enlisted by the magician for his purposes.

Stanza 10. *Agonithetas* from ἀγωνιστής = *combatant*. A has the Anglo-Saxon gloss cempan = *chieftains*. E contains a long gloss on this word, which yields the same result as A.

---

[1] B has misero. The reading miserto is from A and E.

Stanza 11. *Proretas* must be for πρωράτας = *look-out men*. A is glossed Anglo-Saxon stioran from steorra = *a star*. Steor-refra = *steersman* occurs in the Blickling homilies (late tenth century) : Crist wæs on dhæm scipe swa se steorrethra = *Christ was in the ship as a steersman*. E has a long gloss on the word, deriving it from Latin *prora* = the helm.

*Anthletas* for ἀθλητάς = *champions*. A is glossed Anglo-Saxon cempan = *chieftains*. E principes belli.

Stanza 16. *Gibrae*, a suggested origin is Hebrew גֶּבֶר = *man, homo*. A glosses Anglo-Saxon lichoman. Lic and lichama are recognized Anglo-Saxon forms for *body* or *corpse*, cf. German *leichnam*. E glosses id est hominis, gibre.

*Pernas* appears to be equivalent to *flank* or *trunk* ; as such it appears in an eighth-century Anglo-Saxon glossary thus : perna, flicci = *flitch*.[1]

E glosses id est artus id est compur inchleib. The Irish words = *trunk* (?) *of the chest*, according to Stokes.

*Pelta* probably for πέλτη = *shield*. E glosses Irish sciath = *shield*.

Stanza 17. *Tetri* for taetri.

Stanza 18. *Gigram* is glossed by A as Anglo-Saxon hnoll = *crown of the head*, and by E with Irish words of the same significance. The origin of the word *gigram* is unknown. Cockayne's suggestion is גַּרְגַּר, *neck* (rather גַּרְגְּרוֹת). *Gigram* might also be fancifully rendered *high top* (גַּג רָס).

*Cephale* for κεφάλην = *head*.

*Iaris*. W. Wright suggests this word is from שֵׂעָר = *hair* as by error for siaris. The connexion seems distant, but E glosses capillis.

*Conas*. Cockayne's suggestion for עַיִן = *eyes*, giving the full guttural sound to the ע, seems very strained. That conas means *eyes* seems clear from the fact that E is glossed oculos and D Anglo-Saxon egan = *eyes*. Conas is glossed oculos in another tenth-century MS. (Wright, vol. i).

*Pattham* is shown by Irish gloss to E to mean *forehead*. For a source of the word the commentators are driven to Syriac. A glosses Anglo-Saxon onwlite = *face*.

*Liganam* is glossed by E Irish dontengaid = *to the tongue*. The word must therefore stand for linguam.

*Sennas* is glossed by A Anglo-Saxon toef = *teeth*, and by E dentes. Cockayne suggests from שֵׁן = *tooth*.

---

[1] Thomas Wright, *Anglo-Saxon and Old English Vocabularies*, edited by R. P. Wülker, 2 vols., London, 1884, i. 38, 34.

*Michinas* is glossed by A as Anglo-Saxon næsdhyrel = nostrils. A connexion has been suggested with μυκτῆρας = *nostrils*. E glosses with the Irish equivalent of teeth.

Stanza 19. *Cladum* glossed by A as Anglo-Saxon swiran and swioran = sweoro, *neck* or *column*. E glosses collum. For a source W. Wright is again driven to Syriac or Arabic ; Arabic kadhalun, Syriac kedala ; D reads chaladum.

*Crassum* glossed by A as Anglo-Saxon breost and by E pectus. There can therefore be little doubt of its meaning, though no likely suggestion has been made for its source. Crassum is glossed dorsum in a tenth-century MS. (Wright).

*Madianu* glossed by A sidan =*side* and by E latus.

*Talias* glossed by A as Anglo-Saxon lendana = lendenu = *loins, reins*, and by E with the Irish equivalent of *bowels*.

*Bathma* glossed by A as Anglo-Saxon dheeoh = *thews* or *thighs*, and by E with the Irish equivalent of *loins*. Bathma is perhaps from βαθμοί = *steps*, a word which there is evidence from Hesychius Lexicographus (probably fifth century) was used as an out-of-the-way term for *thighs* as βαθμοί ἴχνη πόδες = *thighs, legs, feet*.

*Exugiam* glossed meaninglessly by A as Anglo-Saxon midirnan and by D as Anglo-Saxon micgernu. Micge is the usual Anglo-Saxon for *urine* and micgernu the *place of the urine*, i.e. *the bladder*. To regard it as equal to kidneys, as some have done, is to attribute to the author of the Lorica a physiological conception that he probably did not possess. For him it is probable that the kidneys would have been the seat of some mental rather than urinary function. The Irish gloss gives *tarb gliasta no fathóin*, i.e. the bull (i.e. the thick part as opposed to the calf, the thin part) of the thigh, i.e. the rump or under-rump. In Wülcker the word exigia is glossed Anglo-Saxon gescinco which is surely a collective of sceanca = shank. The agreement of Anglo-Saxon and Irish glosses in this and other places indicates a definite harmony of interpretation that can only have been reached by direct intercourse.

*Idumas* glossed by A as Anglo-Saxon hondas = *hands*, and by E manus. The word itself is probably from יָדַיִם = *hands*.

Stanza 21. *Timpus* is the usual mediaeval form of tempus.

Stanza 23. *Tautonibus* glossed by A as Anglo-Saxon ofer bruun = *upper brows* = *eyebrows*, and by E with the Irish equivalent of *eyelids*, the eyebrows being considered the guardians (tutores) of the eyes ; or perhaps the bony orbit of the skull is meant, cf. Aelfric vocabulary Tauco (? for Tauto), hringban dhæs eagen = *ring-bone of the eye*.

9

*Gingis* glossed by A todhreomum = *tooth-holder*. D reads ignis, but gives the same gloss. The word is probably for gingivis and not a form of Anglo-Saxon cin = *chin*.

*Anile* glossed by A orodhe = *breath* = *anhelae*.

Stanza 24. *Uuae* glossed by A Anglo-Saxon hræctungan = *throat tongue* = *uvula*.

*Gurgulioni* glossed by A Anglo-Saxon dhrotbollan = *throat pan* = *Adam's apple* = *larynx*. E agrees with this.

*Sublinguae* glossed by A Anglo-Saxon tungedhrum = *tongue thread* or *tongue cord* = *under tongue cord*. D has Anglo-Saxon undertunge-dhrum. The meaning is surely the *frenulum linguae* of anatomists.

Stanza 25. *Capitali* glossed by A Anglo-Saxon heafudponnan = *head pan* ; by D Anglo-Saxon heafodlocan = *head guard, head cover*.

*Ceotro* : A reads centro and glosses Anglo-Saxon swiran = *neck*. D reads ceotro ; E reads ceotro and glosses with Irish equivalent of *neck*. Cockayne suggests from χόνδρος, but an eighth-century gloss reads ceruellum, id est centrum brægen = *brain*, and this may well be the meaning.

*Cartilagini* glossed by A Anglo-Saxon gristlan.

Stanza 27. *Sudum* for sudium.

Stanza 29. *Cubis* glossed by A Anglo-Saxon fædhmum = *elbow, arms* ; by D Anglo-Saxon elnbogan = *elbows*.

*Pugnos* glossed fyste = *fist* by both A and D.

*Ungibus* glossed naeglum = *nails* by both A and D.

Stanza 30. *Arctibus* glossed by A Anglo-Saxon liodhum, by D lidh = *joints*.

Stanza 31. *Cata crines* is glossed by A Anglo-Saxon huppbaan = *hip*. The source of the term cata crines is obscure and any derivation from κατακρίνω = *deliver judgement*, seems very difficult, though there was a school of mediaeval thinkers who made the loins the seat of judgement. Williams (*loc. cit.*) thinks that cata may be the Greek κατά, which was commonly used in the Latin of the sixth century as equivalent to ad or juxta.

Stanza 32. *Cambas*. E reads gambas ; A reads cambas, and is glossed Anglo-Saxon homme = *hams*.

*Genuclis*, glossed by A Anglo-Saxon cniethum = *knees*, written above an older and erased gloss that was perhaps hweorfbanum, a word which would bear the meaning *throw-bones*, i.e. *knuckle-bones*.

Stanza 33. *Ramos con crescentes decies* = *the ten growing branches*, i.e. the fingers. Cf. Hesiod, *Works and Days*, 742 : ἀπὸ πεντόζοιο αὖον ἀπὸ χλωροῦ τάμνειν = *to cut the withered from the quick from the five-branched* = *to cut the nails of the hand*.

*Mentagris*, glossed by A Anglo-Saxon tanum = *toes*. No source for the word can be suggested. An eighth-century glossary, printed by T. Wright, gives mentagra, bituihn, which helps no further.

Stanza 34. *Bassibus* from βάσις = step, glossed by A Anglo-Saxon stæpum = *steps*.

Stanza 35. *Iugulam*. Bosworth and Toller (Anglo-Saxon dictionary, Oxford, 1898) suggest that jugulam = *collar-bone*, but the word is glossed by A Anglo-Saxon dhearmgewind, which must mean *abdominal cavity* or *peritoneum* from thearm = *intestine*, dhearmgewind being thus *the parts that enwrap the intestine*.

*Pectusculum* is glossed by A Anglo-Saxon briostban = *breastbone*. E gives an Irish gloss equivalent to *the breast of the palm*.

Stanza 37. *Marsem* perhaps for marsupium = *pouch*. The word is glossed by A Anglo-Saxon bursan = *purse*; E Irish selg = *spleen*.

*Fithrem* is glossed by D Anglo-Saxon snædeldhearm = *intestine*.

*Obligio* is glossed by A Anglo-Saxon nettan = *net*, the usual mediaeval term for the *rete mirabile*, a part of the brain to which especial importance was attached by Galen and all mediaeval writers. E has an Irish gloss, inglais, to which no meaning can be attached.

Stanza 38. *Toliam* glossed by A Anglo-Saxon readan. In Wright's vocabulary there is an Anglo-Saxon gloss ; reada tolia vel porunula (i, 4446–8). Reada = *red*, and Dr. Henry Bradley suggested that toliam may represent the Middle English tuly or tewly = *purple*, a word which he thought might possibly be derived from תְּכֵלֶת or from תּוֹלָע and תּוֹלַעַת = *worm* and also *scarlet*, i.e. the colour obtained from the worm of the shell-fish murex. This tuly and toliam may be the red worm-like structure, the *uvula*.

*Fibras* glossed by A and D Anglo-Saxon smæl = *small*. E gives Irish gloss = *sinews*. Smæl perhaps refers to the *small ends* of the muscles.

*Bucliamini* glossed by A and D Anglo-Saxon heorthoman, for heort-hama = *heart cover* = *pericardium* or *midriff*.

Stanza 39. *Inginem* perhaps for inguinem. B reads iunginam and A glosses Anglo-Saxon tha sceare = *shears* or *scissors* = perhaps for the *crutch* or *fork of the legs*.

Stanza 40. *Pantes* for πάντες = *all*. B reads partes, D pantas. A and H gloss Anglo-Saxon ealle = *all*. E glosses *omnes*.

Stanza 42. *Sensibus cum decim fabrefactis foribus*. A and D gloss Anglo-Saxon mid ten durum = *with ten doors*. The ten doors or portals of entry of sensations is a mediaeval commonplace. The mouth counts for two (œsophagus + trachea), the others being eyes, ears, nostrils, urethra, and anus. Or the five senses may be more strictly followed and the hands reckoned as the organs of feeling.

## § 5. *Appendix*

### Manuscripts of the Lorica of Gildas

The Lorica of Gildas is known from the following six manuscripts :—

(A) *Early Ninth Century.*—Cambridge University Library Ll.I, 10, fol. 43. This MS. is known as the *Book of Cerne*, but is better described as the *Prayer Book of Aedeluald the Bishop*. The section containing the Lorica is fully glossed in the Kentish dialect of Anglo-Saxon by a hand that is probably of the *tenth century*. These glosses are valuable as giving the meaning of many words which would be otherwise untranslatable. The latest edition of it is contained in Dom. A. B. Kuypers, O.S.B., *The Book of Cerne*, Cambridge, 1902, p. 85. The drawings and illuminations of this volume are discussed by J. A. Westwood in his *Facsimiles of the Miniatures and Ornaments of Anglo-Saxon and Irish MSS.*, London, 1868, p. 43. The text is also printed and elaborately compared with the other MSS. and discussed by R. P. Wülcker, *Bibliothek der Angelsachsischen Prosa*, Bd. vi, Hamburg, 1905. See also H. Sweet, *The Oldest English Texts*, Early English Text Society, London, 1885.

(B) *Eighth or Ninth Century.*—British Museum Library, Harley, 2965. A manuscript formerly belonging to St. Mary's Abbey or Nunnaminster at Winchester. The text is printed by W. de Gray Birch, in *An Ancient Manuscript of the Eighth or Ninth Century*, published by the Hampshire Record Society, Winchester and London, 1889. We have in the main reproduced this text. See also *New Palaeographical Society Facsimiles*, plate 163.

(C) *Ninth Century.*—Cologne Cathedral Library, formerly at Darmstadt, where it was numbered 2106. It has been copied from a glossed original and has several corrections in a later hand. The text is printed by Mone in *Lateinische Hymnen*, Freiburg, 1853, vol. i. p. 367.

(D) *Late Tenth Century.*—British Museum Library, Harley, 585, fo. 152. The Lorica is here placed in the midst of an Anglo-Saxon medical receipt book known as the 'Lacnunga' (i.e. Medications, recipes), and is fully glossed by an Anglo-Saxon hand of the eleventh century. This version has been printed by O. Cockayne, *Leechdoms, Wortcunning and Starcraft of Early England*, London, 1864, vol. i. p. 73.

(E) *Fourteenth Century.*—Royal Irish Academy at Dublin, the *Leabhar Breac* or *Speckled Book*. This MS. is an immense collection of ecclesiastical pieces, and has been published in facsimile by the Royal Irish Academy, Dublin, 1876. The text of the Lorica is glossed in Irish, and text and glosses are printed and discussed by Whitley Stokes, *Irish Glosses*, Dublin, 1860, p. 133. It has been printed again by Bernard and Atkinson in the *Irish Liber Hymnorum*.

(F) *Sixteenth Century.*—Vienna Royal Library, 11, 857. This text has been printed by Daniel in the *Thesaurus Hymnologicus*, 1855, vol. iv. p. 364.

PLATE III

SCORPION AND SNAKE FIGHTING

From an Anglo-Saxon Herbal of about 1050 (Cott. Vit. C. iii). The drawing of the scorpion is fairly accurate, showing that the artist of the original, from which this was copied, worked in the Mediterranean region. The plant, which is marked "Solago Minor" in the MS., is perhaps intended to represent the *Heliotropium Europaeum* of botanists. See page 187.

# EARLY ENGLISH MAGIC AND MEDICINE

## *Introduction*

THE practice of the healing art during the centuries that intervened between the fall of Greek science and the rise of the experimental method is a topic from which even the professed historian of medicine has usually averted his gaze. The material is neither edifying nor attractive, while the discipline demanded of one who would investigate it is by no means inconsiderable. Nevertheless the field is not altogether barren, for it can be made to yield valuable information as to the character and direction of cultural streams, and it is perhaps especially productive in just those periods where our other sources of information are most meagre.

The history of medicine in this great stretch of time is sharply divided into two parts by an event of great importance for the development of the human intellect. That event is the arrival in the West of the Arabian learning, the remnant of Greek science that had dwelt in the Moslem world to find its way again to the Occident at a date which varied in different countries but which may roughly be placed at the twelfth century [Fig. 31]. It is with pre-Arabian material only that we shall deal here, and to it we may attach the title of *Dark Age Medicine*.   But it must be remembered that for medicine the *Dark Age* of our notation extends far beyond the limits usually assigned to that period by historians. So far as England is concerned some of its documents undoubtedly date from as late as the thirteenth century. After the first half of that century, however, material, other than pure folk-medicine, free from Arabian influence is distinctly rare.

The magical and medical practice of Early England has come down to us, in a fragmentary state it is true, by two channels, manuscripts and folk-lore.   It is to the manuscripts that we shall here appeal, but in judging written matter produced by a barbarian people among whom the Latin culture was diffusing itself from the shattered fragments of the Roman Empire, certain special precautions are necessary.

Firstly, we must resist the temptation of inferring the primitiveness or the reverse of any practice from the date of the manuscript in which it is found.   The main agent in the spread of Southern culture among the English was the Church, and its instrument—for our purpose at least— the art of writing.   Consider what happens when a savage tribe is converted, under modern conditions, to the religion of a ruling race.   First Bible and Prayer Book are translated and these circulate among the earliest proselytes, who learn to read and write from devotional works.   Later the purposes of Law and Commerce are subserved by the written language.   But it is not until generations have passed, and the art of writing has become far more familiar, that we expect to find the intimate relations of life expressing themselves through the new medium.

So with the documents of Early English origin.   If we turn to an eighth-century writer such as Bede we are faced with purely ecclesiastical material, bearing hardly a trace of the heathenism of his father or grandfather and almost without any indication that the imported culture was a new thing in his part of the world. There is scarcely the mention of a heathen god or hero and practically no word of native magic. The works of Bede might have been written by a foreign missionary instead of by an Englishman, for any information as to native customs that they contain, while of native medicine there is not a particle though there are plenty of medical references. On the other hand, such manuscripts as *Beowulf*, or, more important for our purpose, the *Lacnunga* (Harley 585), are not earlier than the eleventh century, and yet are full of the more primitive material. In spite of its late date the *Lacnunga* is our best source of the primitive medicine of this country untouched by Christian influence, and its compiler does not hesitate to name the northern gods, Woden and the Æsir, in the weaving of his spells. The attitude of the writer of the *Lacnunga* to this material is exhibited by the way in which such purely heathen paragraphs alternate with charms mentioning the sacred personages of Christian tradition. But of any understanding of the nature of the Christian religion he exhibits not a trace ; for him the efficacy of Christ and Peter is wholly on a par with that of Woden and the Æsir. It is this intrusion of primitive elements into late documents and the full Christianization of much earlier records, that make it impossible to describe our material in the chronological order of the manuscripts.

But there is a second source of error against which we must guard. Magic—and all early medicine partakes largely of the nature of magic—is probably among all peoples, and certainly among the North European barbarians, essentially syncretic. Of all forms of cultural influence it is magic that passes most easily and most rapidly from people to people. Any object or process or person, held in esteem by a superior class, may easily acquire magical powers among those of lower culture. Quintus Serenus Sammonicus, a Latin physician of the third century, advised as a remedy for quartan ague the placing of the fourth book of Homer's *Iliad* under the sufferer's head ! But we may

take a more modern and even more absurd instance of the
ease and rapidity of the passage of exotic magical formulae.
It is told of Justice Holt (1642–1710) that he led a wild youth,
and that on one occasion, finding himself near Oxford and
without money, he procured a week's lodging by pretending
to charm away an ague from which his landlady's daughter
was suffering. He scribbled a few words of Greek on a
scrap of parchment that had been used as a label and, rolling
it up, directed that it should be bound to the girl's wrist
and left there till she was well. Many years after, an old
woman was brought before him charged with sorcery. The
evidence showed that she professed to cure the fever-stricken
by the application of a magic bit of parchment. Justice
Holt examined the fragment and found it to be the very
piece with which he had worked his miraculous cure many
years before, for his own Greek words were still legible upon
it. His lordship confessed and the woman, who was acquitted,
was one of the last to be tried for witchcraft in this country.
In the course of our discussion we shall encounter Greek
periapts of this very sort in use among the Anglo-Saxons
(p. 165), but we must not infer from them any more intimate
contact with the Greek originals.

There is yet a third special precaution needed, and this
concerns the language of the documents. Early English
magic and medicine has been investigated mainly by philologists, interested in the material as literature in the Anglo-
Saxon language but paying less attention to the nature
and affinities of its magical elements. For our purposes,
however, we shall have to neglect the linguistic distinction,
for the actual language in which these documents have come
down to us—English or Latin—is hardly more than an
accident. The magic and medicine of Early England must
be studied as a whole if we wish to learn something of the
cultural factors that have gone to make up this remarkable
system, or to gain a true picture of the attitude of the inhabitants of this country towards the healing art, before the
arrival of that scholastic method and Arabian learning

which wrought nearly as great a mental revolution in the thirteenth, as the experimental method and scientific attitude in the seventeenth century (see p. 75 ff).

Before we turn to the medico-magical material itself a word may be said concerning the men for whom it was written and by whom it was used.  It is usually assumed that any documents that come to us from the Dark or Middle Ages must necessarily have been written by clerics, and it

FIG. 50.—Durham Cathedral Library MS., Hunter 100.  [Fo. 122.]  Late Eleventh Century.  A leech branding a patient who has just been shorn.  Neither the leech nor his assistant are tonsured.

is certain that the most beautiful of the Early English medical manuscripts, including all the illuminated specimens, were prepared in monasteries.  The texts of these illuminated manuscripts are, however, copies, or at best little but translations, and the documents to which they go back were hardly, if at all, clericized or even Christianized.  Moreover, there are certain works, such as the *Leech-book of Bald* and the *Lacnunga*, where the scribe himself must have been a layman.  This is emphasized by the frequent demand that certain ceremonies need the aid of a priest, a superfluous direction in a book intended only for monastic use.   There is sufficient evidence to show that, as early as the seventh century, there were lay physicians in this country who were freely consulted by prominent ecclesiastics.   Of the status and character of these leeches we know next to nothing, but we are tempted to fill the gap in our knowledge from the accounts of the hereditary physicians of the Welsh and Gaelic peoples.

In the illuminated Early English manuscripts there are a number of pictures in which a leech makes his appearance, and he is never represented as tonsured [Fig. 50].   It is perhaps dangerous to draw a definite conclusion from this until the source and history of these figures and the degree to which they were mere copies has been finally determined, but it is at least safe to say that the medical writings are less clericized than most Early English material.

The Anglo-Saxon medico-magical writings form a very composite mass in which a great variety of elements may be distinguished.   These may be classed roughly according to the degree to which they have influenced the material that has survived [Fig. 51].

    I.   Greek Medicine filtered through Latin. (True Dark Age Medicine.)
   II.   Ecclesiastical Elements.
  III.   Salernitan Texts.
  IV.   Native Teutonic Magic and Herb-lore.
   V.   Celtic Magic : { (a) Native or Celto-Roman.
                     { (b) Hisperic.
  VI.   A composite mass of herb-lore from Southern Italy.
 VII.   Byzantine Magic and Theurgy.
VIII.   Pagan Roman Spells.

§ 1.  *Greek Medicine filtered through Latin.  (True Dark Age Medicine.)*

Medicine reached the barbarian peoples of the West at a time when the scientific system of Greece was in complete decay, and it came through Latin channels. It was thus merely copied or traditional and had none of those living characteristics so honourably associated with the Hippocratic and Galenic works. Poor as most of this material is, it is yet of importance to us to make some sort of estimate

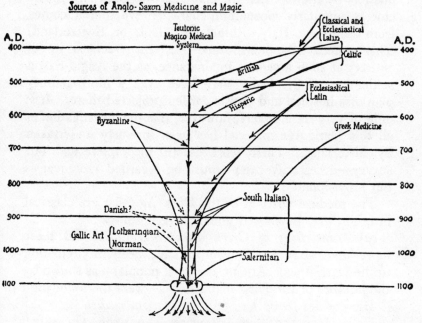

Sources of Anglo-Saxon Medicine and Magic

A composite mass containing in order of importance:-

1. Greek Medicine filtered through Latin (true Dark Age Medicine)
2. Ecclesiastical Elements
3. Salernitan texts etc
4. Native Teutonic Magic and Herblore
5. Celtic (Hisperic + Native) Magic
6. Composite Herblore from South Italy
7. Byzantine Magic and Theurgy
8. Pagan Roman Spells

FIG. 51.

of what Greek medical books were available to the men of the later Empire, in order to estimate the influence of Greek sources on Early English literature.

During the period of Gothic domination in Italy there had been an active process of translation of Greek medical works into Latin. Thus much we learn from Cassiodorus

(490–585).   By an examination of the manuscripts themselves and an investigation of ancient library catalogues we
can form a good idea of the material available for distribution
among the barbarians of the North and West between the
seventh and the eleventh centuries.   The task is rendered
possible by the fact that the characteristic Dark Age medicine is singularly constant in character, whether it comes
from Southern Italy, Rhineland, Gaul, or Switzerland.
This system of monkish medicine was practised in its
entirety at such a centre, for instance, as the Anglo-Saxon
settlement of St. Gall.   We have even a ninth-century
plan of a hospital and physic garden projected there.   It is
only of very recent years, however, that the investigation of
all this Dark Age material has been seriously undertaken
by historians.   Their work is still incomplete and our
survey—necessarily brief—must be regarded moreover as
but provisional.

The medical writings of the Dark Age that are classical
in origin may be classed under three headings :

(a) *Translations of Greek works into Latin*.   Of these
more than sixty are known to have been in circulation
in the Dark Ages.   Among the most popular—as shown by
the number of surviving manuscripts—were the following :

Dioscorides (*circa* A.D. 60), *De materia medica*.

Galen (130–200)—sundry works.   A work *On urines*
    and another *On fevers* were popular.   A good many
    fragments of other works are known.

Oribasius (325–403), *De parabilibus medicamentis (ad
    Eunapium)*.

Alexander of Tralles (525–605), *Therapeutica*.

Paul of Aegina (625–90), Book VII of the *Epitomae
    medicae*.

Of these writers the first two were Latinized at least as
early as the fifth century, the last three probably not until
the seventh or eighth, but it is the last three that had, in
fact, most influence on the English material.   Several
works of Hippocrates, in wretched translations, were also

PLATE IV

'MUGCWYRT' = MUGWORT, *ARTEMISIA PONTICA*

A species foreign to England.

From an Anglo-Saxon Herbal of about 1050 (Cott. Vit. C. iii).
See p. 187.

known in Dark Age Europe, but they appear to have been less used than those we have enumerated, and there is no evidence that any work of Hippocrates was available to early English writers.

(*b*) In addition to the actual translations from the Greek there were a number of *works written in Latin* during the late Empire which, though borrowing from Greek and under the influence of the decaying Greek tradition, were yet composed in the Latin language. These are mostly the work of Provincials, Barbarians, or Graeco-Italians, and are often admixed with local superstitions. Among the more popular were :

Pseudo-Dioscorides, *De herbis feminis* (sixth century ?).

Pseudo-Apuleius, *De herbis* (fourth century).

Sextus Placitus Papyriensis, *De Medicina ex Animalibus* (fourth century ?).

Marcellus Empiricus of Bordeaux, *De Medicamentis* (first half of fifth century).

Pseudo-Hippocratic Epistles (fourth century ?).

The general form of all these works was fixed between the fourth and the sixth centuries.

(*c*) A special position must be accorded to the *Natural History* of Pliny and of his abstractor, Plinius Valerianus, which were available in England at an early date. From Bede and Alcuin onward, Pliny together with Isidore of Seville (560–636) provided the staple of such natural knowledge as was possessed by English writers. Pliny was probably the most widely read of any non-ecclesiastical writer throughout the Dark Ages.

Manuscripts written in England before the Arabian revival contain numerous quotations from all of these works, and indeed they form the groundwork of early English medicine. The medicine derived from these works forms a fairly definite system and is easily traced. Its philosophical basis is the doctrine of the four elements and the four humours, a view which finds ample illustration in English manuscripts. In the belief of the men of the Dark

Ages there was a close relation between the external and the internal world, the macrocosm and the microcosm. Thus

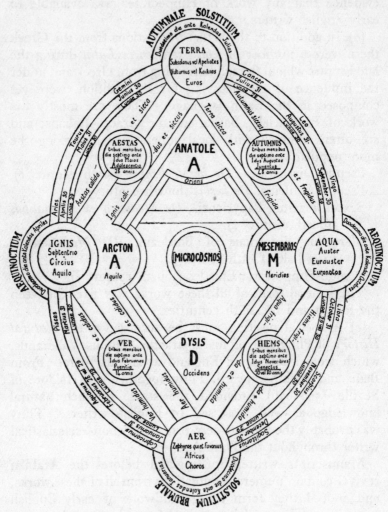

FIG. 52.—Byrhtferð of Ramsey's Diagram of the Relations of Macrocosm and Microcosm. Redrawn from MS. St. John's College, Oxford, 17 (fo. 7 v.), written about 1110 but copied from an original of about 100 years earlier.

they discerned a parallel between the four ages of man and the four seasons, between the humours of the body and the solstices and equinoxes, between the four elements and the four cardinal points, and so on. Such a scheme is elaborated in a diagram drawn up by Byrhtferð of Ramsey

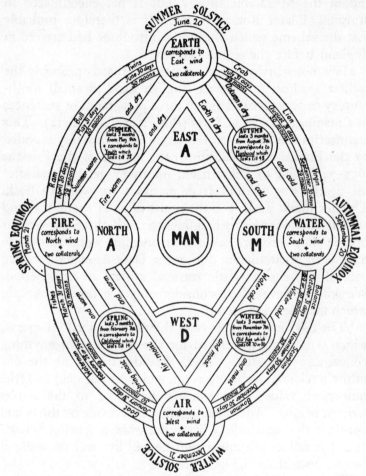

FIG. 53.—English version of Fig. 52.

(*c*. 1000), the commentator of Bede [Figs. 52 and 53]. This diagram is remarkable for associating the initials of the four cardinal points (Arcton, Dysis, Anatole, Mesembrios) with the letters of the name ADAM to whom in the text the term *protoplast* is attached.   The occurrence of this word is itself of interest since it is of liturgical origin and is found in the so-called *Sacramentarium Leonianum* (eighth century) and in the Mozarabic liturgy, but is not encountered in liturgies of later Roman origin.   It is therefore probable that the scheme which Byrhtferð introduces had arrived in England before the eighth century.

More noteworthy is a short passage that is probably the earliest medical text by an English hand, a small ninth-century fragment consisting of three paragraphs or sentences in a manuscript now at Paris (Bibl. Nat. Lat. 11411).   This manuscript was written at Echternach, a monastery founded by the Englishman Willibrord, the apostle of the Frisians (657–738), and to Echternach, for many generations after his death, English and Irish monks were wont to flock. The document itself is in the midst of an Hisperic text and exhibits undoubted Irish influence.   All three paragraphs of this short text are taken from medical works known to have been in circulation during the Dark Ages and forming part of the characteristic medical system of that period. We will, however, here consider only the first paragraph, which may be translated thus :

' The device of the sphere of the philosopher Pythagoras, which Apollonius described for the discovery of anything concerning the sick.   Thou shouldst determine the day of the week and of the moon (on which he fell sick) and (the numerical value) of his name according to the letters written below.   Add them together and divide by thirty and consider the remainder.   Examine what is written below,[1] and if it fall in the upper part he will live and do well; if below, he will die ' [Fig. 54].

The sphere of Pythagoras is a recognized magical device. It is possibly of Egyptian origin, but it certainly spread to Europe through Greek intermediaries.   It is translated

---

[1] The text has here *in spreta*, which is meaningless.  This must stand for a misinterpretation of some such abbreviated form as *in s̄pta* or *īn sc'pta* for *infra scripta*.

from Greek and is known in that language from a third-century papyrus (Leyden V) and in Latin from a large number of early manuscripts from the eighth century onward. During the Dark and Middle Ages this diagram is common in the English manuscripts, where it is variously attributed to Hippocrates, Democritus, Apuleius, Apollonius, Pythagoras, Columcille, Bede, Petosiris, Nechepso, and Plato! Quite a number of specimens date from Anglo-Saxon times.

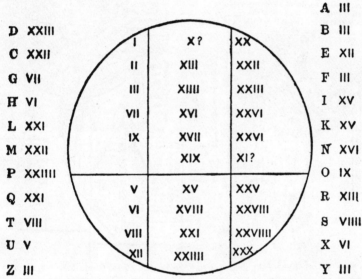

FIG. 54.—The Sphere of Pythagoras according to Bibl. Nat. MS. Lat. 11411, fo. 99, written at the English Monastery of Echternach in the ninth century.

Why is this device so often repeated in the Anglo-Saxon manuscripts ? We can obtain some answer from its associations. The leech-books, whether written in monasteries or no, are, as we have seen, essentially lay products. But the earliest English specimens of magic spheres of Petosiris are nearly all in liturgical books and associated with blood-letting calendars. Thus the earliest, next to that of the Echternach MS., is in the Leofric Missal written for the Bishop of Exeter in 970. In that manuscript it is attached to a venesection text and an apparatus for fixing the date of Church festivals [Fig. 55]. It is thus probable that the magic sphere was employed in monasteries for determining whether venesection might be resorted to or no. Bleeding was periodically performed in these houses both as a regimen of health and as an aid to withstanding the lusts of the flesh.

FIG. 55.—Sphere of Apuleius. From the Leofric Missal (Bodl. MS. 718, fo. 50 v. and 51 r.), written at Glastonbury about the year 970. The figures symbolize Life and Death. The day of death can be discovered by a device similar to that described on p. 144.

But there is another association of the magic sphere. The Leofric Missal is a particularly diminutive specimen of its class. The original binding has disappeared, but similar small missals are frequently provided with wide overlapping leather flaps, so that the volume could be wrapped in them and carried through the wet without injury. Such missals were doubtless used in visiting the sick and the sphere would aid the priest in deciding whether to administer extreme unction.

## § 2.  *Ecclesiastical Elements*

Ecclesiastical elements are found throughout the whole corpus of Anglo-Saxon medicine and magic.  Paternosters accompany every conceivable medical process.  Such elements are perhaps the least interesting of the factors in Anglo-Saxon medicine, since they are known from many sources, are easily recognized, and still survive in folk-custom.  One instance, however, is unusual and worthy of special notice.

In the Ecclesiastical History of Bede (written 731) it is related how John of Beverley, Bishop of Hexham, came to a monastery where a nun laboured under a grievous disease, having been lately bled in the arm.  While engaged in study she had been seized with a violent pain and her wound swelled so that she was now confined to bed and was sick unto death.  The abbess begged the bishop that he would give her his blessing and touch her, for this she believed might aid her.  The bishop then asked when the maiden had been bled, and being told that it was on the fourth day of the moon he said, ' You did very ill and unskilfully to bleed her on that day, for I remember that Archbishop Theodore of blessed memory said that bleeding at that time was very dangerous when the light of the moon and the tide of the ocean is increasing.'  Nevertheless the blessing and touch of the good bishop restored her to health.

The ' blessed Theodore ' was the Greek ecclesiastic who came to this country as Archbishop of Canterbury in 668.  The doctrine that connected bleeding with the tides and the moon was a commonplace of Greek medicine and was certainly adopted at Rome.  It is mentioned in the pseudo-Hippocratic *Epistle of Maecenas*, but the supposed relation of the condition of the blood to the tides and moon is treated more fully in several works of the Galenic corpus, especially in the *Regimen in acute diseases* and the spurious treatise *On crises* from which Theodore more probably derived it.  It is noteworthy that in the very early Celtic

Calendar of Coligny the first half of the lunar month, that is to say, the period of the waxing moon, is held to be unlucky.

## § 3.  *Salernitan Texts*

Salernitan texts, like ecclesiastical elements, are easily traced and therefore need only brief discussion.  Of the early history of the medical school of Salerno our conceptions are still very indefinite, though the surviving early South Italian documents suggest that a knowledge of Greek medicine was widely diffused in what was once Magna Graecia in the seventh and eighth centuries, while hints from Cassiodorus carry us as far back as the sixth century.[1]

In the ninth or tenth century this diffused medical knowledge began to be gathered together at several centres of which Monte Cassino and Salerno were the most important.  At the monastery of Monte Cassino the process went no further than copying and translating, but at Salerno a definite lay medical school arose, and in the eleventh century a certain amount of genuine observation and investigation was being made.  The great monument of that school, the Breslau codex, containing no less than thirty-five separate medical treatises, has been edited, and reference to this enables us to detect Salernitan influence where it occurs in early Western medicine.

One of the medical treatises in the Anglo-Saxon language, the so-called *Peri didaxeon*, is mainly a translation of the works of certain Salernitan writers of the eleventh century, while Latin medical works written in England in the early twelfth century may be traced to similar sources. The influence of the Salernitan school extended far beyond the period of which we treat and forms the basis not only of much modern English folk-medicine but also of some of the practice of the modern herbalist.

[1] The history of the School of Salerno is discussed in greater detail on p. 240.

## § 4.   *Native Teutonic Magic and Herb-Lore*

Native Teutonic magical material may be distinguished from imported elements of Classical, Ecclesiastical, or Salernitan origin by the presence of four characteristic elements : the doctrine of *specific venoms*, the doctrine of *the nines*, the doctrine of *the worm* as the cause of disease, and lastly the doctrine of *the elf-shot*.

We call such material ' Native Teutonic,' but it might more fitly be termed Indo-Germanic, since these doctrines are to be found among all Indo-Germanic peoples and are encountered even in the Vedas.   Yet when we meet these four doctrines in passages of English origin without classical or Celtic elements, and especially when combined with references to Teutonic gods or customs, the material may with reasonable certainty be regarded as having been brought by the Anglo-Saxon tribes from their Continental home.

Perhaps the best specimen of the Native Teutonic magic is the *Lay of the Nine Healing Herbs*, of which we here give a section from the *Lacnunga*.

| | |
|---|---|
| Dha genam woden | Then took Wodan |
| VIIII wuldortanas, | Nine magic twigs, |
| sloh dha tha naeddran | Smote then that serpent |
| thaet heo on VIIII tofleah. | That in nine bits she flew apart. |
| nu magon thas VIIII wyrta | Now these nine herbs avail |
| widh nygon wuldorgeflogenum, | Against nine spirits of evil, |
| widh VIIII attrum | Against nine venoms |
| 7 widh nygon onflygnum : | And against nine winged onsets, |
| | |
| widh dhy readan attre, | 1. Gainst the red venom, |
| widh dhy hwitan attre, | 2. Gainst the white venom, |
| widh dhy [haew]enan attre, | 3. Gainst the purple venom, |
| widh dhy geolwan attre, | 4. Gainst the yellow venom, |
| widh dhy grenan attre, | 5. Gainst the green venom, |
| widh dhy wonnan attre, | 6. Gainst the livid venom, |
| widh dhy wedenan attre, | 7. Gainst the blue venom, |
| widh dhy brunan attre, | 8. Gainst the brown venom, |
| widh dhy basewan attre ; | 9. Gainst the crimson venom, |

| | |
|---|---|
| widh wyrmgeblaed, | 1. Gainst worm blister, |
| widh waetergeblaed, | 2. Gainst water blister, |
| widh thorngeblaed, | 3. Gainst thorn blister, |
| widh thysgeblaed, | 4. Gainst thistle blister, |
| widh ysgeblaed, | 5. Gainst ice blister, |
| widh attorgeblaed, | 6. Gainst venom blister, |
| . . . . . . . . . | 7. [Line missing] |
| . . . . . . . . . | 8. [Line missing] |
| . . . . . . . | 9. [Line missing] |
| gif aenig attor | If any venom |
| eastan fleogan, | Flying from the east |
| [odhdhe aenig sudhan] | [Or any from south] |
| adhdhe aenig nordhan | Or any from north |
| odhdhe aenig westan | Or any from west |
| [genaegan] cume, | Come nigh, |
| ofer werdheode. | Over the world of men. |
| ic ana wat | I alone know |
| ea rinnende, | The running streams |
| 7 tha nygon naedran. | And the nine serpents |
| [nu] behealdadh ; | Now behold. |
| motan calle weoda nu | All weeds must now |
| wyrtum aspringan, | Fail among herbs, |
| saes toslupan, | Seas must dissolve, |
| eal sealt waeter, | All salt water, |
| thonne ic this attor | When I this venom |
| of the geblawe. | From thee blow. |

This passage contains three of the four elements of Teutonic
folk-medicine, namely the doctrine of specific venoms, of the
nines, and of the worm, though the fourth doctrine, the
elf-shot (p.154), is not mentioned.

The opening verses (lines 1–8) tell of Woden warring with
the serpent or worm and how diseases arose from the fragments into which he smote the reptile.  Woden smiting the
worm is a well-known Teutonic myth.  In the mythical
cycle Woden was primarily the dispenser of victory, but
he was also the bringer of many other forms of good luck
and especially of good health.  This part of the poem thus
resolves itself into a charm of that well-known type which
consists in the relation in a few words, usually of verse, of
the story of a cure performed by some sacred personage.

PLATE V

HENNEBELLE = HENBANE = *HYOSCYAMUS RETICULATUS*

A Mediterranean species foreign to England.

From an Anglo-Saxon Herbal of about 1050 (Cott. Vit. C. iii).

See page 187.

A good example of such a charm invoking Woden is to be found in a tenth-century Old High German manuscript at Merseburg Cathedral in Saxony :

Phol ende Wôdan
vuorun zi holza
dô wart demo Balderes
volon sîn vuoz birenkit.

Phol (*Balder*) and Woden
fared to a wood ;
there was Balder's
foal's foot sprained.

. . . . . . . .

dô biguolen Wôdan
so he wola conda
sôse bênrenki
sôse bluotrenki
sôse lidirenki
bên zi bêna
bluot zi bluoda
lid zi geliden
sôse gelîmida sin.

Then charmed Woden
as well he knew how
for bone sprain
for blood sprain
for limb sprain.
Bone to bone
blood to blood
limb to limbs
as though they were glued.

This very charm is still used for sprains in the Northern Highlands, where perhaps the Norsemen brought it. In the Gaelic form, however, Christ has taken the place of Woden. The same charm is known also from other Indo-Germanic sources, as, for instance, the Atharva Veda.

By the Romans Woden was early identified with the god Mercury, whom he resembles in that from him proceed diseases and their cure. He also influenced the casting of lots as a means of bringing good luck. Now the word *tan* in the Lay of the Nine Healing Herbs which we have translated *twig* (line 2) is specifically a twig used in casting lots. 'Augury and Divination by lot,' writes Tacitus of the Germans, ' no people practise more diligently. The use of the lots is simple  A little bough is cut from a fruit-bearing tree and cut into slips ; these are distinguished by runes (*notis quibusdam*), and thrown casually and at random over a white cloth.' From the twig for casting lots *tan* came to mean the *lot* itself. The nine twigs that Woden takes up are these twigs of fate which are to bring a better lot to the sick man on recitation of the magic song.

Following the introduction of Woden and his magic

twigs is a description of their powers (lines 9–26). The nine poisons or flying things are enumerated, and the nine diseases that they produce. The term *geblæd* which we have translated *blister* is from *blæd*, a common term for a breath or spirit, and the description of disease as a *blæd*, blast or blister, is encountered frequently in Teutonic folk-lore. The wind, the results of which are manifest while the agent is invisible, bears an obvious analogy to disease. The *onfligene*, the *on-flying things* (line 8), are the *venoms* which blow about in the air and, reaching the surface of the body, produce their characteristic diseases. They are repeatedly referred to in a refrain of the Lay as ' the loathed things that rove through the land,' a phrase also encountered in modern Danish charms. Thus the best translation both of *onfligen* and of *geblæd* would perhaps be *infection*, though our modern conception of infection is certainly not contained in it. There is a reflection of the nine venoms in *King Lear* (III, 4) where

> Swithold footed thrice the old (i.e. the *wold* or *weald*) ;
> He met the nightmare and her nine-fold.

These nine-fold of the nightmare may be followed at large through Teutonic magic.

After the nine venoms and the nine diseases comes a call addressed to the four quarters of heaven from which the four winds or blasts bring disease (lines 27–33). The division of the winds according to the four cardinal points is of Indo-Germanic origin developed independently of classical influence. The method of description of these winds is in contrast to the usual Greek and Latin system which gave special names to the various prevalent winds, a method more applicable to the regular Mediterranean climate with its periodic recurrence of winds from definite directions. The earliest Anglo-Saxon glosses from the eighth century onward contain the Greek names of winds taken probably from Plinius Valerianus, equated with the suitable geographical direction in terms of cardinal points [Fig. 52].

The custom of uttering a charm against disease successively to the four cardinal points is also of Indo-Germanic
origin and is found in the Atharva Veda.   It occurs over
and over again in Anglo-Saxon literature and is applied
with both Christian and pagan invocations.   The text we
have given is obviously pagan, but there are others in the
same manuscript which have become Christianized, thus :

MS. HARLEY 585, FO. 174 v.

| | |
|---|---|
| Wið fleogendan attre asleah. IIII. scearpan on feower healfa mid æcenan brande ge-blodga ðone brand weorp on weg sing ðis on III | For flying venom, smite four strokes towards the four quarters with an oaken brand, make the brand bloody, throw away, [&] sing this thrice |
| ✠ Matheus me ducað | Matthew leads me. |
| ✠ marcus me conseruæð | Mark preserves me. |
| ✠ lucas me liberat | Luke frees me. |
| ✠ iohannes me adiuuat | John aids me. |

The Magic Lay continues with an obscure passage in
which the disappearance of the disease appears to be
compared to the process of being washed away by water.
The whole body of Anglo-Saxon medicine is full of such
references to the use of water for curative and magical
purposes.   It is related to, though not necessarily derived
from, the Christian view of baptism.

In the last two lines that we have quoted from the Lay
the venom is described as being *blown away* by the power
of the incantation, this being an inversion of the process by
which the flying things were *blown on to* the surface of the
body.   As the winds have blown the disease to the sufferer
so will the magician, by the might of his song, blow it from
him.   The action of blowing is a common accompaniment
of Teutonic magic.

But there remains an English doctrine concerning disease,
which we have not yet discussed, a belief which the English
shared also with the continental Teutons and with the
Celts.   The Teutonic peoples had not the belief in posses-

sion by demons which was so characteristic of the Near East where Christianity took its rise. By the Teutonic tribes a large amount of disease was attributed, not to occupation by, but to the action of supernatural beings, elves, Æsir, smiths, or witches whose shafts fired at the sufferer produced his torments. Anglo-Saxon and even Middle English literature is replete with the notion of disease caused by the arrows of mischievous supernatural beings. This theory of disease we shall, for brevity, speak of as the *doctrine of the elf-shot*.

The Anglo-Saxon tribes located these malicious elves everywhere, but especially in the wild uncultivated wastes where they loved to shoot their envenomed darts at the passer-by. There were water-elves, too, perhaps identical with the Nixies of whom we learn from Celtic sources. Such creatures were perhaps personifications of the deadly powers of marshes and waterlogged land. A water-elf is perhaps thought to have attacked one waterlogged with dropsy in the following passage :

MS. ROYAL 12 D. XVII, FO. 124 V.

Gif mon biþ on wæter ælf adle þonne beoþ him þa handnæglas wonne 7 þa eagan tearige 7 wile locian niþer.

If a man be in the water-elf disease, then are the nails of his hand dusky and his eyes running and he will look downward.

and to prevent future attacks of the elf :

Sing þis manegum siþum. eorþe þe onbere eallum hier mihtum 7 mægenum. þas galdor mon mæg singan on wunde.

Sing this many times. *May Earth bear on thee with all her might and main*. This magic one may [also] sing on a wound.

The effort to bury the elf in the earth in order to prevent his attacks has many parallels in folk-medicine. Thus in Denmark a whitlow is cured by thrusting the finger into the ground and leaving it for some time, and a sick child is lightly covered with earth ; and in Holland, when a man has been struck by lightning—a form of elf-shot—he is interred as far as the neck to extract the evil. But a closer parallel comes to us from a Latin source. Varro (i. 27) has

PLATE VI

VIPERINA = *CARDUUS MARIANUS*

From a Herbal written at Bury St. Edmunds about 1120
(Bodley 130). See pp. 187 and 190.

preserved for us a Roman charm for gout or pain in the feet. The sufferer is to bow to the earth, to spit upon it, and to say thrice nine times the following charm :

Terra pestem teneto.  salus hic maneto.

O earth, bear thou the pain.  Health in my feet remain.

The doctrine of the elf-shot was, however, a view of disease that could hardly persist in its purity. On the one hand the shafts of the elves were so easily confounded with the ' flying venoms.' On the other hand the attacks of elves presented a close similarity to the constant assaults of demons and possession by them from which the Christian ascetic suffered so sorely. In the later Anglo-Saxon material we therefore encounter a fusion of the ideas of demoniacal possession with the attacks of elves, witches, and other beings of the Teutonic mythology and with the effects of flying venoms. But though the human patient tended to become possessed by demons rather than merely elf-shot, the elves continued to make their malignant attacks on the lesser creation, the cattle, whom the more self-respecting demons might be expected to regard as providing but a poor field for their accomplishments. Accordingly we find numerous references to elf-shot cattle.

MS. ROYAL 12 D. XVII, FO. 106

Gif hors ofscoten sie. Nim þonne þæt seax þe þæt hæfte sie fealo hryþeres horn 7 sien III ærene næglas on. Writ þonne þam horse on þam hæfde foran cristes mæl þæt hit blede writ þonne on þam hricge cristes mæl . . . Nim þonne þæt winestre eare þurh sting swigende . . . genimane girde sleah on þæt bæc þonne biþ þæt hors hal . . . Sy þæt ylfa þe him sie. þis him mæg to bote.

If a horse be shot. Take then a knife of which the handle is horn of a roan ox and on which are three brass nails. Inscribe then Christ's cross on the forehead of the horse so that it bleeds, then inscribe Christ's cross on the back. . . . Take then the left ear and prick it through silently . . . Take then a staff, smite (the horse) on the back, then is the horse whole. . . . Whatever the elf, this has power as a remedy.

The process of pricking seems to have been especially efficacious for elf-shot cattle, for we read of it repeatedly.

## Distinction between Elements of Teutonic and Greek Origin

These doctrines then, the doctrine of specific venoms, the doctrine of the worm, the doctrine of the nines, and the doctrine of the elf-shot, separate Teutonic from Greek or Byzantine medicine and all are encountered in the *Lacnunga*. But before we leave the distinction between Teutonic medicine and the debased Greek or Byzantine system we may attempt a wider generalization.

Late Greek medicine is a combination of at least four more or less discordant elements :

(1) The purely scientific medicine which took its rise in the methods of the Ionian philosophers of the seventh century B.C., and was already far advanced by the time of Hippocrates in the fifth century B.C.

(2) Demoniac medicine inherited largely from the civilization of the Tigris and Euphrates. Babylonian-Assyrian medicine was based on the theory that disease was due to the entry of a demon into the patient's body ; hence formulae for exorcism became of great importance. Moreover, what was bad for the demon must be good for the patient ; hence arose the idea of nauseous drugs to disgust the demon and weary him of his habitat. (It should be said that while there is no demonism in early Greek native medicine, there are traces of it in Orphic literature.)

(3) Magic, a term which, while leaving undefined, we may provisionally regard as primitive unorganized belief as to the relation of cause and effect.

(4) ' Common-sense ' empirical knowledge.

As Greek medicine decayed and passed into its Byzantine stage, demoniac and magical elements became more prominent and scientific elements receded. This process, however, had not gone so far but that the Greek medicine distributed among barbarian peoples by the time of the break up of the Empire still contained traces of all four elements.

Now in true *native* Teutonic medicine we can only expect

PLATE VII

'CAMEDRIUM' = *TEUCRIUM CHAMAEDRYS*

From a Herbal written at Bury St. Edmunds about 1120
(Bodley 130). See p. 187.

elements (3) and (4), i.e. magic and empirical knowledge. In the mixture of Teutonic and Byzantine elements that has come down to us under the name of the Anglo-Saxon Leechdoms it will usually be possible to separate magical and empirical elements into the native and the foreign group.

As regards element (1), the true scientific medicine of Greek origin, we can say that it is never difficult to trace when elements of it are found embedded in a native medium. Concerning (2), demoniac medicine, the position is more complicated. Beside the original stratum of demonism in Greek medicine, which was presumably drawn more or less directly from Babylonian sources, much new belief concerning demons had been developed in the Greek system by Christianity, and had been propagated from an early date by the spread of that religion in the West. The pathology of the New Testament is mainly demonic and many of the miracles of healing are exorcisms. There were devils of blindness, dumbness, madness, and epilepsy, and Luke the physician regarded the ' great fever ' of Simon's wife's mother in the light of a demon, for Jesus, he says, ' stood over her and rebuked the fever ; and it left her.' So also the infirmities of Mary Magdalene were of the nature of seven evil spirits—the demons of early Christianity, like those of the Mesopotamian system, were often grouped in sevens—and Peter considered that all those whom Jesus healed had been ' oppressed of the Devil.' The final end of disease is itself a demon's work, since the inspirer of sin is indirectly the author of death, the last enemy that shall be destroyed.

So for the fathers of the Church disease was largely the work of demons. Of some importance for our purpose are the views of Irenaeus (2nd century A.D.) as preserving a record of that early Gallic Christianity which may be supposed to have first influenced the British Isles. He acknowledges the antiquity and effectiveness of exorcisms other than Christian, and thus prepares us for the pagan survivals in our own deeply Christianized material. In writings of Anglo-Saxon origin we have to set off Christological protective charms, such as the *Lorica* prayer or liturgical exorcisms in the divine name of the *creaturae* of water, honey, bread, oil, &c., of liturgical works, against the pagan spells of the Leechdoms.

Now since exorcism proper had no place in the Teutonic system, any protective charms, words of power, and exorcistic formulae designed to expel or to prevent the entrance of the demon, encountered in an Anglo-Saxon setting, must surely be of foreign origin though not necessarily of foreign form. We do encounter, however, Anglo-Saxon magical processes designed to remove, not indeed the demon himself, but the *materies morbi* projected into the body by supernatural beings—in other words formulae for the extraction of the elf-shot.

### § 5. *Celtic Magic*

The Celtic influence in the Anglo-Saxon material is elusive and yet pervasive, but the difficulty of tracing it may be a result of the common heritage of the two cultures and the common external influences to which they were both subjected. Nevertheless, clear cases of the definite incursion of the Celtic magic into the Anglo-Saxon system can be adduced ; these may be roughly classed according as they are derived from (*a*) Celtic magic proper, or from (*b*) that form of Celtic magic which filters through the peculiar Hisperic medium.

(*a*) True Celtic magic in the Leechdoms is betrayed by a number of Celtic words and phrases used as charms. From such phrases, however, we can argue no intimate contact between the two peoples. A somewhat closer connexion is suggested, however, by the use of the so-called ' Circle of Columcille.' The legend of the origin of this magical figure is contained in the Irish life of the Saint by Manus O'Donnell composed in 1532.

' On a time Ethne the mother of Columcille was in the

place called Gartan, and it was the night before Columcille
was born, and their appeared a fair youth in shining raiment,
and he said she should bring forth on the morrow the son
that was promised her to bear. And he told her there
was a broad flagstone in the lake, to the south of the place
where she was. . . . And he told her to let bring that flag-

FIGS. 56 and 57.—Two Early Celtic Stone Crosses. Photographed by the late Mr.
Romilly Allen in County Donegal. The cross to the left is in Glen Columcille,
that to the right in a neighbouring glen.

stone to a certain place . . . and that thereon should God
will the child to be brought forth of her.

' " In what manner shall I get the flagstone, seeing it
is under a lake," saith she, " or whereby shall I know it
from other flagstones ? "

' " Thou shalt find it floating on the bosom of the lake,"
saith he.

' And Ethne found the flagstone on the morrow as it

had been told her, and she let bring it from the foresaid
place.  And albeit it floated on the surface of the lake, and
Ethne's folk brought it away with them without labour,
yet certain it is that it were a task for thirty men to bring it
from the lake to the place where it is to-day. . . .

' And it befell that the foresaid flagstone was under him
at his birth, and the child rested him crosswise thereon,
and the flagstone opened for him in such wise that it left
a place for him therein. *And the figure of that cross is on
that stone from that time to this day.  And that flagstone
remaineth in that place for working of marvels and wonders.*' [1]

Irish archaeologists have frequently described a type of
large flat stone, into the surface of which there has been
cut in remote antiquity a design consisting primarily of a
cross surrounded by a circle.  A fine specimen of this type
of Celtic monument is known from the glen to which
Columcille's name is still attached [Figs. 56 and 57].  To such
stones magical powers were attached and their use passed
over to the English.  In an Anglo-Saxon manuscript of the
eleventh century, over the figure of a circle with a cross
inscribed within it [Fig. 58] we read :

Þis is sancte columcille circul
Writ þisne circul mid þines cnifes
orde on anum mealm stane 7 sleah
ænne stacan on middan þam ymb-
hagan. 7 lege þone stane on
uppan þan stacan þæt he beo
eall under eorðan. butan þam ge-
writenan.

This is the circle of Saint Columcille.  Inscribe this circle with the
point of thy knife on a soft stone
& strike a stake into the middle
of the bee-enclosure, & lay the
stone above the stake so that it
is all under ground except that
which is inscribed.

The stake was presumably to prevent the stone sinking
and the stone thus laid was used for charming bees, but its
form and title betray its Irish affinities.  In the manuscript,
however, the resemblance to the circle of Petosiris has

[1] *Manus O'Donnell's Life of Columcille*, from version of MS. Rawlinson,
B 514, by A. O'Keller and C. Schoepperle, Illinois, 1918.

tempted the scribe to write the days of the moon upon it
after the manner of the Greek device [Figs. 54 and 65].

Columcille seems to have kept his hold on English magic.
In a fifteenth-century English Book of Devotions is this
charm, which surely plumbs the depths of mental imbecility
and bad grammar : ' If a house is on fire stand between

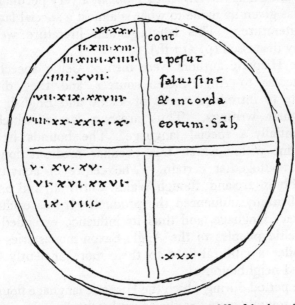

FIG. 58.—The Circle of Columcille. From an Anglo-Saxon MS. of the eleventh century.
(Cott. Vit. E. xviii, fo. 13 v., slightly restored.)

the part that is burning and the part that is not and say
these verses, and the fire will immediately flicker out :

> Sancte columbkille
> Remove mala flamma ille
> Atque columbkillus
> Presérve ab igne domus.'

(MS. ADD. 37787)

(b) *Hisperic*.   The literature of Hisperic origin is more
easily traceable in the English manuscripts than the pure
Celtic magic.   This Hisperic literature is of so peculiar

a character that we must devote a few lines to a general discussion of it.

For the last half-century philogists have been interested and puzzled by a most curious group of early documents of Irish or English origin. The longest of these and in many respects the most striking is a rough metrical composition known as the *Hisperica Famina*, a very peculiar work that has given its name to what is almost a special language and literature. This language and literature we have already discussed (p. 117 ff.).

The Hisperic authors were men of Celtic speech who had access to Anglo-Saxon sources, and they did not hesitate to introduce words of Celtic and English origin into their writings. Thus arose a jargon which was substantially a special language. The bounds in space and time within which this peculiar medium flourished are not altogether certain. The centre of activity was probably in Ireland, though Wales, Cornwall, and possibly even Brittany influenced the product. It was exclusively a literary language, and thus its influence extended from the Celtic peoples to the Anglo-Saxon monasteries which lay under a cultural debt to their more anciently Christianized neighbours.

The period during which the Hisperic language flourished can be roughly stated as the seventh century. It may have been practised for fifty or a hundred years before then, and there is one belated document—copied no doubt for its supposed magical value—of the sixteenth century. There is good evidence, however, that the language was still studied and understood in England as late as the tenth century, since Hisperic words are included in Anglo-Saxon glossaries of that period. The most important manuscripts of the literature are, however, of the eighth or ninth century, and they are mostly in the ' insular ' script.

Certain Hisperic documents, and especially that known as the *Lorica of Gildas the Briton* (p. 122 ff.), were used as charms by the Anglo-Saxon speaking tribes. The *Lorica* is in

FIG. 59.—SNAKE AND SCORPION
FIGHTING

From MS. Bibl. Nat., *Lat.* 6862, tenth
century. Compare Plate III.

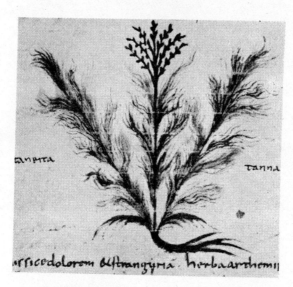

FIG. 60.—' ARTEMISIA ' (*ARTEMISIA PONTICA*)

From MS. Bibl. Nat., *Lat.* 6862, tenth century. Compare Plate IV.

There can be no doubt that the figures of the Anglo-Saxon
herbal are copied from a continental MS. The two figures here
shown from a Latin MS. written in France in the tenth century
may be compared to Plates III and IV, taken from a slightly later
Anglo-Saxon MS.

essence an incantation enumerating all the parts of the body in turn and calling down the blessing and protection of heaven on each, the whole being placed in the form of a passionate and somewhat unbalanced invocation (see Essay III, p. 111). Such invocations shade off into the more ordinary liturgical material of the type encountered in the chapter *De exorcizandis obsessis a daemonis*, of the *Rituale Romanum*. An intermediate stage, still betraying strong Celtic influence, is represented by a conjuration, in corrupt Latin uttered as a preservative against pestilence, part of which may be thus translated :

### MS. HARLEY 585, FO. 191

In the name of Father, Son, and Holy Ghost, Amen.   May the Saviour help [names].   We [names] ought to give thanks to the God of Heaven, the King of Kings, and to beseech him that, he ward off from us [names] the plague of this pest. . . .   Preserve and defend us [names] from the agony of the Igniculum (St. Anthony's fire, Erysipelas) and from the power of the Variola (? Measles) and protect us from the danger of death.   Free us [names] from the most evil languors and dangers of this season, amen. brigitarum dricillarum tuarum *malint uoarline dearnabda murde murrunice domur brio rubebroht.*   Scē rehhoc. & scē ehwalde. & scē cassiane. & scē germane. & scē sigismundi regis gescyldað me wið ða laþan poccas 7 wið ealle yfelu. amen.   [Saint Rehhoc, Saint Ehwald, Saint Cassian, Saint German, and Saint Sigmund the king protect me against the loathed pocks and against all ills.   Amen.]

The italicized sentence is corrupt Irish and is said to contain the equivalent of *Immaculate Maid of Heaven, Mary of God*.   Whether this be so or no, the saints mentioned are certainly, in the main, a Celtic group.   *Brigita* is Bridget.   *Sanctus Rehhoc* is the Celtic Rioc, who is perhaps identical with Riaghail and Regulus the legendary founder of St. Andrews (? eighth century).   *Sanctus Sigmundus rex* was the son of Gundebald, King of Burgundy ; he was converted from Arianism in 515 and became king in 516.   *Sanctus Germanus* (378 ?–428) was Bishop of Auxerre and missionary to Britain ; he had a high reputation for his power over demons, and there are many Celtic stories of him.   *Sanctus Cassianus* is perhaps the Alexan-

drian of that name who became Bishop of Autun, and died
in 355. *Sanctus Ehwaldus* is probably one of the Hewalds
(Edwald), ' two priests of the English nation who had long
lived in Ireland for the sake of the eternal inheritance '
(Bede) ; they were martyred in the seventh century.[1]

## § 6.  *Southern Plant-Lore*

Of all the elements in the Anglo-Saxon medical system,
by far the most attractive is the plant-lore.  The English
were a people who early exhibited some power in the
observation of nature and considerable artistic skill, but their
achievements in these matters were greatly hampered by
the respect paid by them to the written records of a higher
civilization.  Thus the Early English texts containing
descriptions of plants are merely bad copies or worse
translations of works which had existed in Latin dress from
at least as early as the seventh century, and in these no new
or original element can be expected.  But when we turn to
the figures with which these herbals are illustrated we are
met with an entirely new and very interesting series of
phenomena.  Indeed, the story of plant representation
throughout early barbarian Europe is a peculiar and in
many ways an isolated development which cannot easily
be fitted into the general account of the history of art, and
for this there is a special reason.  Most expressions of the
mediaeval artistic spirit were prepared only with an eye
to the emotions that they raised, but in the case of the
illustrations to herbals there was a definite utilitarian object.
As, however, we devote a special essay to the descent of the
herbal texts and figures, we need not deal with it further
here.  (See Essay V, p. 168, Plates III-IV and Figs. 59-64.)

## § 7.  *Byzantine Magic and Theurgy*

Instances of Byzantine theurgy occur scattered throughout Anglo-Saxon writings.  Sometimes there is a use of

---

[1] The relationship of Irish and English magic has recently been discussed by the
author's pupil Dr. W. Bonser in a valuable article in *Folk-lore*, vol. xxxvii.,
December 1927.  See also his article on Elf-shot, December 1926.

FIG. 61.—Additional 21115, Italian workmanship, fifteenth century.

FIG. 62.—Pierpont Morgan MS., Byzantine workmanship, tenth century.

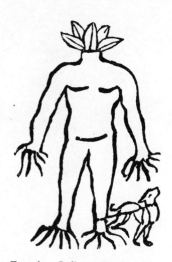

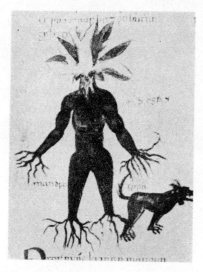

FIG. 63.—Italian printed work, 1484 A.D.

FIG. 64.—Cotton Vitellius C. iii., Anglo-Saxon workmanship, about 1050.

FIGS. 61–64.—FIGURES OF MANDRAKES, SHOWING THE CLOSE SIMILARITY OF THE TRADITIONAL MODES OF DRAWING THESE FIGURES. FIGS. 63 and 64 ARE ESPECIALLY NEARLY RELATED DESPITE THEIR SEPARATION IN TIME.

Greek script in the writing of a word of power, but there is no case where such a charm clearly involves a knowledge of the Greek language. These charms are thus comparable to the piece of magic of Sir John Holt quoted above (p. 136).

Among the most striking of these Byzantine tags is perhaps the curious charm used to stop intractable haemorrhage which is found in several eleventh and twelfth-century manuscripts (e.g. St. John's College, Oxford, XVII and Durham Cathedral, Hunter 100). This charm consisted of the following words, which had to be written on the part affected or else worn as a periapt :

> Stomen calcos stomen meta fofu.

The sentence is merely a corrupted passage from the Greek Liturgy of St. Chrysostom :

> στῶμεν καλῶς· στῶμεν μετὰ φόβου.
> Let us stand seemly, let us stand in awe.

These words, coming in the most solemn part of the service before the elevation of the elements, would be regarded with special reverence, and thus easily pass over with magic significance into the practice of a people of lower culture. The phrase is still used as a charm by Macedonian peasants.

A second Greek liturgical passage put to an exorcistic use is encountered in an eighth-century English manuscript and runs as follows :

MS. Royal 2 A. xx, fo. 45 v.

Eulogumen . patera . cae yo . cae agion . pneuma . cae nym . cae ia . cae iseonas . nenon amin . adiuro te satanae diabulus *aelfae* . per dominum uiuum ac uerum . et per trementem diem iudicii ut refugiatur ab homine illo qui abeat hunc aepistolam scriptum secum in nomine dei patris et filii et spiritus sancti.

The Greek in this passage is an attempt to transliterate the doxology εὐλογοῦμεν πατέρα καὶ υἱὸν καὶ ἅγιον πνεῦμα καὶ νῦν καὶ ἀεὶ καὶ εἰς αἰῶνας αἰώνων ἀμήν. The italicized

word *ælfa* is the *elf* who is equated with Satan, a natural
and common priestly identification.

The same manuscript gives us also a charm to arrest
haemorrhage which yields us a hint as to the route by which
such Greek liturgical material may have reached England.
The charm runs as follows :

MS. ROYAL 2 A. XX, FO. 49 V.

Per illorum uenas cui siccato dominico lauante coniuro sta. . . . In
nomine sanctae trinitatis atque omnium sanctorum ad sanguinem restrin-
gendum scribis hoc COMAPTA OCOΓMA CTYΓONTOEMA EKTYTOΠO
+ . . . . . Beronice libera me de sanguinibus Deus Deus salutis meae
AMICO CAPΔINOPO ΦIΦIPON.

The underlined Greek words are the equivalent of
στυγοῦν τὸ αἷμα ἐκ τοῦ τόπου. Beronice or Veronica is
the traditional name of the woman who was healed of the
issue of blood, and the herb Veronica, also called Betonica
in the herbals, our Betony, was used to stop haemorrhage.
The gibberish Greek words are similar to words used for
a like purpose by Marcellus Empiricus of Bordeaux.

Another instance of the importance attached to Greek
words is yielded by the occurrence of the Greek script
in some of the Anglo-Saxon specimens of the Circle of
Petosiris [Fig. 65]. These, being used to foretell the life or
death of the patient, would easily become invested with a
special solemn importance. The corruptness of the Greek
of some of these circles is almost incredible.

## § 8. *Pagan Roman Spells*

Lastly, it is interesting to observe that the Latin herbal,
being copied ultimately from Pagan Roman sources, contained certain Pagan Roman spells which are known to
occur also in certain early Continental manuscripts, of
which the earliest dates from the seventh century. It
is very remarkable that these should have survived in their
full and unexpurgated heathenism in herbals of twelfth-
and even thirteenth-century English workmanship. We

terminate our discussion with a translation of one of these conjurations.

### MS. HARLEY 1585, FF. 12 V.–13 R.

Earth, divine goddess, Mother Nature, who generatest all things and bringest forth anew the sun which thou hast given to the nations ; Guardian of sky and sea and of all gods and powers ; through thy power all nature falls silent and then sinks in sleep. And again thou bringest back the light and chasest away night, and yet again thou coverest us most

FIG. 65.—Circle of Petosiris with Greek Script. From MS. St. John's College, Oxford, 17 (fo. 8 r.), written at Ramsey about 1110.

securely with thy shades. Thou dost contain chaos infinite, yea and winds and showers and storms. Thou sendest them out when thou wilt and causest the seas to roar ; thou chasest away the sun and arousest the storm. Again when thou wilt thou sendest forth the joyous day and givest the nourishment of life with thy eternal surety. And when the soul departs to thee we return. Thou indeed art duly called great Mother of the gods ; thou conquerest by thy divine name. Thou art the source of the strength of nations and of gods, without thee nothing can be brought to perfection or be born ; thou art great, queen of the gods. Goddess ! I adore thee as divine ; I call upon thy name ; be pleased to grant that which I ask thee, so shall I give thanks to thee, goddess, with due faith.

# V

# EARLY HERBALS

A HERBAL is a collection of descriptions of plants usually put together for medical purposes. The term is perhaps nowadays used most frequently in connexion with the finely illustrated works produced by the 'fathers of botany' in the fifteenth, sixteenth, and seventeenth centuries. Behind the tradition they represent, however, are a host of manuscript works equally entitled to be described as herbals. These take us back into remote antiquity and their origins must be sought in the history of man.

Yet despite the antiquity of the herbal tradition it is truly remarkable at what a late stage in his development man first began to observe plants closely. Palaeolithic man has left us many samples of his artistic skill. Indeed, like his modern successor the diminutive Bushman, who is also an expert in the portrayal of animal life, palaeolithic man was often an artist to the finger-tips. Yet with all his powers he seems always to have neglected the portrayal of plants. The whole repertory of palaeolithic art may be

FIG. 66.—Representation of branch with leaves scratched in Palaeolithic times on a piece of reindeer horn from Arcy-sur-Cure, Dep. Yonne, France. There are but few Palaeolithic representations of plants and of them this is, perhaps, the best.

searched through without finding a representation of a plant the species of which can be recognized [Fig. 66].

The reason for this neglect may be sought in the artist's motive. It is believed that these paintings were of a magical character; by representing the forms of animals

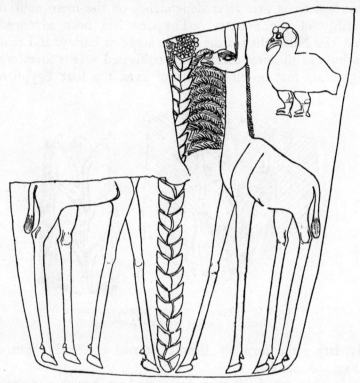

FIG. 67.—Pre-dynastic Egyptian palette of a palm-tree flanked on either side by a Gerunak gazelle. Above hovers a vulture. The figure is put together from two fragments, one in the Ashmolean Museum at Oxford, and the other at the British Museum.

on the walls of his cave the hunter thought to bring the animals themselves within his power. The plant, since it needed no hunting, was neglected by the artist. It is at least noteworthy that not until we reach a time and a country where man is beginning to domesticate plants and is becoming more dependent on them for his food, do we encounter any adequate representation of vegetable life. The earliest figure of a recognizable species of plant is carved by a pre-dynastic Egyptian on a piece of slate and represents a rudely cut palm-tree [Fig. 67]. The valley of the Nile is one of the earliest sites of tillage—the art that first freed man from dependence on the mere natural fertility of the country. The view has been advanced that the Nile valley is the native home of barley, and that barley was the first cereal to be cultivated. It is therefore significant that on monuments of even the first Egyptian

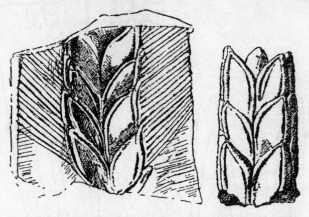

FIGS. 68 and 69.—Egyptian carvings, representing cereals, from a tomb of the first dynasty at Abydos.

dynasty some form of bearded cereal is clearly figured [Figs. 68 and 69].

The history of Egyptian art as a whole, however, repeats the history of palaeolithic art in its relative backwardness in the correct rendering of plants. Egyptian art reached its finest development in the fourth dynasty. Egyptian artists of that period have seldom been excelled in human portraiture, and reached a high standard in the rendering of the moving bodies of animals, but from this artistic development botanical delineation gained very little. This is remarkable when we consider certain other developments of Egyptian activity. The Egyptians indeed never

PLATE VIII

'PEONIA' = *OROBUS SP.*

From a Herbal written at Bury St. Edmunds
about 1120 (Bodley 130). See p. 188.

reached the philosophical level in which men consciously seek to draw new general laws from co-ordinated observation of nature. They did, however, cultivate the ' collector's instinct,' which may be regarded as an earlier and more primitive stage in the progress of the human mind towards science and is the stage represented by the herbal. In the eighteenth dynasty, about 1500 B.C., Thothmes III sent out an expedition to Syria which brought back with it a number of new and strange plants. The figures of these plants were sculptured on the walls of Karnak, where they may be seen to this day [Fig. 70]. They are diagrammatic to a degree and few can be actually identified. On them, however, is an inscription which may be translated thus :

Year 25 of the King of Upper and Lower Egypt, Living for Ever. Plants which His Majesty found in the country of Syria. All plants that grow, all goodly flowers that are in the Divine Land (i.e. country east of Egypt) . . . His Majesty saith, ' As I live, all these plants exist in very truth ; there is not a line of falsehood among them. My Majesty hath wrought this to cause them to be before my father Amon, in this great hall for ever and ever.'

Is not this perpetuation the motive of the herbal, and have we not here a herbal in stone ? It was among another people, however, that the more permanent herbal tradition arose. The herbal tradition that we inherit comes to us from Greece.

The three great influences that converged on the Greeks, those spoiled darlings of history, were the culture of Egypt, of Mesopotamia, and of the Minoan peoples. The arts of Mesopotamia and of Crete, so far as plants are concerned, go through much the same history that we have traced in Egypt. Nor is the great art of the Greeks themselves very different in relation to our subject. In Greek art of the classical age we find no worthy representations of vegetable life. Plants are freely used for design and woven into the motives of patterns, but living and growing plants are hardly ever found. The triumphs of Greek art

are to be found in the treatment, and especially the idealiza-
tion, of the human form.   When the Greek artist treats

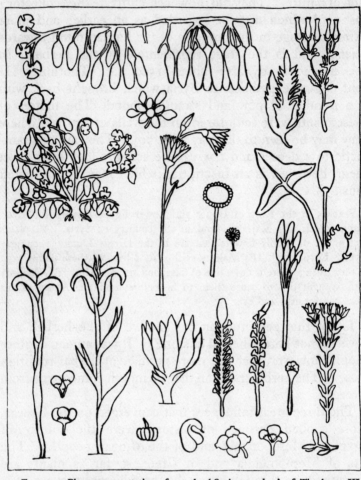

FIG. 70.—Plant representations from the ' Syrian garden' of Thothmes III
on his temple at Karnak.   Gourds, a heath, a lotus, two irises, a seedling arum,
and other plants and parts of plants may be distinguished.

animals, he treats them in relation to man.   Plants and
inorganic nature he almost entirely neglects.   Greek science,
Greek philosophy, but most of all Greek art was, according
to our ideas, strangely anthropocentric.

If we consider (says Plato in the *Critias*) the works of the painter, we shall see that we are satisfied with one who is able *in any degree* to imitate the earth, its mountains, rivers, and woods, and the universe, and the things that are and move therein. Knowing nothing precise about such matters, we do not examine or analyse the paintings. All that we ask is a sort of indistinct and deceptive mode of shadowing them forth. But when our artist treats the human form we are quick to find faults, and our familiar knowledge makes us severe judges of one who does not render every point exactly.

At a very early date the Greeks brought the art of medicine within the range of the sciences, and thus provided the theme for the herbal. We have a number of Greek medical works of the fifth and fourth centuries before the Christian era in the so-called *Hippocratic Collection*. From that group of works modern investigators have gathered a list of between three and four hundred plants. It is remarkable that no contemporary ancient author seems to have thought of doing this. It was not until towards the end of the Hippocratic period that the first Greek herbal was put together.

The author of this first Greek herbal was Diocles of Carystus in Euboeia. He practised in Athens with enormous reputation in the first half of the fourth century B.C., and is believed to have influenced Aristotle deeply. His book on plants has unfortunately disappeared even more completely than his other works. We know only enough of it to say that it was a systematic treatise in which short descriptions of plants and their habitats were followed by an account of their uses in medicine.

In the period in which Diocles worked, the tiny independent States of Greece were beginning to be overshadowed by the growing power of Macedon. The generation which followed saw the profound modification of the Greek outlook that Alexander's career was to bring. Starting across Asia Minor and penetrating to the remotest recesses of Syria and Egypt, of Babylonia, Persia, Media, Turkestan to Afghanistan and Baluchistan, and reaching the

Punjab, he and his followers not only found themselves in contact with strange new forms, but beheld completely new regions of plant geography of which previous generations had not dreamed.

The campaigns of Alexander were something far more than mere manœuvres of conquest. They were carried on with all the scientific resources of the day. The navy especially, then as now the most scientific branch of the fighting force, was active in collecting such data, and much of the information concerning foreign plants, found in the pages of later Greek botanists, was taken from these naval records. Chief among Alexander's admirals was Nearchus, who led the fleet from the mouth of the Indus, near Karachi, along the Baluchistan coast to Hormuz in the mouth of the Persian Gulf, and then up the eastern side to the head of the Gulf. Fragments of an account of this journey by Nearchus himself contain admirable descriptions of the banyan tree or Indian fig, of the various species of mangrove along the coast, of the cotton plant found in the islands of the Gulf, and of the great spiny Euphorbias of the Baluchistan wastes. Another expedition under Androsthenes explored Bahrein on the western side of the Gulf, and its leader prepared a monograph of his voyage which was largely devoted to botanical topics. Thus the Alexandrian expeditions brought to Greece a wealth of the botanical material out of which a herbal might be built.

While the conquests of Alexander were in progress, Aristotle, himself an admirable naturalist, found time among his philosophical labours to make a complete sketch of organic nature containing a section devoted to plants. This Aristotelian treatise on plants has disappeared, but by way of compensation we have works by Aristotle's pupil, Theophrastus of Eresus, sometimes spoken of as the ' father of botany.' They contain descriptions of a large number of plants, native and foreign, with accounts of their uses, and these accounts may therefore be regarded

PLATE IX

'MERCURY' BRINGS THE HERB ELECTROPION TO
'HOMER'

From an Anglo-Norman Herbal of the thirteenth century (Ashmole
1462). See p. 191.

as making up a herbal—though they are in fact also much
more. The works of Theophrastus were among the Greek
sources of the later herbals. They were the best, but not
the only sources.

Although uncivilized peoples do not as a rule observe
plants closely, yet at an early cultural stage they begin to
employ them for the treatment of disease. Nearly all
peoples, ancient or modern, seem to have developed something of a medical herb-lore, frequently mixed with much
magical material. The recipients of this traditional herb-
lore among the Greeks were the so-called *rhizotomists*.
These, as a class, were ignorant men corresponding in a
measure to our herbalists. They were very superstitious
and practised a complex ritual in the gathering of their
drugs, as still do many people on the same cultural level.
Fragments of this ritual have survived, and we can detect
in it ceremonies similar to those recorded in mediaeval
herbals and leech-books and still closely followed by
European peasants. The profession and the tradition of
the rhizotomists extended from Greek into mediaeval and
even to modern times, and they and their work are not
infrequently illustrated in the manuscripts and early
printed books [Fig. 71]. Of their practices Theophrastus
has much to tell us.

The herbal as we know it was not yet formed. Theophrastus was one of its remotest—and its best—sources,
but the works of Theophrastus were scientific treatises
which endeavoured to set forth a real system of plants.
The key-note of the herbal proper, however, is its *practical*
character : that vague and foolish word with which ignorant
and unpractical people have been accustomed in all ages
to hide the nakedness of their minds. The earliest collection of this sort that we have is perhaps the *Alexipharmaca*
of Nicander, written in the century following Theophrastus.
It is a wretched production—in spite of the praise of
Cicero—ill-written and obscure, with nothing poetic about
it save its form. It deals with a number of poisons and

their antidotes, mostly of a vegetable character, and

Fig. 71.—Rhizotomists gathering plants upon a mountain. From a fifteenth-century drawing in a MS. now destroyed. Restored from P. Giacosa, *Magistri Salernitani*, Turin, 1901.

savours far more of the rhizotomists and their magical practices than of the scientific Theophrastus.

The effective source for the surviving and viable tradition of the illustrated herbal is, however, to be sought a
little later in the first century before the Christian era.
It is the work of the rhizotomist Crateuas, one of the
most intelligent and instructed of his class, who occupied
himself not only with collecting but also in describing and

FIG. 72.—*Adonis aestivalis*, from a sixth-
century copy of a drawing, now lost, by
Crateuas (first century B.C.).

FIG. 73.—*Aristolochia
pallida*, from a sixth-century copy of a drawing,
now lost, by Crateuas.
Contrast Fig. 79.

drawing plants. He is thus the father of the department
of plant illustration. Of the work of Crateuas, who was
the attendant of Mithridates VI of Parthia (reigned 111–64
B.C.), fragments have survived. By a lucky chance copies
of his actual drawings, not very remote from second-
hand, have come down to us, so that we can form a pretty
good idea of the general character of his work [Figs. 72–4].

12

In the first century of the Christian era appeared a
number of works, each of which had its influence in shaping
the herbals of the Middle Ages that were to follow.   One
was by Pamphilus, a Greek physician, who practised in
Rome and wrote a work on plants which, for the first
time, was arranged in alphabetical order, a device
commonly adopted in later herbals.   If Galen is just in
his criticisms, it resembled later herbals in several other
respects, for he tells us that Pamphilus described plants
which he had never seen, and mingled much absurd and
superstitious matter
with his imperfect des-
criptions.

FIG. 74.—*Asarum Europaeum*, from a sixth-
century copy of a drawing, now lost, by Crateuas
(first century B.C.).

The art of plant
illustration founded by
Crateuas was extended
if not developed during
the first century of the
Christian era.   This ex-
tension was encouraged
by the appearance of
several botanical works
among which Pliny's
*Natural History* and
Dioscorides' *Materia
Medica* must be especially mentioned.

In Pliny we have a collection of current views on the
nature, origin, and uses of plants, such as we might expect
from an honest, industrious, and gullible gentleman
devoid of critical or scientific skill.   Pliny is the compiler
*par excellence*, the learned collector who will put down
anything he is told or can read, without verification.
Scientifically the work is therefore worthless.   Yet it was
not only the actual basis of later herbals but also for
centuries a main conduit of the ancient teaching and
observations on natural history.   Read throughout the
ages, alike in the darkest as in the more enlightened periods,

copied and re-copied, translated, commented on, extracted
and abridged, a large part of Pliny's work has gradually
passed into folk-keeping, so that through his agency the
gipsy fortune-teller of to-day is still reciting garbled

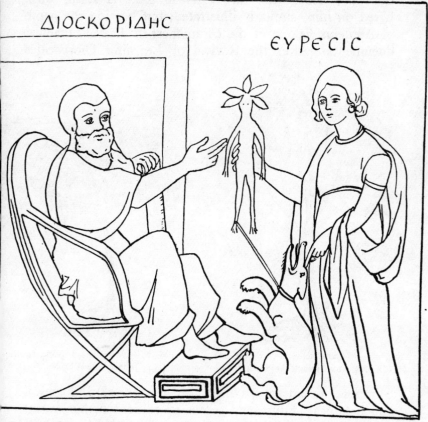

ΔΙΟCΚΟΡΙΔΗC

ΕΥΡΕCΙC

FIG. 75.—Scene traced from a miniature of the Juliana Anicia Codex, written A.D. 512.
The nymph Discovery (Εὕρεσις) presents a mandrake to the physician Dioscorides. The mandrake
is still tethered to the hound whose life is sacrificed to obtain it.

versions of the formulae that Pliny himself took from works
of Aristotle and Hippocrates, written two and a half
millennia ago (compare p. 12 ff.).

The fate of Dioscorides (flourished A.D. 60) has been
not dissimilar. His work *On Materia Medica* is a series

of short accounts of plants and their uses, often provided
with terse descriptions which sometimes deal with habits
and habitats. It has been one of the most influential
botanical treatises ever penned. Illustrated Latin translations of Dioscorides were early in use. A Latin work
based on him, similarly illustrated, but bearing the name
of Apuleius, is one of the commonest mediaeval botanical
documents. After the Revival of Learning Dioscorides

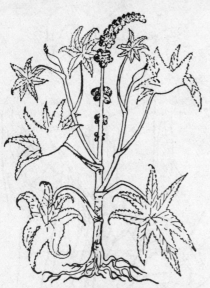

Fig. 76.—*Ricinus communis*. Young castor
oil plant, from Juliana Anicia Codex.

Fig. 77.—Young bean plant, from
Juliana Anicia Codex.

continued to attract an immense amount of philological
and botanical ability, and scores of editions of his works,
many of them nobly illustrated, poured from the presses.
The work decided the general form of every ancient and
most modern pharmacopoeias, both Oriental and Occidental.
Dioscorides practically determined modern plant nomenclature both popular and scientific—he is the main source
of the herbals.

Translated into nearly every language, from Anglo-
Saxon and Provençal to Persian and Hebrew, appearing in

innumerable beautifully illuminated manuscripts, some of which are among the fairest treasures of the great national libraries, Dioscorides, the drug-monger, appealed to scholasticized minds for centuries. One of the earliest datable Greek codices in existence is a glorious illustrated volume of Dioscorides, written in capitals, the chief adornment of what was once the Royal Library of Vienna. This manuscript was thought worthy to form a wedding gift for the lady Juliana Anicia, the daughter of Anicius Olybrius, Emperor of the West in 472, and of his wife Placidia, herself the daughter of Valentinian III. The Juliana Anicia manuscript forms a land-mark not only in the history of botany in general and the herbal in particular, but also in the history of art. It is the earliest and also the finest of the Greek herbals [Figs. 75-8].

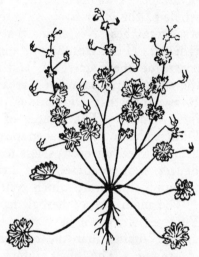

FIG. 78.—*Geranium molle*, from Juliana Anicia Codex.

There are several frag-ments of earlier Greek herbals written on papy-rus. They show that long before the Juliana Anicia manuscript was prepared the art of plant painting had begun to deteriorate. The later history of the Greek herbal is one of yet further decay. A number of illustrated Greek herbals are known, extending down to the present century. They all tell the same tale of copying not even exact enough to be called slavish. At each remove the plants become less like their originals, until they are unrecognizable save by one who has studied the course of their tradition. So far as the Greek world is concerned the evolution

of the herbal is closed with the Juliana Anicia manuscript.

One interesting branch was, however, given off by the
Greek herbal tradition in its decline. As the general
character of the Greek mind deteriorated, such science as
survived passed into the hands of the various Oriental
peoples who went to make up the Byzantine Empire. Of
these the Nestorian Christians entered most freely into
medical studies and turned into Syriac the more popular
of the Greek medical works. In after centuries, when the
whole of the Near East came under the power of Islam, it
was from these Nestorians that medical knowledge mainly
radiated. First Gondisapur and then Baghdad became the
centre of their activities, and at the last centre most of
the work of translation of Greek wisdom was accomplished.
It was thus that Dioscorides passed into Arabic and later
into Persian. The figures of the plants of the Greek
Dioscorides tradition, taken mostly from the Mediterranean
littoral, were however useless to the Oriental reader. New
figures were prepared and items were added. A new
tradition thus arose which continues to this day.

The main line of herbal development, that of Western
Europe, which we have now to consider, has shown far
greater vitality than the original Greek stock from which
it sprang. The chief interest of the Western herbal
depends on the history of the art which it embodies. An
understanding of the development of any form of Western
art in the first centuries of the Christian era depends on the
realization of the early differentiation of the outlook of
East and West within the Roman Empire. To the political
historian the breach between the Eastern and the Western
Empire is marked by certain important events, such as
the separation of the Empire into an Eastern and a Western
realm in 364, or its final division in 395. To the student
of cultural history these events are only the expression of
tendencies which lay much deeper and existed long before
their political results declared themselves. Those differ-

PLATE X

A CENTAUR HOLDS THE PLANT CENTAURY

From an Anglo-Norman Herbal of the thirteenth century
(Ashmole 1462). See p. 191.

182]

ences are expressed in the contrast between the art of the East and that of the West.

The classical art of Greece, with its immense power in the production of idealized types, corresponded to the capacity for abstract thought among its men of science. The West took less kindly both to idealized types and to abstract thought ; on the other hand it was more productive in the realm of portraiture and in the close and detailed observation of nature. The country gentleman's love of nature, so typical of the Roman noble, corresponds to the power to express nature in plastic art. Greek art, which had few triumphs of nature representation to record on its own soil, brought however a most valuable element to the development of Western art. It was the technique of Greek artists that combined with the taste of Roman patrons to produce the development known as the Augustan style. In this type of art, devoid of the freedom and the idealism of the great art of Greece, plants were treated as they had never been before (p. 2 ff.). In such specimens as the Tomb of the Haterii in the Lateran Museum, or the famous well-head at Vienna, we have the work of a faithful student of nature (see Figs. 1–3). In the mural paintings in the Villa Livia we have a treatment of plants so close and natural that they would serve for a modern botanical textbook.

Roman art had, however, but a meteoric career. After the first century it steadily deteriorated. The causes of this deterioration may be sought in many directions. The growing estrangement of East and West deprived Roman art of a source of inspiration. The social disturbances of the time, the rise of the new religion and the character of what survived of the old pagan philosophy were none of them favourable to the free development of an independent art. Most of all, the exclusively literary character of education in the late Empire told against all originality and independence of thought. The whole stress was on classical models, and imitation was elevated into the very standard of excellence. As Christianity gained way on paganism it too developed an art, but it was an art in which even the details were copied from an older source. Such was the atmosphere in which the Western herbal tradition arose.

In the first instance the Latin or Western herbals were nothing but translations of Greek works. They were part of a regular system of translation of medical works which began with the rendering of Celsus in the first pre-Christian century, and extended to Cassiodorus in the sixth century of the Christian era. In the case of the herbals the earliest Latin production seems to have been a translation of such a work on herbs about the year 400. To this the name of Apuleius became attached. The herbal of Apuleius was probably illustrated in the original, for though the Greek source has not been found, fragments of a very similar Greek work with illustrations comparable to those in the earliest known manuscript of the Latin Apuleius have been recovered.

During the third and fourth centuries the diversity of tongues within the Empire had created a difficulty of comprehending medical terms. Provincials, however perfectly they might understand Latin, retained their local names for such familiar objects as herbs. To meet their difficulty, lists or lexicons of plant synonyms were prepared and one of these was very early incorporated into the text of the Apuleius herbal.

A manuscript of the Apuleius herbal, dating from the sixth or early seventh century, is one of the treasures of the library at Leyden [Figs. 79 and 80]. Like the Juliana Anicia manuscript, it is a landmark in the history both of botany and of manuscript illustration. There is good evidence that the illustrations of this Leyden manuscript are copied from a manuscript two centuries older. It contains, too, the dictionary of synonyms that continued to be slavishly repeated through scores of generations on to the end of the Middle Ages, when not only were the dialects of the

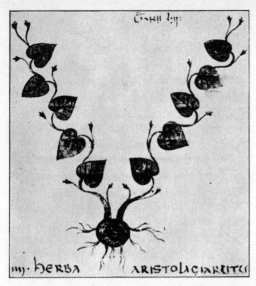

FIG. 79.—(Above) *ARISTO LOCHIA PALLIDA*

From the Leyden Apuleius, written about A.D. 600. Contrast the stiffness and rigidity of this figure from an early Latin MS. with the freedom of the Greek in Fig. 73.

FIG. 80.—(Below) BLACK-BERRY

From the Leyden Apuleius, written about A.D. 600.

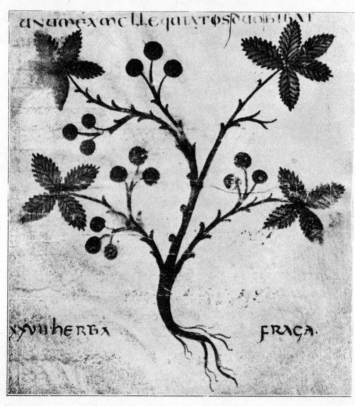

lexicon forgotten but the very fact of their existence had passed out of recollection. The Leyden Apuleius is the very recognizable ancestor of a whole host of manuscript herbals. These were copied and re-copied throughout the ages, naturally deteriorating a little at each stage.

Finally, the period of printing is reached. The first printed herbal is again our Apuleius ; some of its old figures pass into print [Fig. 63, cf. Fig. 64] and with them the same synonyms of the dead and forgotten tongues. Man is an imitative animal, but we doubt if any better instance of his imitativeness could be found than this constant copying and re-copying, for over a thousand years, with enormous labour and technical skill, of a futile work with its unrecognizable figures and its incomprehensible vocabulary.

The herbarium of Apuleius represents perhaps the first attempt to turn a Greek work of this type into Latin. Soon, however, a considerable part of the work of Dioscorides himself became available. When the actual work of translation took place we cannot be quite sure, but it was probably during the course of the Gothic domination (493–555). We see in it the handiwork of Cassiodorus (490–585), the Chancellor of the Emperor Theodoric the Goth. Cassiodorus grew tired of political power at an early age, and spent the very long evening of his life— he retired at 50, and died at 95—at his birthplace, Squillace, a town in the extreme south, which looks into the Gulf between the toe and heel of Italy. At Squillace was a Benedictine house, and Cassiodorus took great interest in its literary welfare. It was an age which looked exclusively to the past, and Cassiodorus was a creature of his age. Fortunate it is for us that he was so, for but for his activity it is possible that no complete Latin literary work—save that of Virgil—would have reached our time.

In his *Institutiones divinarum et humanarum litterarum* he tells his monks that : ' If you have not sufficient facility with Greek writing, then you can turn to the herbarium of Dioscorides, which describes and figures the herbs of

the field with wonderful faithfulness.' Copies of this
Latin translation of Dioscorides exist. They are richly
illustrated and some of the figures can be traced to the
Juliana Anicia and its congeners. In them we see passing
on to the Middle Ages some of the old figures which
Crateuas had prepared in the first century B.C. Others of
the figures of the Latin Dioscorides were prepared in Italy
at a later date, and in them we may see the deteriorated
descendants of Augustan art.

Besides the genuine translation of the work of Dioscorides
there were, however, other herbals to which his name
became attached. These were put together in the earlier
Middle Ages. One of them is the so-called *De herbis
feminis Dioscoridis*. This pseudo-Dioscoridean work was
compiled in Latin at some early date out of sources such
as Apuleius and the Latin Dioscorides. Another document,
which scholars have been accustomed to distinguish by
spelling the name in the mediaeval fashion, ' Dyascorides,'
was put together at Salerno from numerous Latin sources
which do not include the true Dioscorides. Manuscripts
of these works are provided with figures, and they form
the bases of later mediaeval herbals.

The figures of these herbals are more interesting than
the texts which they illustrate. The copying of the figures
from hand to hand, century after century, gave rise to
traditions or schools of plant illustration. Even in the
Leyden Apuleius most of the pictures are already heavily
stylized and far removed from nature drawing [Figs. 79 and
80]. This model remained little altered till the tenth century,
and herbals of that period from the Rhineland and Italy
still preserve pictures very close to the original type.
Then, however, there set in a new method of drawing
which, taking old models, deeply modified them. The
new type of plant-drawing appeared perhaps first in
northern France, but soon spread over Europe. The
plants depicted became more and more diagrammatic and
the drawing heavier. The style reached its climax in the

FIG. 81.

The Figure of 'Earth' from Botticelli's Primavera, with anemones, roses, and centauries issuing from her mouth. Twigs of spruce fir can be seen in the background. The picture was painted in 1478, and in feeling marks the passage from mediaeval to modern.

thirteenth century, at which period heavily diagrammatized and geometrical figures were being produced, rigidly enclosed in frames of burnished gold. The pictures are technically remarkable, but as plants they have become totally unrecognizable [Plates IX and X].

In the earlier Middle Ages an especial interest attaches itself to the Anglo-Saxon manuscripts. Magnificent documents in themselves, they gain additional interest from being the first vernacular treatises of the kind in existence. The investigator approaches them with hopes that they may yield a harvest of Anglo-Saxon custom and folk-lore. Alas! the hope is destined to disappointment. With insignificant exceptions the only thing English about these works is their language. When they differ from their classical original it is usually due to an error of the translator or the scribe, to some misarrangement of the text, or to the introduction of some copied passage from another classical source. Even the figures can be shown to be taken from French or Italian documents [Figs. 59, 60, 63, 64, and Plates III, IV, V].

Though the figures in the manuscript herbals up to the fifteenth century almost always correspond very closely to a fixed tradition, there are yet a very few exceptions to this rule. Most interesting of these is a Latin manuscript written at Bury St. Edmunds about 1120. The majority of its figures are traditional, but others are convincing naturalistic studies. Some monastic plant-lover had set himself the task of preparing a book of plant pictures. He had before him this ancient herbal, and proceeded to identify figures in it with the plants in his monastery garden. Thus, for the ‘ Viperina ’ of the old book, he adopted a milk thistle, *Carduus marianus* [Plate VI], then a garden plant from southern Europe, where it is common in waste places, and now a weed of escape in Britain. Similarly, for the ‘ Camedrum ’ of the ancient herbal he took *Teucrium chamaedrys* [Plate VII], another south European and western Asiatic form, which though now established in parts of England is unquestionably a garden escape. Again, for ' Paeonia ' he depicted a non-British *Orobus* [Plate VIII]. His naturalistic drawings are a reflex of a very characteristic Anglo-Saxon form of art. That school, though very seldom occupying itself with the plant-forms—which were usually merely copied —was very active in his day. Unfortunately the Anglo-Saxon style perished soon after and naturalism in Art had to await the Renaissance.

As the mediaeval centuries wore on, new influences began to affect the medical world. The most important of these, so far as the herbals are concerned, is that which comes from the ' Arabian ' writers. This influence is indeed the key to mediaeval science (see pp. 71–81). Islam, nowadays the client of Christendom, was from the ninth until the twelfth or thirteenth century the envied possessor of all the science and philosophy then accessible, and the West had to wrest it from her. The process led to a remarkable intellectual upheaval, the result of which is embedded in the great development known as ' Scholasticism ' (see pp. 85–90).

The first exponent of this Arabian influence was Constantine the African, an adventurer who came from North Africa, where he seems to have been in contact with Jewish physicians. He settled at Salerno, and later became a monk at the ancient Benedictine monastery of Monte Cassino, where he spent many years translating works from Arabic. He died in 1087. About a century later, in 1161, one Odo, of Meune on the Loire, composed a poem about herbs, drawing on Constantine and on certain older Latin sources. This was the first independent herbal to be produced in the West in mediaeval times, and it became one of the most popular. Odo, or his successors, attached the name of ' Macer ' to it, and it can be found in innumerable manuscripts and printed editions, some of which are illustrated along traditional lines.

Another herbal of about the same date as ' Macer ' was

FIG. 82.—COLUMBINE

By Leonardo da Vinci, Windsor Library.

put together by the physician Mathaeus Platearius, at Naples. It is known by its opening words *Circa instans*. This work relies partly on the old Latin sources, but like Macer draws also on Arabian material. Platearius knew of the old dictionary of synonyms, now quite incomprehensible (p. 185), and substituted for it a series of Greek, Latin, and colloquial Italian plant names. This list is philologically interesting as an early specimen of the Italian language. The *Circa instans* was translated into several vernaculars and had considerable influence. It is interesting, too, as the prototype in the mediaeval West of a new style of literature, the *synonyma*, or dictionary of drug synonyms. These works are occasionally illustrated and they also approach the herbal type.

The study of plants now begins to take an upward turn. ' Macer ' and the *Circa instans* are merely literary efforts and contain no real observation, but they herald the dawn. More scientific is the work *On plants* of the great Dominican, Albertus Magnus (1206–?1280). Primarily a compilation based on a pseudo-Aristotelian work, it too is essentially a learned product. It contains, however, in places, evidence of careful first-hand observation. This botanical treatise gives a very pleasing impression of the common-sense and open-mindedness of the great mediaeval scholar who has thus a place among the grandfathers, if not among the fathers, of modern botany.

In the century following Albert, Conrad von Megenberg (1309–98) produced in German his *Book of Nature*, a complete work on natural history and the first of its kind in the vernacular. He has a long section devoted to plants, which contains some original observations, though it is founded mainly on the work of Albert's contemporary and intimate, Thomas of Cantimpré (1201–70), who in turn based his work on Latin versions of ancient biological works made from the Arabic.

The scholastic movement, to the furthering of which Albert's chief efforts were directed, was essentially inimical

to first-hand study, and the great scholastic centuries from
the twelfth to the fifteenth were infertile in botanical
works exhibiting any first-hand knowledge. In one department, however, there was some revival of the spirit of
the naturalist. The artistic spirit early showed its kinship
with the scientific by the closeness with which some illuminators of manuscripts sought to imitate nature. The
texts of the herbals remained fixed, while the illustrations,
even of the older texts, underwent a definite development
in the direction of increased naturalism, though still retain-
ing a traditional element.

To explain the development of illustration of the later
mediaeval herbals some reference must be made to the
manner in which they were prepared. The text was
usually written before the figures were inserted, and
writing and illumination were the work of different hands.
The illuminator had the advantage over the scribe in being
without learning, for in certain stages of human development freedom from tradition is a positive advantage. Thus
the figures are as a rule a little later and may occasionally
be much later than the text, and are not infrequently produced in a different spirit. Sometimes the provenance of
the model can be determined from an examination of the
figures. Thus in one of the figures from the Anglo-Saxon
herbarium of about the year 1050, the plant representing
the henbane, or to call it by its earlier English name,
*hennebelle*, is not our familiar *Hyoscyamus niger* but *Hyoscyamus reticulatus*, a Mediterranean form not found in this
country [Plate V]. Again, the herbal prepared at Bury
St. Edmunds in 1120, to which we have already referred,
can be shown to reproduce a figure of a thistle that
grows in southern France [Plate VI].

It must always be remembered too that those who used
these herbals had no idea of plant distribution. The
conception that flora had local peculiarities, familiar enough
in antiquity, had been lost in the Middle Ages. When
the scribe copied his text he usually left a space into which

FIGS. 83 and 84.—SCABIOUS AND ACORNS
By Jean de Bourdichon, 1508.

the illustrator could then fit his figure. Many manuscript
herbals are known in which the illustrator has either not
completed or not begun his work, so that these spaces
remain blank. The gaps might be filled in later, according
as the owner of the book had the talent or the financial
resources at his disposal. Sometimes the original model
was not available when the later figures were inserted, so
that these do not always fit the spaces left for them.

Such figures of plants being copied from earlier figures,
became further removed from nature at each stage. But
the degradation of the copied herbarium had its limits, and
those limits were reached when the figures had so utterly
deteriorated that no semblance to an indigenous plant
could be discerned by the native scribe or owner of the
book. At this point it was necessary, if the herbal was to
be of use in practice, that there should be a return to
nature so as to give some impression of a local plant. The
point of lowest illustrational degradation corresponds in
general to the full development of the heavy stylized
manner ·at the beginning of the thirteenth century
[Plates IX and X]. From this period we can trace the
rise towards modern methods of plant illustration. The
movement was continuous and in manuscripts of the
fourteenth and fifteenth centuries we can distinguish
beautiful attempts to imitate nature, comparable in their
degree to the work of the artists who employed their
talents on grander themes.

Although some advance in herbal illustration began in
the thirteenth century, we have again the history repeated
of the capacity to represent plants lagging behind other
forms of art. This delay is very noticeable in the art of
the great painters. Thus the plants of Giotto (1267 ?–1337)
can rarely be identified, and Orcagna (1308 ?–68) is hardly,
if at all, more easy to interpret. Even Fra Angelico
(1387–1455) still belongs in this respect to the Middle
Ages. The first great plant painter is undoubtedly
Botticelli himself (1444–1510). In the ' Birth of Venus '

and in the ' Primavera ' are dozens of plants accurately
and faithfully rendered.  Especially good from the botanic
point of view is the beautiful cloud of flowers that falls
from the mouth of ' Earth ' in the latter great picture
[Fig. 81].

With Leonardo (1452–1519) and Dürer (1471–1528) we
encounter a new type.  The study of the minute details of
plants—botanical structure—is the strong point of the
former with his instinctive scientific bias, the rendering
of plant habits one of the glories of the latter.  The discussion of the works of such men as these would take us far
beyond our subject, but they are important for our purpose
because of the repercussion of the movements which they
represent upon the schools of manuscript illumination and
so upon the herbals [Fig. 82].

The faithful rendering of minute details of nature is the
special field of the miniature painter.  This power is
beautifully brought out in many manuscripts of the later
fifteenth century, and in none better illustrated than in
the famous manuscript of Bartholomaeus Anglicus (c. 1350),
in the Royal Collection at the British Museum.  This
grand volume was prepared at Bruges in 1482, and a large
part of its text is itself of the nature of a herbal.  There
was a contemporary type of manuscript too which linked
itself especially with plant illustration.  This was the
' Book of Hours,' on which the illuminators expended
much of their best art.  One great book of hours—itself
one of the finest specimens of manuscript illustration in
existence—contains also a valuable example of herbal
illustration.  It is the document known as *Les grandes
heures de la Reine Anne de Bretagne*, in the National Library
at Paris.  The illumination of this manuscript is the work
of Jean de Bourdichon, and was wrought in the year 1508.
It contains scores of plants portrayed in an interesting
manner intermediate between mere design and free drawing.
The plants are shown with the insects which infest them,
and these also are most carefully and exactly represented.

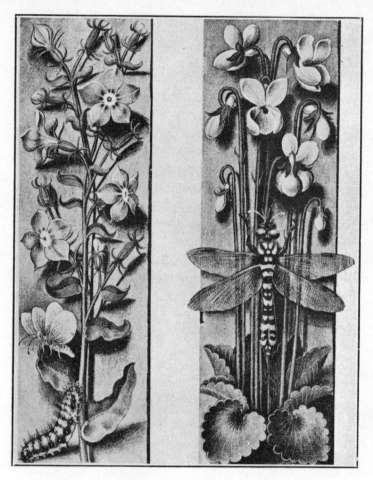

FIGS. 85 and 86.—CAMPANULA (Garden variety) AND VIOLETS
By Jean de Bourdichon, 1508.

The work of Jean de Bourdichon is unquestionably a monument of accurate nature study [Figs. 83–6].

While these artistic developments were continuing the art of printing was being perfected. Much attention has been paid to the earliest printed herbals, and they are

Fig. 87.—From the *Buch der Natur* of Conrad von Megenberg, printed at Augsburg in 1475.

certainly of great interest as illustrating the evolution of the woodcut. From the point of view of botanical history, or even in the limited field of the evolution of the herbal, they are, however, of little significance. In the first printed herbal, the Latin Apuleius, which appeared at Rome in 1484, there is nothing noteworthy about the illustrations

13

save their badness [Fig. 63]. It was printed from an inferior
and well-known type of manuscript original closely allied to
the Anglo-Saxon herbal of five hundred years earlier.
Again, the 'Bartholomaeus Anglicus,' printed first in 1470,
and reprinted by Wynkyn de Worde in England in 1495,
and Conrad von Megenberg's *Das Buch der Natur*, produced at Augsburg in 1475 [Fig. 87], are utterly inferior

FIG. 88.—Wallflower with Dodder.        FIG. 89.—Yellow Flag.
From the *Gart der Gesundheit*, printed at Mayence, 1485.

to the magnificent work of the Royal Bartholomaeus or
Bourdichon's 'Hours.'

Among these early printed books there is only one small
group of early printed herbals, the so-called *Gart der
Gesundheit*, in which there is evidence of a definite appeal
to nature, and some of its figures set a standard for the
next generation. The extension of the printer's art to
the service of scientific botany had thus its first home in
Germany. It consisted in the attempt to portray faithfully

a series of plants with all the new power that printing had placed in the herbalists' hands. The great step was only taken with the complete renunciation of the manuscript tradition [Figs. 88 and 89].

FIG. 90.—Anemone, from Brunfels, Strassburg, 1530.

It is the distinction of Otto Brunfels (1464–1534) that he was the first to produce a herbal which relied entirely on observation. His work, which he justly called *Herbarum vivae eicones*, was produced in parts that began to appear at Strassburg in 1530. The blocks were executed by Hans Weiditz, who deserves to be remembered by

historians of botany. His drawings are firm, sure, and
faithful, and it is instructive to compare them to those of a
good modern hand-book of plant form [Fig. 90]. The text

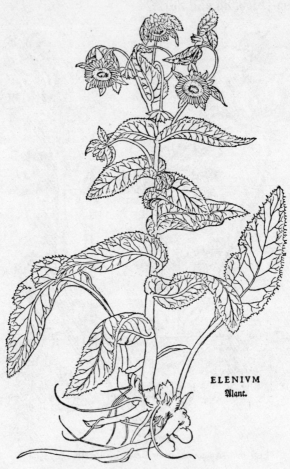

ELENIVM
Alant.

FIG. 91.—Elecampane, from Fuchs, Basel, 1542.

of Brunfels is inferior to the figures, for it is befogged by a
curious fallacy from which the botanical world took long
to free itself. He seeks always to identify his plants with
those of Dioscorides. As Dioscorides described the flora
of the eastern Mediterranean littoral, and Brunfels that of

the Rhine, the attempt naturally gives rise to much confusion.

The next important German botanist was Hieronymus Bock (1498–1554), whose work is significant as containing for the first time since Greek days adequate descriptions of the mode of occurrence and localities of the plants.

The most remarkable of the early illustrated herbals, however, is that of Leonhard Fuchs (1501–66). Fuchs was well known as a practising physician and apart from his herbal he has a definite place in the history of medicine. His masterpiece, however, is his *De historia stirpium*, which appeared at Basel in 1542. This work is a fine achievement in every direction, and a landmark in the history of natural knowledge. Fuchs was an excellent scholar, with a good acquaintance with the Greek and Latin classics, and his identifications with the plants mentioned by other writers are based on adequate study. The woodcuts that illustrate the work are of extraordinary beauty and truth, and based on a first-hand study

FIG. 92.—Cowslip, from Fuchs, Basel, 1542.

of the habits and structure of plants. These figures established a tradition and standard of plant illustration which is clearly traceable down to the middle of the following century, and is perceptible to this day [Figs. 91 and 92].

With Fuchs we reach the high-water mark of the Renaissance herbal. The history of the herbal continued for long after his time, and important books were produced by later authors. From now on, however, such works were to develop on more strictly botanical lines. Fuchs was essentially a herbalist in the limited sense. His plants were arranged in alphabetical order and there is in his pages nothing of the nature of classification, hardly anything that can be called plant geography, little or nothing concerning the essential nature of plants, or of their relation to other living things. It is a herbal pure and simple, containing none of the scientific elements except systematic observation. But modern science was dawning. The year after the *De historia stirpium* appeared at Basel there was printed at the same town the *De fabrica corporis humani* of Andreas Vesalius, and in the same year the *De revolutionibus orbium celestium* of Nicholas Copernicus was published at Nürenberg. With these two fundamental works dealing with the microcosm and the macrocosm respectively modern science had dawned. The day of the herbal and all that it represented was over.

PLATE XI

VISION OF THE TRINITY

From a MS. of Hildegard's *Scivias* at Wiesbaden, written at Bingen about 1180.
For description see page 232.

# VI

## THE VISIONS OF HILDEGARD OF BINGEN

## § 1. *Hildegard and her Works*

HILDEGARD of Bingen was born in 1098, of noble parentage, at Böckelheim, on the River Nahe, near Sponheim. Destined from an early age to a religious life, she passed nearly all her days within the walls of Benedictine houses. She was educated and commenced her career in the isolated convent of Disibodenberg, at the junction of the Nahe and the Glan, where she rose to be abbess. In 1147 she and some of her nuns migrated to a new convent on the Rupertsberg, a finely placed site, where the smoky railway junction of Bingerbrück now mars the landscape. Between the little settlement and the important mediaeval town of Bingen flowed the River Nahe. The stream was, and is, here spanned by a bridge of Roman origin, to which still clings the name of the pagan Drusus (15 B.C.–A.D. 19). At this spot [Fig. 93], a place of ancient memories, secluded and yet linked to the world, our abbess passed the main portion of her life, and here she closed her eyes in the eighty-second year of her age on September 17, 1179.

Hildegard was a woman of extraordinarily active and independent mind. She was not only gifted with a

thoroughly efficient intellect, but was possessed of great
energy and considerable literary power, and her writings
cover a wide range, betraying the most varied activities

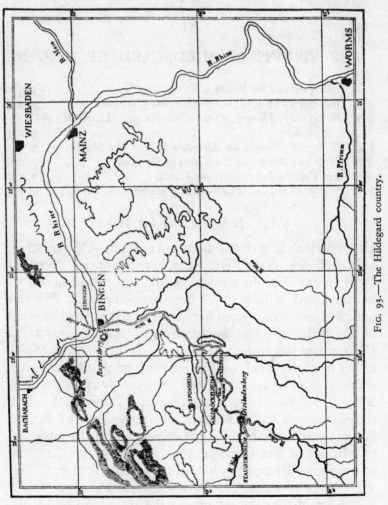

FIG. 93.—The Hildegard country.

and remarkable imaginative faculty. The most interesting
of her works are her books of visions. She was before
all things an ecstatic, and both of her great mystical works,
the *Scivias* (written between 1141 and 1150), and the

*Liber divinorum operum simplicis hominis* (written between 1163 and 1170), contain passages of real power and beauty. Less valuable is her third long mystical work (the second in point of time), the *Liber vitae meritorum* (written between 1158 and 1162). She wrote an interesting mystery-play and is perhaps responsible for a collection of musical compositions, while her life of St. Disibode, the Irish missionary (594–674) to whom her part of the Rhineland owes its Christianity, and her account of St. Rupert, a local saint commemorated in the name 'Rupertsberg,' bear witness to her narrative powers, to her capacity for systematic arrangement, and to her historical interests. Her extensive correspondence demonstrates the influence that she wielded, while certain other works by her give us glimpses of her activities as head of a religious house.

Her biographer, the monk Theodoric, records that she also busied herself with the treatment of the sick and credits her with miraculous powers of healing. Some of the cited instances of this faculty, as the curing of a love-sick maid, are but manifestations of personal ascendancy over weaker minds. Notwithstanding her undoubted acquaintance with such feeble remains of ancient science as existed in her day, and notwithstanding the claims that have been made for her as a pioneer of the hospital system, there is no serious evidence that her treatment extended beyond exorcism and prayer. There is a medical compilation ascribed to her, which is an interesting relic of Dark Age medicine. We are, however, unconvinced by the evidence that Hildegard was its authoress.

For her time and circumstance Hildegard saw a fair amount of the world. Living on the Rhine, the highway of Western Germany, she was well placed for observing the traffics and activities of men. She had journeyed as far north as Cologne, and had traversed the eastern tributary of the great river to Frankfort on the Main and to Rothenburg on the Taube. Her own country, the basin of the Nahe and the Glan, she knew intimately. She was in

constant communication with Mayence, the seat of the
archbishopric in which Bingen was situated, and there
has survived an extensive correspondence with the ecclesiastics of Cologne, Speyer, Hildesheim, Treves, Bamberg,
Prague, Nürenberg, Utrecht, and numerous other towns
of Germany, the Low Countries, and Central Europe.

Hildegard's journeys, undertaken with the object of
stimulating spiritual revival, were of the nature of religious
progresses.   Like those of her contemporary, St. Bernard of
Clairvaux, they were in fact largely directed against the
heretical and most cruelly persecuted Cathari, an Albigen-
sian sect widely spread in the Rhine country of the twelfth
century.   In justice to her memory it is to be recalled that
she herself was ever against the shedding of blood.   It was
not an age of tolerance, but had her less ferocious views
prevailed, some more substantial relic than the groans and
tears of this people might have reached our time, while the
annals of the Church would have been spared the defilement
of an indelible stain.

Hildegard's correspondence with St. Bernard, then
preaching his crusade, with four popes, Eugenius III,
Anastasius IV, Adrian IV, and Alexander III, and with the
emperors Conrad and Frederic Barbarossa, brings her into
the current of general European history.   She comes into
some slight contact with the story of England by her horta-
tory letters to Henry II and his consort Eleanor, the divorced
wife of Louis VII.

To complete a sketch of her literary activities, mention
should be made of a secret script and language attributed
to her.   It is a foolishly empty device that hardly merits
the dignity of the term ' mystical.'   It has, however,
exercised the ingenuity of several learned philologists.

There is ample material for a full biography of Hildegard,
and many accounts have appeared of her.   Most of them
are the work of men devoid of critical judgement and are
marked by a desire for edification that neither adds to their
attractiveness as literature nor conduces to our assurance

Fig. 94.—THE STRUCTURE OF THE SPHERE OF THE EARTH.

From a MS. at Lucca of Hildegard's *Liber Divinorun. Operum Simplicis Hominis*, written about 1200.
For description see page 222.

of their truthfulness. It would demand more skill than her biographers have exhibited to interest a detached reader in the minutiae of monastic disputes that absorbed a considerable part of her activities. Perhaps the best life of her is the earliest. It is certainly neither the most credulous nor the worst written and is by her contemporaries, the monks Godefrid and Theodoric.

Hildegard was never canonized. Attempts towards that end were made under the Popes Gregory IX (1237), Innocent IV (1243), and John XXII (1317). Miraculous cures and other works of wonder were claimed for her, but either they were insufficiently miraculous or insufficiently attested. Those who have impartially traced her life in her documents will, we believe, agree with the verdict of the Church. Hers was a fiery, a prophetic, in many ways a singularly noble spirit, but she exhibited defects of character which prevent us from regarding her as a woman of truly saintly mind or life. From her doctrine of *Nous* (p. 217) the orthodox may derive evidence of her heresy as an author and the pious draw comfort for her failure to achieve canonization as a saint.

In attempting to interpret the views of Hildegard on scientific subjects, certain special difficulties present themselves. First is the confusion arising from the writings to which her name has been erroneously attached. From the discussion which follows we omit certain works ascribed to her on what seem to us inadequate grounds. A second difficulty is due to the receptivity of her mind, so that views and theories that she accepts in her earlier works become modified, altered, and developed in her later writings. A third difficulty, perhaps less real than the others, is the visionary and involved form in which her thoughts are cast. But a fourth and more vital difficulty is the attitude that she adopts towards phenomena in general. To this difficulty we must devote a little special attention.

To Hildegard's mind there is no distinction between physical events, moral truths, and spiritual experiences.

This´view, which our children share with their mediaeval ancestors, was developed but not transformed by her visionary powers. Her fusion of internal and external universe links Hildegard to a whole series of mediaeval visionaries, culminating with Dante. In Hildegard, as in her fellow-mystics, we find that ideas on Nature and Man, the Moral World and the Material Universe, the Spheres, the Winds and the Humours, Birth and Death, on the Soul, the Resurrection of the Dead, and the Nature of God, are not only interdependent but closely interwoven. Nowadays we separate our ideas into categories, scientific, ethical, theological, philosophical, and so forth, and we even esteem it a virtue to retain and restrain our thoughts within limits that we deliberately set for them. To Hildegard the segregation of ideas in this manner would have been incomprehensible. Such terms as *parallelism* or *allegory* do not cover her views of the relation of the material and spiritual. In her mind the material and spiritual are really interfused, or rather they have not yet been separated.

Therefore, although in the following pages an attempt is made to estimate her scientific views, yet this method must, of its nature, interpret her thought only in a very partial fashion. Hildegard presents to us scientific thought as an undifferentiated factor, and an attempt is here made to separate it, by the artificial but not unscientific process of dissection, from the organic matrix in which it is embedded.

The interest of the works of Hildegard is greatly heightened by the existence of certain early and most remarkably illuminated manuscripts of her visions. Some knowledge of the miniatures in two of these, one at Wiesbaden and one at Lucca, is essential for the understanding of her meaning.

The illuminated manuscript of Hildegard's *Scivias* in the provincial library at Wiesbaden is a truly noble volume, in excellent preservation and of the highest value for the history of mediaeval art. It was prepared in or near Bingen at about the time of Hildegard's death. Its miniatures help greatly in the interpretation of the visions,

## VISION OF THE 'SEDENS LUCIDUS'

From a MS. of Hildegard's *Scivias* at Wiesbaden, written at Bingen about 1180. The figure is typical of migraine. It consists of a glittering background, here represented in gold, on which appears a very bright shimmering point of red light. From this point fortification figures radiate. The vision is identical in pathological basis with that depicted in Plate XIII and both are combined in the 'reconstructed' vision of Plate XIV. The Frontispiece, Plate XI, and Fig. 108 are migrainous appearances of rather different types. See page 233.

illustrating them often in the minutest details. In view of the great difficulty in visualizing much of her narrative, there can be little doubt that the preparation of these miniatures was either supervised by the prophetess herself or under her immediate tradition [Frontispiece, Plates XI–XIV, Figs. 95, 97–9, 107–9].

The other important illuminated manuscript of Hildegard is that of the *Liber divinorum operum simplicis hominis* in the municipal library at Lucca. It was written very early in the thirteenth century. Of its most remarkable miniatures, some are of special value for the interpretation of Hildegard's theories on the relation of Macrocosm and Microcosm, of which more hereafter. They represent the meaning of the text with a convincing sureness of touch. Without the clues provided by the Lucca miniatures, many passages in the book would be wholly incomprehensible. It is probable that the traditional interpretation of Hildegard's works, thus preserved to our time by these miniatures and by them alone, had its origin from the mouth of the prophetess herself [Plate II, Figs. 94 and 101–3].

We have here to consider especially Hildegard's view of the material world, the scientific contents of her visions. These are all grouped round her theory of the macrocosm and microcosm. It will be convenient to consider her views under four heads. Firstly, her conception of the structure of the Universe, the Macrocosm (§ 2). Secondly, the doctrine of the relation of Macrocosm and Microcosm (§ 3). Thirdly, her view of the structure of the body of Man, the Microcosm (§ 4). Fourthly, her view of the nature of the soul (§ 5).

## § 2. *Hildegard's View of the Universe the Macrocosm*

To the student of mediaeval science Hildegard's beliefs as to the nature and structure of the universe are among the most interesting that she has to impart, and here the miniatures aid us greatly.

In the middle of Hildegard's universe is a spherical earth.

Around this are arranged a number of concentric shells or zones. The inner zones, like the earth itself, tend to be spherical. The outer zones are, however, oval, and the

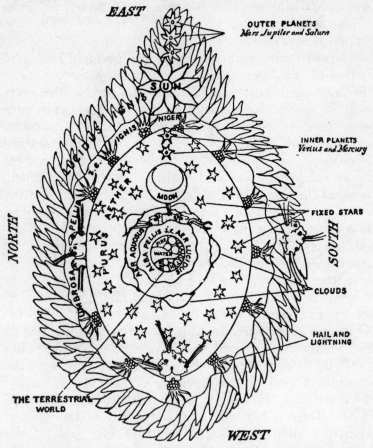

FIG. 95.—Hildegard's first scheme of the universe, slightly simplified from a figure in the Wiesbaden Codex.

outermost of all is egg-shaped, with one end prolonged and more pointed than the other [Fig. 95].

The concentric structure of the universe with the earth in the middle is a commonplace of mediaeval science. In most mediaeval works, as for instance in Dante (p. 86), the universe is, however, described as spherical. The egg-shape, as exhibited by Hildegard, is unusual, but is encountered among other mediaeval writers. Many of the so-called *Mappaemundi* exhibit the *surface* of the habitable earth itself as oval, and it was probably from the misunderstanding of such charts that Hildegard and other writers gained their conception of an oval universe. In her method of orientation also she follows the *Mappaemundi*, placing the east at the top of the page, where we are accustomed to place the north.

It is unfortunate that Hildegard does not deal with geography in the restricted sense, and so we are not in full possession of her views on the antipodes, a subject of derision to patristic and of misconception to scholastic writers. She does, however, vaguely refer to the inversion of seasons and climates in the opposite hemisphere, though she confuses the issue by the adoption of a theory, widespread in the Middle Ages and reproduced in the *Divina Commedia*, that the antipodean surface of the earth is uninhabitable, since it is either beneath the ocean or in the mouth of the Dragon [Fig. 94]. The nature of the antipodean inversion of climates was clearly grasped by her contemporary, Herrade de Landsberg [Fig. 96].

Hildegard's views as to the internal structure of the terrestrial sphere are more difficult to follow. Her doctrine of Purgatory and Hell is confused, but she held that the interior of the earth contained two vast spaces, shaped like truncated cones, where punishment was meted out and whence many evil things had issue. Her whole scheme presents analogies as well as contrasts to that of her kindred spirit Dante [Fig. 95 and cf. Fig. 39]. Hildegard, however, who died before the thirteenth century had dawned, presents us with a scheme far less definite and elaborated than that of her great successor, who had all the stores of the golden age of scholasticism on which to draw.

In Hildegard's first diagram of the universe, which is of the nature of a ' section,' the world, the *sphaera elementorum* of mediaeval writers, is diagrammatically represented as compounded of earth, air, fire, and water confusedly mixed in what her younger contemporary, Alexander of Neckam (1157-1217), calls 'a certain concordant discord of the elements.' In the illustrations, the four elements have each a conventional method of representation, which appears again and again in the different miniatures [Figs. 98-9].

Around this world with its four elements is spread the atmosphere, the *aer lucidus* or *alba pellis*, diagrammatically

FIG. 96.—Scheme of the 'zones' of the world, the Frigid, the Temperate, and the Tropic (perusta), from Herrade de Landsberg's *Hortus deliciarum*.

represented, like the earth which it enwraps, as circular. Through this *alba pellis* no creature of earth can penetrate. Beyond are ranged in order four further shells or zones. Each zone contains one of the cardinal winds, and each cardinal wind is accompanied by two accessory winds, represented, in the traditional fashion, by the breath of supernatural beings.

Of the four outer zones the first is the *aer aquosus*, also round, from which blows the east wind. In the outer part

FIG. 97.—THE LAST JUDGEMENT AND THE FATE OF THE ELEMENTS

From a MS. at Wiesbaden of Hildegard's *Scivias*, written at Bingen about 1180.   For description see page 210.

of the *aer aquosus* float the clouds, and according as they contract or expand or are blown aside the heavenly bodies above are revealed or concealed.

Enwrapping the *aer aquosus* is the *purus aether*, the widest of all the zones. The long axis of this, as of the remaining outer shells, is in the direction from east to west, thus determining the path of movement of the heavenly bodies. Scattered through the *purus aether* are the constellations of the fixed stars and arranged along the long axis are the moon and the two inner planets. From this zone blows the west wind. The position and constitution of this *purus aether* is evidently the result of some misinterpretation of Aristotelian writings.

The next zone, the *umbrosa pellis* or *ignis niger*, is a narrow dark shell, whence proceed the more dramatic meteorological events. Here, following on the hints of the *Wisdom of Solomon* (chap. v) and the *Book of Job* (chap. xxxviii), are situated the diagrammatically portrayed treasuries of lightning and of hail. From here the tempestuous north wind bursts forth. The presence of this *ignis niger* suggests some contact on the part of the authoress with the teaching of the *Meteorologica* of Aristotle. The nature of this contact we shall consider later.

The outermost layer of all is a mass of flames, the *lucidus ignis*. Here are the sun and the three outer planets, and from here the south wind pours its scorching breath [Fig. 95].

The movements of the four outer zones around each other, carrying the heavenly bodies with them, are attributed to the winds in each zone. The seasonal variations in the movements of the heavenly bodies, along with the recurring seasons themselves, are also determined by the prevalent winds, which, acting as the motive-power upon the various zones, form a celestial parallelogram of forces. In this way is explained also why in spring the days lengthen and in autumn they shorten, until in either case an equinox is reached.

' I looked and behold the east and the south wind with their collaterals, moving the firmament by the power of their breath, caused it to revolve over the earth from east to west ; and in the same way the west and north wind and their collaterals, receiving the impulse and projecting their blast, thrust it back again from west to east. . . .'

' I saw also that as the days began to lengthen, the south wind and his collaterals gradually raised the firmament in the southern zone upwards towards the north, until the days ceased to grow longer. Then, when the days began to shorten, the north wind with his collaterals, shrinking from the brightness of the sun, drove the firmament back gradually southward until by reason of the lengthening days the south wind began yet again to raise it up.' [1]  [Fig. 95.]

Intimately bound up not only with her theory of the nature and structure of the universe but also with her beliefs as to the end of things is Hildegard's doctrine of the elements. Before the Fall of Man these were arranged in a harmony, which was disturbed by that catastrophe [Fig. 98], so that they have since remained in the state of mingled confusion in which we always encounter them on the terrestrial globe. This *mistio*, to use the mediaeval Aristotelian term, is symbolized by the irregular manner in which the elements are represented in the central sphere of the diagram of the universe [Fig. 95]. Thus mingled they will remain until subjected to the melting-pot of the Last Judgement [Fig. 97], when they will emerge in a new and eternal harmony, no longer mixed as matter, but separate and pure, parts of the new heaven and the new earth [Fig. 99].

' But the heavens and the earth which are now . . . are kept in store and reserved unto fire against the day of judgement and perdition of ungodly men. . . . But the day of the Lord will come . . . in the which the heavens shall pass away with a great noise, and the elements shall melt with fervent heat, the earth also and the works that are therein shall be burned up. . . . Nevertheless we, according to his promise, look for new heavens and a new earth, wherein dwelleth righteousness.' (2 *Peter* iii, 7, 10, and 12.)

So Hildegard, acting on a scriptural hint, is enabled to dematerialize her doctrine of the after-things.

But, although since man's fall the elements have lost their

[1] Migne, cols. 789–91.

Fig. 98.—MAN'S FALL AND THE
DISTURBANCE OF THE PRIMORDIAL
ELEMENTAL HARMONY.

For description see page 210.

Fig. 99.—THE NEW HEAVENS AND
THE NEW EARTH AND THE NEW
ORDERING OF THE ELEMENTS.

For description see page 210.

From a MS. at Wiesbaden of Hildegard's *Scivias*, written at Bingen about 1180.

order, and their harmony on this terrestrial orb, yet is that harmony still in part preserved in the celestial spheres that encircle and surround our globe ; and water, air, earth, and fire have each their respective representatives in the four concentric zones, the *aer aquosus*, the *purus aether*, the *umbrosa pellis*, and the *lucidus ignis* [Fig. 95]. These are the ' superior elements ' which still retain some at least of their individuality and primal purity. From each of their spheres blows, as we have seen, one of the cardinal winds, and each wind partakes of the elemental character of the zone whence it issues, and has a corresponding influence on man's body, since each of the four humours is specifically affected by the element to which it corresponds.

' Then I saw that by the diverse quality of the winds, and of the atmosphere as they in turn sweep through it, the humours in man are agitated and altered. For in each of the superior elements there is a breath of corresponding quality by which, through the power of the winds, the corresponding element (below) is forced to revolve in the atmosphere, and in no other way is it moved. And by one of those winds, with the agency of sun, moon and stars, the atmosphere which tempers the world is breathed forth.' [1] [Cf. Fig. 101.]

This doctrine of the relation of the various winds to the four elements and through them to the four humours is found in the *De Rerum Natura* of Isidore of Seville, and is illustrated in European manuscripts from the ninth century onward, but we meet it set forth with special definiteness in the twelfth century in the translations from Messahalah (p. 236). It is encountered also in the work of Herrade de Landsberg (p. 237). In and after the thirteenth century it had become a common-place.

The description we have given of the universe was set forth by Hildegard in her first mystical work, the *Scivias* (1141–50). Subsequently she became dissatisfied with the account she had given and, while not withdrawing it, she sought in her later *Liber Divinorum Operum* (1163–70) so to modify the original presentment as to bring it more

[1] Migne, col. 791.

into line with accepted views which treated the universe as
a series of concentric spheres.   Thus she writes :

' There appeared to me in vision a disk very like that object which
I saw twenty-eight years ago of the form of an egg, in the third vision
of my book *Scivias*.   In the outer part of the disk there was as it were
the *lucidus ignis*, and beneath it the circle of the *ignis niger* was portrayed . . . and these two circles were so joined as to be one circle.'

There was thus one outer zone representing the fire.

' Under the circle of the *ignis niger* there was another circle in the
likeness of the *purus aether* which was of the same width as the two
conjoined (outer) fiery circles.   And below this circle again was the
circle of the *aer aquosus* as wide as the *lucidus ignis*.   And below this
circle was yet another circle, the *fortis et albus lucidusque aer* . . . the
width whereof was as the width of the *ignis niger*, and these circles were
joined to make one circle which was thus again of width equal to the
outer two.   Again, under this last circle yet another circle, the *aer
tenuis*, was distinguishable, which could be seen to raise itself as a cloud,
sometimes high and light, sometimes depressed and dark, and to diffuse
itself as it were throughout the whole disk. . . . The outermost fiery
circle perfuses the other circles with its fire, while the watery circle
saturates them with its moisture (cf. *Wisdom of Solomon* xix. 18–20).
And from the extreme eastern part of the disk to the extreme west a
line is stretched out (i.e. the equator) which separates the northern
zones from the others.' [1]   [Fig. 100, Plate II, and Figs. 101, 103.]

The earth lies concentrically with the *aer tenuis* and its
measurements are given thus :

' In the midst of the *aer tenuis* a globe was indicated, the circumference of which was everywhere equidistant from the *fortis et albus
lucidusque aer*, and it was as far across as the depth of the space from
the top of the highest circle to the extremity of the clouds, or from
the extremity of the clouds to the circumference of the inner globe.' [2]
[Fig. 100.]

In her earlier work, the *Scivias*, Hildegard apparently had
not realized the need of accounting for the independent
movements of the planets other than the sun and moon.
She had thus placed the moon and two of the moving stars
in the *purus aether*, and the sun and the three remaining

---

[1] Migne, cols. 403–14.        [2] Migne, col. 751.

moving stars in the *lucidus ignis*. Since these spheres were moved by the winds, their contained planets would be subject to the same influences. In the *Liber Divinorum Operum*, however, she has come to realize how independent the movements of the planets really are, and she invokes a special cause for their vagaries.

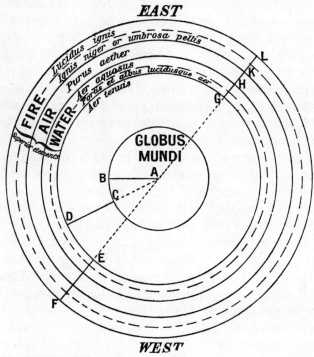

FIG. 100.—Hildegard's later scheme of the universe reconstructed from her measurements. AB, CD, and EF are all equal and GH, HK, and KL are all equal. The clouds are situated in the outer part of the *Aer tenuis* and are formed by an extension of the *Aer aquosus* towards the earth.

' I looked and behold in the outer fire (*lucidus ignis*) there appeared a circle which girt about the whole firmament from the east westward. From it a blast produced a movement from west to east in the opposite direction to the movement of the firmament. But this blast did not give forth his breath earthward as did the other winds, but instead thereof it governed the course of the planets.' [1]   [Cf. Fig. 101.]

[1] Migne, col. 791.

The source of the blast is represented in the Lucca manuscript as the head of a supernatural being with a human face [Fig. 101].

These curious passages were written at some date after 1163, when Hildegard was at least 65 years old. They reveal our prophetess attempting to revise much of her earlier theory of the universe. Note that (a) the universe has become round ; (b) there is an attempt to arrange the zones according to their density, i.e. from without inwards, fire, air (ether), water, earth ; (c) exact measurements are given ; (d) the water zone is continued earthward so as to mingle with the central circle. In all these and other respects she has adapted her opinions to the general current of mediaeval science which was just beginning to be moulded by Aristotelian works translated from the Arabic. Her knowledge of the movements of the heavenly bodies is entirely innocent of the doctrine of epicycles, but in other respects her views have come to resemble those, for instance, of Messahalah, one of the simplest and easiest writers on the sphere. Furthermore, her conceptions have developed so as to fit in with the macrocosm-microcosm scheme which she grasped about the year 1158. Even in her latest work, however, her theory of the universe exhibits differences from the typical scholastic view, as exemplified for instance by Dante [Fig. 39 and compare Fig. 100].

Like many mediaeval writers, Hildegard would have liked to imagine an ideal state of the elemental spheres in which the rarest, fire, was uppermost, and the densest, earth, undermost. Her conceptions were however disturbed by the awkward facts that water penetrated below the earth, and indeed sought the lowest level, while air and not water lay immediately above the earth's surface. Mediaeval writers adopted various devices and expended a vast amount of ingenuity in dealing with this obvious discrepancy. Hildegard devotes much space and some highly involved allegory, both in the *Scivias* and in the *Liber Divinorum Operum*, to the explanation of the difficulty, while Dante himself wrote a

FIG. 101.—THE MACROCOSM, THE MICROCOSM, AND THE WINDS

From a MS. at Lucca of Hildegard's *Liber Divinorum Operum Simplicis Hominis*, written about 1200. For description see pages 213–4.

treatise in high scholastic style on this very subject. These works of two mystics illustrate the essential difference between mediaeval and modern science. Both writers attach a far greater demonstrative value to analogy than we now allow, and the reasoning of both is almost exclusively *a priori*. The vast stress on analogy and the constant use of *a priori* methods are the two chief elements which separate the scientific thought of the Middle Ages from that of our own time.

## § 3. *Hildegard's Theory of the Relation of Macrocosm and Microcosm*

The winds and elements of the outer universe, the Macrocosm, become in Hildegard's later schemes intimately related to structures and events within the body of man himself, the Microcosm, the being around whom the universe centres. The terms *macrocosm* and *microcosm* are not employed by her, but, in her last great work, the *Liber Divinorum Operum*, she succeeds, in most eloquent and able fashion, in synthesizing into one great whole, centred around this doctrine, her theological beliefs and her physiological knowledge, together with her conceptions of the working of the human mind and of the structure of the universe. The work is thus an epitome of the science of the time viewed, however, through the distorting medium of this theory. In studying it the modern reader is necessarily hampered by the bizarre and visionary form into which the whole subject is cast. Nevertheless, the scheme, though complex and difficult, is neither incoherent nor insane, as at first sight it may seem. It is, in fact, a highly systematic and skilful presentment of a cosmic theory which for centuries dominated scientific thought.

As an explanation of the complexity of existence which thinkers of all ages have sought to bring within the range of some simple formula, this theory of the essential similarity of macrocosm and microcosm held in the Middle Ages, during the Renaissance and even into quite modern times, a position comparable to that of the theory of evolution in our own age. If at times it passed into folly, fantasy, and even madness, it should be remembered that it also fulfilled a high purpose. It gave a significance to the facts of nature and a formula to the naturalist, it unified philosophic systems, it exercised the ingenuity of theologians, and furnished a convenient framework to prophecy, while it seemed to illumine history and to provide a key and meaning to life itself. Even now it is not perhaps wholly devoid of message, but as a phenomenon in the history of human thought, a theory which appealed to such diverse scientific writers as Seneca, Albertus Magnus, Paracelsus, William Gilbert, William Harvey, Robert Boyle, and Leibnitz is surely worthy of attention. We may turn now to Hildegard's presentation of this doctrine.

Hildegard's *Liber Divinorum Operum* opens with a remarkable and beautiful vision illustrated by a no less remarkable picture [Fig. 102] :

' I saw a fair human form and the countenance thereof was of such beauty and brightness that it had been easier to gaze upon the sun. The head thereof was girt with a golden circlet through which appeared another face as of an aged man. From the neck of the figure on either side sprang a pinion which swept upward above the circlet and joined its fellow on high. And where on the right the wing turned upward, was portrayed an eagle's head with eyes of flame, wherein appeared, as in a mirror, the lightning of the angels, while from a man's head in the other wing the lightning of the stars did radiate. From either shoulder another wing reached to the knees. The figure was robed in brightness of•the sun, while the hands held a lamb shining with light. Beneath, the feet trampled a horrible black monster of revolting shape, upon the right ear of which a writhing serpent fixed itself.' [1]

The image declares its identity in words reminiscent of the Wisdom literature or of passages in the Hermetic writings, but which are, in fact, partly borrowed from Bernard Sylvester (see pp. 230 and 237).

' I am that supreme and fiery force that sends forth all the sparks of life. Death hath no part in me, yet do I allot it, wherefore I am girt

[1] Migne, col. 741.

FIG. 102.—*NOUS* PERVADED BY THE *GODHEAD* AND CON-
TROLLING *HYLE*

From a MS. at Lucca of Hildegard's *Liber Divinorum Operum Simplicis Hominis*,
written about 1200. For description see pages 216–7.

about with wisdom as with wings. I am that living and fiery essence of
the divine substance that glows in the beauty of the fields. I shine
in the water, I burn in the sun and the moon and the stars. Mine is
that mysterious force of the invisible wind. I sustain the breath of
all living. I breathe in the verdure and in the flowers, and when the
waters flow like living things, it is I. I formed those columns that
support the whole earth . . . I am the force that lies hid in the winds,
from me they take their source, and as a man may move because he
breathes, so doth a fire burn but by my blast. All these live because
I am in them and am of their life. I am wisdom. Mine is the blast of
the thundered word by which all things were made. I permeate all
things that they may not die. I am life.' [1]

Hildegard thus supposes that the whole universe is
permeated by a single living spirit, the figure of the vision.
This spirit of the macrocosm [Fig. 102], the *Nous* or ' world
spirit' of Hermetic and Neoplatonic literature, the imper-
sonated *Nature*, as we may perhaps render it, is in its turn
controlled by the Godhead that pervades the form and is
represented rising from its vertex as a second human face.
Nature, the spirit of the cosmic order, controls and holds
in subjection the hideous monster, the principle of death
and dissolution, the *Hyle* or *primordial matter* of the Neoplatonists whose chaotic and anarchic force would shatter
and destroy this fair world unless fettered by a higher power.

With the details of the visionary figure we need not delay,[2]
but we pass to the description of the structure of the macrocosm itself, to which the second vision is devoted [Fig. 103].
Here appears the same figure of the macrocosmic spirit.
But now the head and feet only are visible, and the arms
are outstretched to enclose the disk of the universe which
conceals the body. Although the macrocosm now described is considerably altered from Hildegard's original
scheme of the universe, she yet declares that ' I saw in the
bosom of the form the appearance of a disk of like sort

[1] Migne, col. 743.
[2] It is outside our purpose to attempt a full elucidation of Hildegard's
allegory. The eagle in the right wing signifies the power of Divine Grace,
while the human head in the left wing indicates the powers of the natural
man. To the bosom of the figure is clasped the Lamb of God.

to that which twenty-eight years before I had seen in the vision, set forth in my book *Scivias*.' [1]   The zones of this disk are then described [Fig. 100].   They are from without inwards :

(*a*) The *lucidus ignis*, containing the three outer planets, the sixteen principal fixed stars, and the south wind.

(*b*) The *ignis niger*, containing the sun, the north wind, and the materials of thunder, lightning, and hail.

(*c*) The *purus aether*, containing the west wind, the moon, the two inner planets, and certain fixed stars.

(*d*) The *aer aquosus*, containing the east wind.

(*e*) The *fortis et albus lucidusque aer*, where certain other fixed stars are placed.

(*f*) The *aer tenuis*, or atmosphere, in the outer part of which is the zone of the clouds.   All these zones are represented in the accompanying plates and diagram.

From all these objects, from the spheres of the elements, from the sun, moon, and other planets, from the four winds each with their two collaterals, from the fixed stars, and from the clouds, descend influences, indicated by lines, towards the figure of the microcosm [Figs. 101 and 103 and Plate II].

The microcosm is then introduced.

' And again I heard the voice from heaven saying, " God who created all things, wrought also man in His own image and similitude, and in him He traced [*signavit*] all created things, and He held him in such love that He destined him for the place from which the fallen angel had been cast." ' [2]

The various characters of the winds are expounded in a set of curious passages in which the doctrine of the Macrocosm and Microcosm is further mystically elaborated.   An endeavour is made to attribute to the winds derived from the different quarters of heaven qualities associated with a number of animals.[3]   The conception is illustrated and made comprehensible by the miniatures in the Lucca manuscript [Plate II and Figs. 101 and 103].

---

[1] Migne, col. 751.          [2] Migne, col. 744.
[3] *Liber Divinorum Operum*, part i, visions 2 and 3.

An associated vision is devoted to a comparison of the organs of the human body, the Microcosm [Fig. 103], to the parts of the macrocosmic scheme. Some of these views are set forth below (pp. 224–6).

Another vision explains the influence of the heavenly bodies and of the ' superior elements ' on the power of nature as exhibited on the surface of the earth. It is illustrated by a charming miniature in the Lucca manuscript [Plate II].

' I saw that the upper fiery firmament was stirred, so that as it were ashes were cast therefrom to earth, and they produced rashes and ulcers in men and animals and fruits.'

These effects are shown in the left upper quadrant of Plate II, where the ashes are seen proceeding from the *lucidus ignis*, the ' upper fiery firmament.' Two figures are seen, a female semi-recumbent, who lifts a fruit to her mouth, and a male figure fully recumbent, on whose legs a rash is displayed. The trees also in this quadrant show the effects of the ashes, two of them being denuded of fruit and foliage.

' Then I saw that from the *ignis niger* certain vapours (*Nebulae*) descended, which withered the verdure and dried up the moisture of the fields. The *purus aether*, however, resisted these ashes and vapours, seeking to hold back these plagues.'

These vapours may be seen in the right upper quadrant of Plate II. They descend from the *ignis niger*, attenuate for a space in the *purus aether*, and then descend through the other zones on to an arid and parched land. Here are two husbandmen ; one sits forlornly clasping his axe, while the other leans disconsolately upon his hoe. On the legs of the latter a rash may be distinguished.

' And looking again I saw that from the *fortis et albus lucidusque aer* certain other clouds reached the earth and infected men and beasts with sore pestilence, so that they were subjected to many ills even to the death, but the *aer aquosus* opposed that influence so that they were no hurt beyond measure.'

This scene is portrayed in the right lower quadrant of
Plate II. Here is a husbandman in mortal anguish. He
has gathered his basket of fruit and now lies stricken with
the pestilence. His left hand is laid on his heart, while
his right hangs listless on his thigh, pointing to tokens of
plague upon his legs. Beyond lies the dead body of a
beast on which a carrion bird has settled.

' Again I saw that the moisture in the *aer tenuis* was as it were boiling
above the surface of the earth, awakening the force of the earth and
making fruits to grow.' [1]

This happier scene is represented in the left lower
quadrant of Plate II. Here the beneficent fertilizing
influence is falling on trees and herbs, and the happy husbandmen are reaping its results.

The main outline of the *Liber Divinorum Operum*, in
which these visions are to be found, is borrowed from the
work of her contemporary Bernard Sylvester of Tours,
*De mundi universitate sive megacosmus et microcosmus*. In
this composition, written about 1150 by a teacher in a
cathedral school, gods and goddesses of the classical pantheon flit across the stage as though the writer were a pagan.
The mythology of Bernard is founded mainly on Plato's
*Timaeus*. The eternal *seminaria* of created things are mentioned and the general line of thought is Neoplatonic. Thus
the *anima universalis* of Neoplatonic writings can be identified with the *Nous* of Bernard. This principle is contrasted
with primordial matter or *Hyle*. The general setting of
Hildegard's work is quite different, but Hildegard's figure
of the spirit of the Macrocosm is identical with Bernard's
*Nous*. *Hyle*, on the other hand, becomes in Hildegard's
plan the monstrous form, the emblem of brute matter, on
which the spirit of the universe tramples.

Hildegard's conception of macrocosm and microcosm,
which was thus borrowed from Bernard Sylvester, has
analogies also to those well-known figures illustrating the

[1] Migne, col. 807.

PLATE XIII

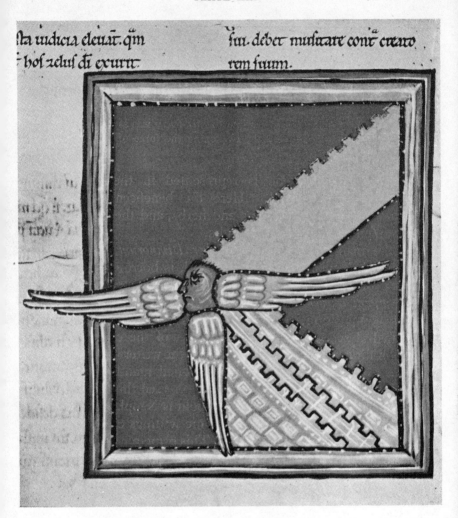

## VISION OF THE 'ZELUS DEI'

From a MS. of Hildegard's *Scivias* at Wiesbaden, written at Bingen about 1180. This figure is a representation of a vision of migrainous origin. In its essential parts it is identical with Plate XII, and it recurs in the 'reconstructed' vision shown in Plate XIV. It should be compared to the other types of migrainous vision shown in the Frontispiece, in Plate XI, and in Figure 108. See page 233.

supposed influence of the signs of the zodiac on the different parts of the body. Such figures, with the zodiacal symbols arranged around a figure of Christ, may be seen in manuscripts anterior to Hildegard [Fig. 30] and may be traced back to pagan sources in which Hercules takes the place of Christ. The influence of the ' Melothesia '—to give it the name assigned by Porphyry—has been traced through its period of efflorescence at the Renaissance [Fig. 38] right down to our own age and country, where it still appeals to the ignorant and foolish, and is still to be found in popular calendars and prophecies.

Hildegard often interprets natural events by means of a peculiarly crude form of the doctrine of the parallelism of Macrocosm and Microcosm. Thus she tells us that ' if the excess of waters below are drawn up to the clouds (by the judgement of God in the requital of sinners), then the moisture from the *aer aquosus* transudes through the *fortis et albus lucidusque aer* as a draught drunk transudes into the urinary bladder ; and the same waters descend in an inundation.' [1]

Again, events in the body of man are most naively explained on the basis of the nature of the external world as she has pictured it.

' The humours at times rage fiercely as a leopard and again they are softened, going backwards as a crab ; or they may show their diversity by leaping and goring as a stag, or they may be as a wolf in their ravening, and yet again they may invade the body of man after the manner of both wolf and crab. Or else they may show forth their strength unceasingly as a lion, or as a serpent they may go now softly, now violently, and at times they may be gentle as a lamb and at times again they may growl as an angered bear, and at times they may partake of the nature of the lamb and of the serpent.' [2] These animals will be seen represented in Plate II and in Figs. 101 and 103.

The word *cancer* is here used, but the crab goes sideways, not backwards. By *cancer* Hildegard, who had never seen the sea, means the freshwater crayfish *Astacus fluviatilis*, an animal common in the Rhine basin. It is the head of a

---

[1] Migne, col. 757.　　　　[2] Migne, cols. 3, 791–2.

crayfish that is figured in the miniatures of the vision of
the macrocosm in the Lucca manuscript.

Having completed her general survey of the Macrocosm
and having investigated in detail the structure of man's
body, the Microcosm, in terms of the greater universe, and
discussed the influence of the heavenly bodies on terrestrial
events, Hildegard turns to the internal structure of the terrestrial sphere [Fig 94].

Upon the surface of the earth towards the east stands the
building which symbolizes the *aedificium* of the church, a
favourite conception of our authoress. This church is
surmounted by a halo, whence proceed a pair of pinions
which extend the shelter over a full half of the earth's
circumference. As for the rest of the earth's surface, part
is within the wide-opened jaws of a monster, the Destroyer,
and the remainder is beneath the surface of the ocean.
Within the earth are five parts analogous, as she holds, to
the five senses of man. An eastern clear arc and a western
clouded one signify respectively the excellence of the
Orient where Zion is situated, and the Cimmerian darkness
of the occidental regions over which the shadow of the
dragon is cast. Centrally is a quadrate area divided into
three zones where the qualities of heat and cold and of a
third intermediate ' temperateness ' (*temperies*) are stored.
North and south of this are two areas where purgatory is
situate. Each is shaped like a truncated cone, and composed
also of three sectors. Souls suffer the torment of flame in
one section, the torment of water in another, while in the
third or intermediate section lurk monsters and creeping
things which add to the miseries of purgatory or at times
come forth to earth's surface to plague mankind [Fig. 94].
These northern and southern sections exhibit by their reversed arrangement the belief in the antipodean inversion
of climate, an idea hinted at several times in Hildegard's
writings, but more definitely illustrated by a figure of
Herrade de Landsberg [Fig. 96].

Macrocosmic schemes of the type illustrated by the text

Fig. 103.—*NOUS* PERVADED BY THE GODHEAD AND EMBRACING BOTH THE
MACROCOSM AND THE MICROCOSM

From a MS. at Lucca of Hildegard's *Liber Divinorum Operum Simplicis Hominis*, written about 1200. For
description see page 217.

of Hildegard and by the figures of the Lucca MS. had a great vogue in mediaeval times, and were passed on to later ages. Some passages in Hildegard's work read curiously like extracts from Paracelsus (1491–1541), and it is not hard to find a link between these two difficult and mystical writers. Trithemius, the teacher of Paracelsus, was abbot of Sponheim, an important settlement almost within sight of Hildegard's convents on the Rupertsberg and Disibodenberg. Trithemius studied Hildegard's writings with great care and attached much importance to them, so that they may well have influenced his pupil.

The influence of mediaeval theories of the relation of Macrocosm and Microcosm is encountered among numerous Renaissance writers beside Paracelsus. But as knowledge accumulated, the difficulty in applying the details of the theory became ever greater. Facts were strained and mutilated more and more to make them fit the Procrustean bed of an outworn theory, which became untenable when the heliocentric system of Copernicus, Kepler, and Galileo replaced the geocentric and anthropocentric systems of an earlier age. The idea of a close parallelism between the structure of man and of the wider universe was gradually abandoned by the scientific, while among the unscientific it degenerated and became little better than an insane obsession. As such it appears in the ingenious ravings of the English follower of Paracelsus, the Rosicrucian, Robert Fludd, who reproduced, often with fidelity, the systems which had some novelty five centuries before his time. As a similar fantastic obsession this once fruitful hypothesis still occasionally appears in modern works of perverted learning.

### § 4. Hildegard's View of the Structure of Man, the Microcosm

One of the visions of the *Liber Divinorum Operum* is devoted to a description of man's body according to the theory of the macrocosm and microcosm.

An investigation of her account reveals the fact that she is making an independent attempt to fit the anatomical knowledge of her day into her favourite theory. To understand her results we must know something of the material on which she is drawing, as well as of the theory into which she is trying to fit it.

The list of works containing anatomical descriptions that was available to a German writer of the twelfth century is not long. A perusal of them reduces her sources of information to three. One of these was the book *On the Nature of Man* by Constantine the African (died 1087. See p. 75). This book was translated by him about 1085, at the Benedictine Abbey of Monte Cassino, from some unknown Arabic original. The other anatomical work to which Hildegard was able to refer was a series of five diagrams representing respectively the arteries, veins, bones, nerves, and muscles [Fig. 104]. These diagrams were very widespread during the Middle Ages and were copied in the most servile fashion for centuries. Her account of the structure of the body was also in part derived from the work of Hugh of St. Victor *On the Members and Parts of Man*. On this, however, her dependence is less direct than upon the other two. The resultant is a curious visionary system of anatomy, physiology, and pathology, which we set forth in an abbreviated translation :—

' The humours may pass to the liver, where wisdom is tested, having been already tempered in the brain by the strength of the spirit, and having absorbed its moisture so that now it is plump, strong, and healthy.

' In the right of man is the liver and its great heat, so that the right is swift to act and to work [1] . . . the vessels of the liver, affected by the agitation of the humours, trouble the venules of the ear of man and sometimes confound the organ of hearing. . . .

' I saw also that sometimes the humours seek the navel, which covers the viscera as a cap, and holds them in, lest they be dissipated,

---

[1] An idea that occurs in Aristotle, *Parts of Animals*, ii, c. 2, but is rejected by Galen.

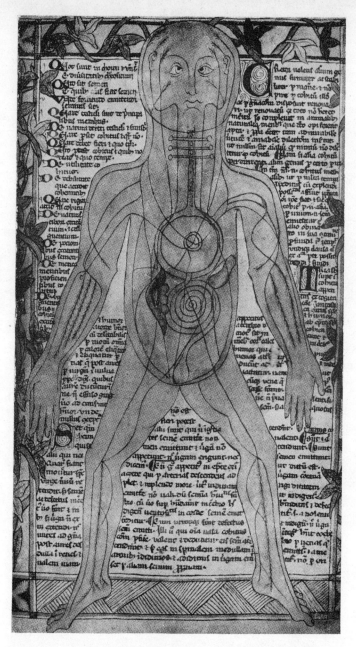

FIG. 104.—AN ANATOMICAL DRAWING OF THE THIRTEENTH
CENTURY, REPRESENTING THE VEINS

From MS. Ashmole 399.  See page 224.

and maintains their course and preserves the heat both of them and of the veins. . . .

'And the same humours go to the vessels of the reins and of other members, and pass in their turn to the vessels of the spleen, and then to the lungs and to the heart ; and they meet the viscera on the left where they are warmed by the lungs, but the liver warms the right-hand side of the body. And the vessels of the brain, heart, lung, liver, and other parts carry strength to the reins, whose vessels descend to the legs, strengthening them ; and returning along with the leg vessels, they unite with the virile organ or with the womb as the case may be.

'Again, the muscles of the arms, legs, and thighs contain vessels full of humours ; and just as the belly has within it viscera containing nourishment, so the muscles of arms, legs, and thighs have both vessels and the (contained) humours which preserve man's strength. . . . But when a man runs or walks quickly, the nerves about the knees and the venules in the knees become distended. And since they are united with the vessels of the legs, which are numerous and intercommunicated in a net-like manner, they conduct the fatigue to the vessels of the liver, and thus they reach the vessels of the brain, and so send the fatigue throughout the body.

'The humours in man are distributed in just measure. But when they affect the veins of the liver, his humidity is decreased and also the humidity of the chest is attenuated ; so that thus dried, he falls into disease of such a nature that the phlegm is dry and toxic and ascends to the brain. There it produces headache and pain in the eyes and wasting of the marrow, and thus if the moon is in default he may develop the falling evil (epilepsy).

'The humidity also which is in the umbilicus is dispersed by the same humours, and turned into dryness and hardness, so that the flesh becomes ulcerated and scabby as though he were leprous, if indeed he do not actually become so. And the vessels of his testicles, being adversely affected by these humours, are dried up within them ; and thus, the humours being withdrawn, impetigos may arise . . . and the marrow of the bones and the vessels of the flesh are dried up, and so the man becomes chronically ill, dragging out his days in languor.

'But sometimes the humours so affect breast and liver . . . that various foolish thoughts arise . . . and they ascend to the brain and infect it and again descend to the stomach and generate fevers there, so that the man is long sick. Yet again they vex the minor vessels of the ear with superfluity of phlegm ; or with the same phlegm they infect the vessels of the lung, so that he coughs and can scarce breathe and the phlegm may pass thence into the vessels of the heart and give pain there, or the pain may pass into the side, exciting pleurisy ; under such circumstances also, the moon being in defect, the man may lapse into the falling sickness.' [1]

Sometimes Hildegard's visionary anatomical ideas can be paralleled among her contemporaries.  Thus the following passage on the relationship of the planets to the brain is well illustrated by a diagram of Herrade de Landsberg.

' From the summit of the vessel of the brain to the extremity of the forehead seven equal spaces can be distinguished.  Here the seven planets are designated, the uppermost planet in the highest part, the moon in front, the sun in the middle, and the other planets distributed among the other spaces' [Fig. 105].

## § 5.  *Birth and Death and the Nature of the Soul*

The method by which the soul enters the body is set forth in a very striking vision in the *Scivias* and is illustrated in the Wiesbaden Codex by a no less remarkable miniature [Fig. 106].  The soul, which contains the element of wisdom, passes into the infant's body, while yet within the mother's womb.  The *Wisdom of God* is represented as a four-square object, with its angles set to the four quarters of the earth, this form being the symbol of stability.  From it a long tube-like process descends into the mother's womb.  Down this there passes into the child a bright object, described variously as ' spherical ' and as ' shapeless,' which ' illumines the whole body,' and becomes or develops into the soul.

The birth scene is strikingly portrayed.  In the foreground lies the mother with the head and shoulders supported and the right arm raised.  In her womb is the infant in the position known to obstetricians as a ' transverse presentation.'  Around the child may be distinguished clear traces of the uterine membranes.  Near the couch are ranged a group of ten figures who carry vessels containing the various qualities of the child.  Above and to the left the Evil One may be seen pouring some noxious substance into one of

[1] Migne, cols. 792–3.

these vessels, or perhaps abstracting some element of good. The whole scene suggests the familiar fairy story in which, while all bring pleasant gifts to the child's birth, there

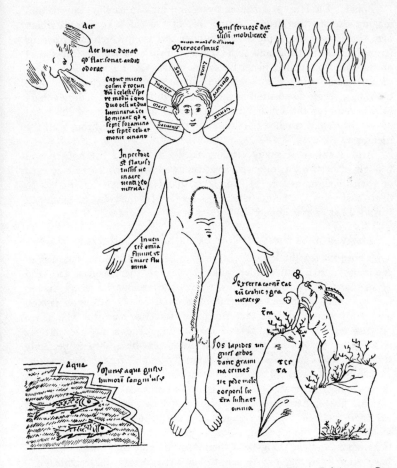

FIG. 105.—The Microcosm from Herrade de Landsberg's *Hortus Deliciarum*. Over the head of the figure are written the names of the seven planets. Air and fire stand one on each side. The inscription against the head may be rendered : ' The head of the microcosm is round like the heavenly sphere. In it are two eyes as the two luminaries shine in the heavens and there are seven orifices adorn it like the seven heavens of harmony.' Against the thorax is written : ' In the chest is breath and cough like to winds and thunder.' Against the abdomen : ' Into the belly all things flow like rivers to the sea.' By the legs stand the emblems of Earth and Water and the analogy is similarly carried on.

comes at last the old witch or the ill-used relative who
adds a quota of spitefulness.

The scene is described and expounded as follows :

' Behold, I saw upon earth men carrying milk in earthen vessels and
making cheeses therefrom.  Some was of the thick kind from which
firm cheese is made, some of the thinner sort from which more porous
[tenuis] cheese is made, and some was mixed with corruption [tabes] and
of the sort from which bitter cheese is made.  And I saw the likeness
of a woman having a complete human form within her womb.  And
then, by a secret disposition of the Most High Craftsman, a fiery sphere
having none of the lineaments of a human body possessed the heart
of the form, and reached the brain and transfused itself through all the
members. . . .

' And I saw that many circling eddies possessed the sphere and
brought it earthward, but with ever renewed force it returned upward
and with wailing asked, " I, wanderer that I am, where am I ? " " In
death's shadow." " And where go I ? " " In the way of sinners."
" And what is my hope ? "  " That of all wanderers." ' [1]

The vision is then further explained as follows :

' Those whom thou seest carrying milk in earthen vessels are in
the world, men and women alike, having in their bodies the seed
of mankind from which are procreated the various kinds of human
beings.  Part is thickened because the seed in its strength is well
and truly concocted, and this produces forceful men to whom are
allotted gifts both spiritual and carnal. . . . And some had cheeses
less firmly curdled, for they in their feebleness have seen imperfectly
tempered, and they raise offspring mostly stupid, feeble, and useless.
. . . And some was mixed with corruption . . . for the seed in that
brew cannot be rightly raised, it is invalid and makes misshapen men
who are bitter, distressed, and oppressed of heart, so that they may not
lift their gaze to higher things.[2] . . . And often in forgetfulness
of God and by the mocking devil, a mistio is made of the man and of
the woman, and the thing born therefrom is deformed, for parents who
have sinned against me return to me crucified in their children.' [3]
[Compare Constantine, De humana natura, sections ' De perfectione '
and ' De impeditione.']

Hildegard thus supposes that the qualities and form of a
child are inherited from its parents, but that two factors,
the formless soul from the Almighty and the corrupt fluid

[1] Migne, col. 415.    [2] Migne, col. 421.    [3] Migne, col. 424.

Fig. 106.—THE ARRIVAL OF THE SOUL IN THE
BODY OF THE INFANT

From a MS. at Wiesbaden of Hildegard's *Scivias*, written at
Bingen about 1180.   For description see pages 226–8.

instilled by the devil, also contribute to the character of offspring. This is the usual mediaeval view and is broadly portrayed in the figure.

The strange conception of the body being formed from the seed as cheese is precipitated and curdled from milk, is doubtless derived from a passage in the Book of Job :

> Hast thou not poured me out as milk,
> And curdled me like cheese ?
> Thou hast clothed me with skin and flesh,
> And knit me together with bones and sinews.[1] (*Job* x. 10, 11.)

When the body has thus taken shape there enters into it the soul, which, though at first shapeless, gradually assumes the form of its host, the earthly tabernacle ; and at death the soul departs through the mouth with the last breath, as a fully developed naked human shape, to be received by devils or angels as the case may be [Fig. 107].

During its residence in the body the soul plays the part usually assigned to it in the earlier mediaeval psychology. Hildegard regards the brain as having three chambers or divisions, corresponding to the three parts of man's nature, an idea encountered in the writings of St. Augustine. Parallel to these there are, she tells us :

' three elements in man by which he shows life ; to wit, soul (*anima*), body (*corpus*), and sense (*sensus*). The soul vivifies the body and inspires the senses ; the body attracts the soul and reveals the senses ; the senses affect the soul and allure the body. For the soul rules the body as a flame throws light into darkness, and it has two principal powers or limbs, the intellect (*intellectus*) and the will (*voluntas*). . . . For the intellect is attached to the soul as the arms to the body ; for as the body is pro- longed into arms with fingers and hands attached, so the intellect is produced from the soul by the operations of its various powers.' [2]

We need follow Hildegard no further into her maze of micro-cosmology, in which an essential similarity and

---

[1] The Aristotelian writings also compare the transformation of the material humours into the child's body with the solidification of milk in the formation of cheese.

[2] Migne, col. 425.

relationship is discovered between the qualities of the soul, the constitution of the external cosmos, and the structure of the body, a thought which appears as the culmination of her entire system and provides the clue to the otherwise incomprehensible whole.[1]

## § 6.   *The Pathological Basis of the Visions*

For the physical accompaniments and phenomena of Hildegard's visions we have three separate lines of evidence : her own account ;  the statements of her contemporary biographers, Theodoric and Godefrid ;  and the miniatures of the Wiesbaden Codex, probably prepared under her supervision.

It is clear that despite the length and activity of her life Hildegard did not enjoy normal health.   From a very early age she was the subject of trances and visions, and from time to time she was prostrated with protracted illness.

' God punished me for a time by laying me on a bed of sickness so that the blood was dried in my veins, the moisture in my flesh, and the marrow in my bones, as though the spirit were about to depart from my body. In this affliction I lay thirty days while my body burned as with fever, and it was thought that this sickness was laid upon me for a punishment.  And my spirit also was ailing, and yet was pinned to my flesh, so that while I did not die, yet did I not altogether live.   And throughout those days I watched a procession of angels innumerable who fought with Michael and against the Dragon and won the victory . . . And one of them called out to me, " Eagle, Eagle,[2] why sleepest thou ? . . . All the eagles are watching thee. . . . Arise ! for it is dawn, and eat and drink " . . . And then the whole troop cried out with a mighty voice . . . " Is not the time for passing come ?  Arise, maiden, arise ! " Instantly my body and my senses came back into the world ; and seeing this, my daughters who were weeping around me lifted me from the ground and placed me on my bed, and thus I began to get back my strength.

' But the affliction laid upon me did not fully cease ;  yet was my spirit daily strengthened. . . . I was yet weak of flesh, timid of mind, and fearful of pain . . . but in my soul I said, " Lord, Lord, all that

---

[1] Especially in the *Liber Divinorum Operum*, pars i, vis. iv.

[2] The eagle is frequently in mediaeval writings a symbol of the power of Divine Grace.

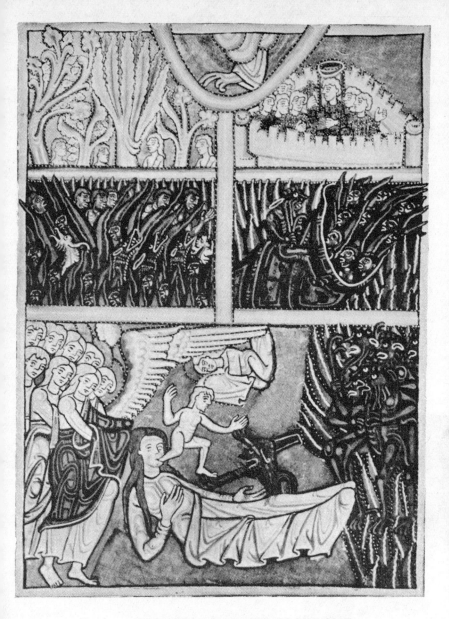

FIG. 107.—DEPARTURE AND FATE OF THE SOUL

From a MS. at Wiesbaden of Hildegard's *Scivias*, written at Bingen about 1180. For description see page 229.

Thou puttest upon me I know to be good . . . for have I not earned these things from my youth up ? " Yet was I assured He would not permit my soul to be thus tortured in the future life.[1] . . . Thus was my body seethed as in a pot . . . yet gave I thanks to God, for if this affliction had not been from Him I had surely not lived so long. But although I was thus tortured, yet did I, in supernal vision, often repeat, cry aloud, and write those things which the Holy Spirit willed to put before me.'

' Three years were thus passed during which the Cherubim thus pursued me with a flaming sword . . . and at length my spirit revived within me and my body was restored again as to its veins and marrows, and thus I was healed.'[2]

This illness of Hildegard was the longest and most typical but by no means the only one through which she passed. She describes her affliction as continuing for long periods, but there can be little doubt, from her history, that during much of the time she was able to carry on some at least of her functions as head of a religious house.

The condition from which she was suffering was clearly a functional nervous disorder ; this is sufficiently demonstrated by her repeated complete recoveries, her activity between the attacks, and the great age to which she lived. At first sight the long procession of figures and visions suggests that she might have been the victim of a condition similar to that of which Jerome Cardan has left us so complete a personal record. But on reading the books of visions the reader will easily convince himself that we are not here dealing with a dream-state. The visions are indeed essentially vivid. ' These visions which I saw,' she repeatedly assures us, ' I beheld neither in sleep, nor in dream, nor in madness, nor with my carnal eyes, nor with the ears of the flesh, nor in hidden places ; but wakeful, alert, with the eyes of the spirit and with the inward ears, I perceived them in open view and according to the will of God. And how this was compassed is hard indeed for human flesh to search out.'[3]

Nevertheless, though the visions exhibit great originality and creative power—the reader will often be reminded of

<hr>

[1] Migne, col. 110.    [2] Migne, col. 111.    [3] Migne, col. 384.

William Blake—all or nearly all present certain characters in common. In all a prominent feature is a point or a group of points of light, which shimmer and move, usually in a wavelike manner, and are most often interpreted as stars or flaming eyes [Frontispiece]. In quite a number of cases one light, larger than the rest, exhibits a series of concentric circular figures of wavering form [Plate XI]; and often definite fortification figures are described, radiating in some cases from a coloured area [Plates XII, XIII]. Often the lights gave that impression of *working*, boiling, or fermenting, described by so many visionaries, from Ezekiel onwards.

This outline of the visions Hildegard herself variously interpreted. We give examples from the more typical of these visions, in which the medical reader or the sufferer from migraine will, we think, easily recognize the symptoms of ' scintillating scotoma.' Some of the illuminations, here reproduced in their original colours, will confirm this interpretation.

' I saw a great star most splendid and beautiful, and with it an exceeding multitude of falling sparks which with the star followed southward. And they examined Him upon His throne almost as something hostile, and turning from Him they sought rather the north. And suddenly they were all annihilated, being turned into black coals . . . and cast into the abyss that I could see them no more.' [1]    [Frontispiece.]

This vision, illustrated by the beautiful figure of stars falling into the waves, is interpreted by her as signifying the *Fall of the Angels*.

The concentric circles appear in numerous visions, and notably in that of the *Days of the Creation of the World and the Fall of Man*, illustrated by what is perhaps the most beautiful of all the miniatures of the Wiesbaden Codex [Fig. 108]. It is in this concentric form that Hildegard most frequently pictures the Almighty, and the idea again appears in the eleventh miniature, here reproduced in its original colours, which she describes as 'a most shining light

---

[1] *Scivias*, lib. iii, vis. 1 ; Migne, col. 565.

FIG. 108.—THE DAYS OF CREATION AND THE FALL OF MAN

From a MS. at Wiesbaden of Hildegard's *Scivias*, written at Bingen about 1180.   See page 232.

and within it the appearance of a human form of a sapphire colour which glittered with a gentle but sparkling glow' [Plate XI]. Appearances of this type are recorded again and again.

The type with fortification figures is encountered in a whole series of visions, of which we reproduce the account and illumination of the *Zelus Dei* [Plate XIII, and *Sedens Lucidus*, Plate XII].

' I looked and behold, a head of marvellous form . . . of the colour of flame and red as fire, and it had a terrible human face gazing northward in great wrath. From the neck downward I could see no further form, for the body was altogether concealed . . . but the head itself I saw, like the bare form of a human head. Nor was it hairy like a man, nor indeed after the manner of a woman, but it was more like to a man than a woman, and very awful to look upon.

' It had three wings of marvellous length and breadth, white as a dazzling cloud. They were not raised erect but spread apart one from the other, and the head rose slightly above them . . . and at times they would beat terribly and again would be still. No word uttered the head, but remained altogether still, yet now and again beating with its extended wings.'

From the head extended a series of fortification lines, and this peculiar form of vision is reproduced on several occasions and variously interpreted [Plate XIII]. It is united with similar visions in what we regard as a reconstructed conception of exceedingly complex structure. This she claims to see separately, and she interprets it as the *aedificium* of the city of God [Plate XIV]. Such reconstructed visions are clearly of a different type and origin to the simple group in which a shining light or group of lights is encountered and interpreted as a speaking figure.

Hildegard's visions, perhaps without exception, contain this element of a blinding or glittering light, which she interprets in a more or less spiritual manner. We terminate our account with the passage in which she sums up her experiences of it.

' From my infancy,' she says, ' up to the present time, I being now more than seventy years of age, I have always seen this light in my spirit and not with external eyes, nor with any thoughts of my heart nor with help from the senses. But my outward eyes remain open and the other corporeal senses retain their activity. The light which I see is not located but yet is more brilliant than the sun, nor can I examine its height, length, or breadth, and I name it the " cloud of the living light." And as sun, moon, and stars are reflected in water, so the writings, sayings, virtues, and works of men shine in it before me. And whatever I thus see in vision the memory thereof remains long with me. Likewise I see, hear, and understand almost in a moment and I set down what I thus learn. . . .

' But sometimes I behold within this light another light which I name " the Living Light itself " . . . And when I look upon it every sadness and pain vanishes from my memory, so that I am again as a simple maid and not as an old woman.[1]

' And now that I am over seventy years old my spirit, according to the will of God, soars upward in vision to the highest heaven and to the farthest stretch of the air and spreads itself among different peoples to regions exceeding far from me here, and thence I can behold the changing clouds and the mutations of all created things ; for all these I see not with the outward eye or ear, nor do I create them from the cogitations of my heart . . . but within my spirit, my eyes being open, so that I have never suffered any terror when they left me.'[2]

## § 7. *Sources of Hildegard's Scientific Knowledge*

In our discussion we have often referred to works consulted by Hildegard. In this section we have to consider her sources in more general terms. Her imaginative power and mystical tendency make an exhaustive search into the origin of her ideas a difficult task. Unfortunately, she does not herself refer to any of her sources other than the Biblical books ; to have cited profane writers would have involved the abandonment of her claim that her knowledge was derived by immediate inspiration from on high. Nevertheless, it is possible to form some idea, on internal evidence, of the origin of many of her scientific conceptions.

The most striking point concerning the sources of Hildegard's mystical writings is negative. There is no German linguistic element distinguishable, and the writings show little or no trace of native German folk-lore. She claims to be a simple unlearned woman, unskilled in the Latin tongue ; but with the testimony before us of the writings

[1] Migne, col. 18.        [2] Migne, col. 18.

themselves, and of her use of Latin, the statement may be
set down to a mere literary formula, accentuated by the
desire to magnify the element of inspiration.  So far from
her having been illiterate, we perceive that not only the form
—which might have been modified by a contemporary
editor—but also the structure and details of her writings
betray much painstaking study of the works of others.

Hildegard lived at rather too early a date to drink fully at
that broad stream of new knowledge that was soon to flow
into Europe through Paris from its reservoir in Moslem
Spain.  Such drops from that source as may have reached
her must have trickled in either from Italy, with the works
of Constantine the African (died 1087), or perhaps from the
Jews who had settled in the Upper Rhineland.

Her science is primarily of the usual degenerate Greek
type, of the earlier Middle Ages.  We may distinguish in
it disintegrated fragments of Aristotle and Galen, coloured
and altered by the customary mediaeval attempts to bring
theory into line with scriptural phraseology, though a
degree of independence is at times obtained by the visionary
form in which her views are set.  Hildegard exhibits, like
all mediaeval writers on science, the Aristotelian theory of
the elements, but her statement of the doctrine is illuminated by flashes of her own thoughts and is coloured
by suggestions from St. Augustine, Isidore of Seville,
Bernard Sylvester, and from writings attributed to
Boethius.

The great translator from the Arabic, Gerard of Cremona
(1114–87), was her contemporary, and his labours at
Toledo made available for Latin readers a vast number of
scientific works which had previously circulated only among
Arabic-speaking peoples.  Several of these works, notably
Messahalah's *De Orbe*, and the Aristotelian *De Caelo et
Mundo*, and parts of the *Meteorologica*, which contain
material on the form of the Universe and on the nature of the
elements, evidently reached the Rhineland in time to be
used by Hildegard.  On the subject of the form of the earth

Hildegard expressed herself definitely as a spherist, a point of view more widely accepted in the earlier Middle Ages than is perhaps generally supposed. She considers in the usual mediaeval fashion that this globe of ours is surrounded by celestial spheres that influence terrestrial events. But while she claims that human affairs are controlled, under God, by the heavenly cosmos, she yet commits herself to none of that more detailed astrological doctrine that was developing in her time, and came to efflorescence in the following centuries. In this respect she follows the earlier and more scientific spirit of such writers as Messahalah, rather than the wilder theories of her own age. The short-ness and simplicity of Messahalah's tract on the sphere made it very popular. It was one of the earliest to be translated into Latin ; and its contents would account for the change which, as we shall see, came over Hildegard's scientific views in her later years.

The general conception of the universe as a series of concentric elemental spheres had penetrated to Western Europe centuries before Hildegard's time. Nevertheless, the prophetess presents it to her audience as a new and striking revelation. There is another favourite mediaeval cosmic theory, however, which she developed along indivi-dual lines. Hildegard exhibits in a peculiar and original form the doctrine of the macrocosm and microcosm (see pp. 224-6). Hardly distinguishable in the *Scivias* (1141-50), it appears definitely in the *Liber Vitae Meritorum* (1158-62), in which work, however, it takes no very prominent place, and is largely overlaid and concealed by other lines of thought. But in the *Liber Divinorum Operum* (1163-70) this belief is the main theme. The book is indeed an elaborate attempt to demonstrate a similarity and relationship between the nature of the Godhead, the constitution of the universe, and the structure of man, and it thus forms a valuable com-pendium of the science of the day viewed from the standpoint of this theory.

From whence did she derive the theory of macrocosm

and microcosm ? In outline its elements were easily accessible to her in Isidore's *De Rerum Natura*. But the work of Bernard Sylvester, *De mundi universitate sive megacosmus et microcosmus*, corresponds so closely both in form, in spirit, and sometimes even in phraseology to the *Liber Divinorum Operum*, that Hildegard must have had access to it. Bernard's work can be dated between the years 1145-53. This would correspond well with the appearance of his doctrines in the *Liber Vitae Meritorum* (1158-62) and their full development in the *Liber Divinorum Operum* (1163-70).

Another older contemporary with whom Hildegard presents points of contact is the mystical writer Hugh of Saxony (1096-1141), head of the monastic school of St. Victor at Paris. In Hugh's writings the doctrine of the relation of macrocosm and microcosm is more veiled than with Bernard Sylvester. Nevertheless, the symbolic universe in his work *The Mystic Noah's Ark* is on the lines of Hildegard's belief, and presents many parallels to the visions of Hildegard.

At Hildegard's date very complex cabalistic systems involving the doctrine of macrocosm and microcosm were being elaborated by the Jews, and Rabbinic mysticism specially flourished in her district. The famous traveller Benjamin of Tudela, who visited Bingen during Hildegard's lifetime, tells us that he found there a congregation of his people. It is clear from her writings that she was familiar with Jews, and it is possible that she may have derived some of the very complex macrocosmic conceptions, with which her last work is crowded, from local Jewish students.

The Alsatian Abbess, Herrade de Landsberg (died 1195), a contemporary of Hildegard, developed the microcosm theory along similar lines. A combination of circumstances thus make it probable that the theory, in the form in which these writers present it, reached the Upper Rhineland somewhere about the middle or latter half of the twelfth century, and that it was conveyed by works coloured by Neoplatonism and depending on Arabic sources.

Apart from the Biblical books, the work which made the deepest impression on Hildegard was Augustine's *City of God*, which forms the background of a large part of the *Scivias*. *Ezekiel*, *Daniel*, and the *Apocalypse* among the Biblical books, the *Gospel of Nicodemus* and the *Shepherd of Hermas* among Apocryphal books, contain a lurid type of vision which her own spiritual experiences enabled her to utilize, and which fitted in well with her microcosmic doctrines. Ideas on the harmony and disharmony of the elements she picked up from the *Wisdom of Solomon* and from the Pauline writings, supplemented by Isidore of Seville.

Her figure of the Church in the *Scivias* reminds us irresistibly of Boethius' vision of the gracious feminine form of Philosophy, and Boethius was very widely read in Hildegard's day. The visions of the punishments of Hell which Hildegard recounts in the *Liber Vitae Meritorum* bear resemblance to the work of her contemporary Benedictine, the monk Alberic the younger of Monte Cassino (1101– *c.* 1160), to whom Dante also became indebted.

Hildegard repeatedly assures us that most of her knowledge was revealed to her in waking visions. Some of these, we have seen, had a pathological basis and she was a sufferer from a condition that would nowadays probably be classified as hystero-epilepsy. Too much stress, however, can easily be laid on the ecstatic presentment of her scientific views. Visions, it must be remembered, were a common literary device at the period. Her contemporary Benedictine sister, Elizabeth of Schönau, as well as numerous successors, as for example Gertrude of Robersdorf, adopted the same framework for their message. The use of the vision for this purpose remained popular for centuries, and we may say of these writers, as of Dante, that the visions gave, not the genius nor the poetic inspiration, but the form merely in which they were realized.

PLATE XIV

'RECONSTRUCTED' VISION OF 'THE HEAVENLY CITY'
(Compare Plates XII and XIII.)

From a MS. of Hildegard's *Scivias* at Wiesbaden, written at Bingen about 1180. Note that the visions represented in Plates XII and XIII reappear here. The other parts of this picture are represented separately in other miniatures in the same MS. See page 233.
238]

The contemporaries of Hildegard who provide the closest analogy to her are Elizabeth of Schönau (died 1165), whose visions are recounted in her life by Eckbert, and Herrade de Landsberg, Abbess of Hohenburg in Alsace, the priceless manuscript of whose *Garden of Delights* was destroyed in the siege of Strassburg in 1870. With Elizabeth of Schönau, who lived in her neighbourhood, Hildegard was in frequent correspondence. With Herrade she is not known to have had direct communication ; but the two were contemporaries, lived not very far apart, and under similar political and cultural conditions. Elizabeth's visions present some striking analogies to those of Hildegard, while the figures of Herrade, of which copies have fortunately survived, often suggest the illustrations of the Wiesbaden or of the Lucca manuscripts of the works of Hildegard.

In fine, Hildegard presents us with the science of the Dark Ages just emerging into the Arabian twilight. In spite of the extreme mystical form in which her material is cast, we can discern the Aristotelian and Neoplatonic tendencies which the new Arabian science was conveying to Western Europe. We can perceive in Hildegard something of the nature of a complete and coherent philosophy, which separates her from the ages that went before her. Hildegard's works are heralds of the dawn of a new movement.

# VII

## THE SCHOOL OF SALERNO AND ITS LEGENDS

## § 1.   *Introduction*

THE earliest European institution to develop an organization that bore a semblance to a university is said to have been the medical school at Salerno, an ancient seaport in southern Italy not far from Naples.  For centuries the Byzantine Empire, securely ensconced on the Adriatic sea-board, disputed the mastery of southern Italy with native chiefs, and, from the eighth century onwards, with Saracens also.  The prevailing language of the South remained, even into modern times, a dialect of Greek.  The imperfect grasp of the Byzantines, however, gave an opportunity for the entrance of other tongues.  A Latin speech of a peculiar southern type was spoken in many places ; in others Greek was replaced by some form of Arabic speech.  Nor were Latin, Greek, and Saracen cultures the only competitors.  Material and literary remains combine to tell us of a considerable development of a Jewish culture in this region.

Into this welter of futile and static archaism, of linguistic and cultural strife, three great solvent forces entered. First came the stimulus of Moslem energy and enterprise. Secondly, there was the Norman invasion and conquest, with the resulting reorganization of society and the strengthening of law.  Thirdly, there was Jewish learning and the Jewish habit of syncretizing. The finished product of these forces at Salerno was the first medical school in Europe which flourished in the eleventh and twelfth centuries. But in 1224 a university was formally instituted at Naples by the Emperor Frederick II. This measure was fatal to the neighbouring school, and the importance of Salerno immediately began to wane, although the literary activity of the place continued to some extent, and the school prolonged a progressively more feeble existence to the beginning of the nineteenth century. It gradually became a place of 'bogus degrees.' When Napoleon closed it in 1811, it was but a corpse that he slew.

As with all established things, legends had gathered round the Salernitan School. All ancient institutions tend to develop such stories to account for their origin. The school of Salerno, as we may more than suspect, was never really 'founded' at all, rather it 'just growed.' It was a natural product of certain very peculiar and complex cultural surroundings. To follow all its legends would be quite beyond our purpose; we shall, however, discuss four, of peculiar interest and of peculiar persistence.

## § 2.  *The Four Masters*

The first of our legends relates that ' the school of Salerno was founded by *four masters*, a Greek, a Latin, an Arab, and a Jew.' A book is in existence actually fathered on these ' four masters.' Their historicity was credited until quite modern times, and is assumed in the works of several living historians, though it is generally scouted by critical writers. Yet the idea of the foundation of the school by a Greek, a Latin, an Arab, and a Jew, though not literally true, does correspond, as we have seen, to the mingled influences under which the school arose. Can we associate it with any historical individual? The names mentioned in the legend have not been traced back to any real personages. But there is an historical personage who seems to unite the four masters in himself, and seems to typify-

16

in his own person the influences under which the school of Salerno arose. This is the Jew Donnolo.

The name Donnolo is but a variation of *Domnulus*, a diminutive of *Dominus*, and his full name was Shabbethai ben Abraham ben Joel. He was born near Otranto in 913, and he died there about 984. His life course therefore corresponds to the period which just precedes the time when our records of the medical school of Salerno begin. He represents the legendary stratum. When he was twelve years of age, Donnolo and his family were captured by Moslem raiders, and carried off to Palermo, which had long been under Moslem rule. While a Saracen prisoner Donnolo made his first acquaintance with the Arabic language. After a time he was ransomed by relatives and returned to Otranto, and later he practised medicine there and at Rossano. A considerable fragment has survived of a medical treatise by him. At Otranto Donnolo managed to secure a teacher of Arabic from Baghdad. The fact that he was able to do so bears witness to the mixed character of the population of South Italy at that date. He learned from him the wisdom of the East : he afterwards claimed to have ' studied all the sciences of the Greeks, Arabs, Babylonians, and Indians.'

This hankering after Eastern learning may seem a strange thing to us, but we must recall the circumstances of the times. During the centuries between the eighth and twelfth, the hegemony of the philosophical and scientific world, as of the world of arms and affairs, lay not with Christendom but with Islam, whose sway extended athwart the world from India to the Atlantic [Fig. 32]. Teeming with intellectual activity, this great stretch of lands became united not only by a religion but also by a language. From Andalusia to Persia the tongue of the Koran was used for the purpose of learning and philosophy, and mediaeval Islam thus enjoyed an advantage never attained by any civilization of like extent. In such a civilization there had naturally grown up a portentous accumulation of scientific and medical works. These were based on the heritage of Greek science that Islam had received from ancient Greece, mainly through Syriac sources. In this great Arabic literature advances had been made in some departments, notably in mathematics, though in most departments, as in medicine, the Arabian material was a deterioration from the best Greek standards. Such as it was, however, it was the most effective and most living then available. It was material of this sort that Donnolo studied.

Donnolo's medical work is written in Hebrew, but in a peculiar Hebrew that contains many Arabic idioms and a few Arabic words. The basis of the treatment detailed in it is in many respects that usual in the Arabic medical works of ultimate Greek origin. Of some of the herbs he mentions he gives the Greek form, of others the Latin form—in both cases transliterated into Hebrew. We know, too, both from his own statements and from those of his contemporary St. Nilus of Rossano, that Donnolo had travelled among the Latins.

Have we not therefore here a very personification of the first legend of Salerno ? It is untrue that the school was founded by a Greek, a Latin, an Arab, and a Jew ; but it is true that the four influences that those names represent were at work in South Italy in the tenth century. We find an individual in South Italy practising the art of medicine and exhibiting the influence of all four cultures in his writings. As in so many cases, therefore, we may discern an element of truth at the back of the legend, and may treat it, like many other legends, as but "history misunderstood." It is these four cultural influences, Greek, Latin, Hebrew, and Arabic, that we see being welded together as the first university in Europe emerges into the light of historic day.

## § 3. 'The Ladies of Salerne'

The second legend is that of the ' ladies of Salerne.' The claim has often been maintained that Salerno was quite unique among mediaeval institutions in the free way in which both women and Jews were admitted to its teaching, even in the early period. Alas ! as regards the ' ladies of Salerne ' at least, the cold light of history dissipates the romantic story ! There, as elsewhere in the earlier Middle Ages, women doubtless acted as midwives and nurses, and to this extent they may have been connected with the medical school. But the works to which their names have been connected with such assurance, where are they ? Let us glance at the answer.

A lady of Salerno, known as Trotula, whose life course is placed in the earlier eleventh century, is said to have been the authoress of the only two books by Salernitan women that the ages have spared to us. Her name passed long ago into the fairy-tales as *Dame Trot*, and has been known in every nursery for four hundred years. Alas ! she had no real existence. The treatises by the so-called Trotula are in fact compilations from sources far more ancient than the Middle or even the Dark Ages. The very name *Trotula* is due to a misunderstanding. One Trottus, indeed, there was, a doctor of Salerno, and a mere male. His works, or rather his compilations, were spoken of as *the Trotula*, according to a common habit of the Italian schools. As these works happened to deal with aspects of women's life and contained something of the ' Peeping Tom ' about them, they were naturally mothered on a woman. The situation is not devoid of humour—and thus fades into nothingness the first woman professor whose life a learned medical historian once essayed to write ![1]

## § 4. *The Falsifications of Constantine the African*

We now turn to shatter the reputation of the most considerable and most influential writer that the school of Salerno has produced, Constantinus Afer. The ' High Salernitan ' period, when the fame of the medical school

[1] Salvatore De Renzi, *Collectio Salernitana*, 5 vols. (Naples, 1852–8), i. 149–61.

was at its height, is inaugurated by the works of Constantine the African, of Salerno and Monte Cassino, a Christian convert from Islam, who died in 1087. He is an historical character right enough, and we now have a considerable amount of information about him, most of it by no means to his credit.

The works that bear Constantine's name are all, in fact, versions of the compositions of Greek medical writers, but they are neither translated from the Greek nor are they traditional South Italian material. Some of them he had translated from Arabic writers, altering them considerably for the worse in the process ; of others he gives us the names of the authors, but he gives them falsely ! Many other confusions are to be found in these works of Constantine. Some of these errors, it is evident, were deliberately introduced, with the intention of deceiving. The wiles of Constantine have occupied the attention and exercised the ingenuity of scholars for generations. We are now in the happy position of being able to unmask him. The writer on whom Constantine mainly leaned was Abu Jakub Ishak ben Suleiman al Israeli (died 953), an excellent and respectable Jewish physician who practised in the tenth century, first in Egypt and later in Kairouan, and wrote voluminous Arabic works. He was known to the Latin West as Isaac Judaeus. The further details of the literary depredations of Constantine need not occupy us, for they have been expounded in detail by that most learned of Orientalists, Moritz Steinschneider.

## § 5. *Salerno and the King of England*

There is yet a fourth legend of Salerno, however, with which we must deal faithfully. The most popular medical work ever written is the *Regimen Sanitatis Salerni*. It has been translated into nearly every European and some Asiatic languages. It has run into hundreds of editions. Verses of it are still repeated by herbalists in every country, and it forms the basis of much medical folk-lore. It is a series of verses of mediaeval origin, the received text beginning with the line *Anglorum regi scribit Schola tota Salerni*. This long poem was admirably Englished by Sir John Harrington in the seventeenth century. The introduction runs as follows :

> The Salerne Schoole doth by these lines impart
> All health to Englands King, and doth advise
> From care his head to keepe, from wrath his heart,
> Drink not much wine, sup light, and soone arise.
> When meat is gone, long sitting breedeth smart;
> And after-noone still waking keep your eyes.
> When mov'd you find your selfe to Natures Needs
> Forbeare them not, for that much danger breeds.
> Use three Physicions still ; first Doctor Quiet,
> Next Doctor Merry-man, and Doctor Dyet.

The advice is doubtless admirable. More scepticism may be expressed as to the identity of this English king than as to the wisdom of the restraint urged upon him. We are firmly of the opinion that he is another historical Mrs. 'Arris, fit mate for Trotula herself. Some of the MSS. speak of him as ' Robert.' The older editions—and an undue proportion of the modern ones—identify him with Robert Duke of Normandy (1054 ?–1134), the eldest son of William the Conqueror. On his way back from the Crusade the graceless Robert sojourned a while at Salerno in the years 1099–1100, to be healed of a wound. His stay in the ' Hippocratic city ' is said to have cost him the English crown. It certainly cost him another wound, that of love, for it was there that he fell a victim to the charms of the lady that he married. The ascription of the poem to Robert would refer the work to about the year 1100, and it is usually so dated. This view, however, is untenable.

The Salernitan poem, in the form at present recognized, was certainly put together at a much later date than 1100, and in the period of Salernitan decline. Manuscripts of it are very common, but the earliest known in its present form is from the beginning of the fourteenth century, and in the recension of the Catalan, Arnald of Villanova (1238 ?–1311, pp. 94–5). Arnald was a strange combination of charlatan and genius, who had himself studied at Salerno. He is under strong suspicion—to say the least of it—of having concocted practically the whole thing himself. As for the ascription to the King of England, it would be completely in the manner of the time to inset this as a recommendation of the poem to the reader. Some manuscripts of it are, in fact, dedicated to the ' King of Arragon,' others to the ' King of the Franks,' and others to Charlemagne himself. In these circumstances it is scarcely worth the scholar's while to spend time in the identification of this particular king of England. In the Middle Ages, as now, medicine good enough for the great was held to be more than good enough for the small. The word of an eminent actress or cricketer is held by our advertisements to justify the use of a nerve tonic, a pill, or an ointment. So it was also in the Middle Ages, though the contemporary idea of greatness differed somewhat from ours. After all, these manuscripts had to be sold, and what better way than to attach a king's name to them ? So passes our fourth legend !

But as the legend of *Dame Trot* still rejoices the nursery, so does that of the *Regimen* still console the kitchen and the cottage. The pen of that poet whose name is legion has been busy with the Salernitan verses. One of his best and best-known efforts has been exerted on the introduction to Duke Robert. That passage contains the exquisite lines,

> Si tibi deficiant medici, medici tibi fiant
> Haec tria, mens laeta, requies, moderata diaeta.

These the unknown poet has thus immortalized,

> Joy, Temperance, and Repose
> Slam the door on the doctor's nose.

Classical scholars have assured us that Virgil's tomb is none the worse for never having seen the bones of

Virgil. The important thing, forsooth, is not the fact but the tradition! Such a one would have us believe that a fib ceases to be a fib if it be but old enough. We, on our side, may at least claim that medical advice is certainly none the worse for never having been given to Duke Robert. History permits us to hear little good of that scapegrace, but his remedies will be none the worse—and none the better—for that! The herbs of Salerno still send forth a sweeter savour than his memory.

# INDEX OF NAMES

*Numbers in ordinary type refer to pages. Numbers in heavy type refer to figures or coloured plates.*

# A SHORT HISTORY OF ANATOMY AND PHYSIOLOGY FROM THE GREEKS TO HARVEY (The Evolution of Anatomy)

## by Charles Singer

This corrected edition of a classic work on the history of anatomy and physiology is still the most interesting intermediate study of the subject currently available. It traces the evolution of anatomy from prescientific times through the Greek and Roman periods, the Dark Ages and the Renaissance, up to the age of Harvey and the beginning of modern scientific concepts. Primary attention is centered on individuals, movements and periods that definitely advanced anatomical knowledge.

In the first of four chronological sections, the author considers the period before 50 B.C., in Sicily, Ionia, Athens and Alexandria. He covers the work of Plato, Diocles, Aristotle, Theophrastus, Herophilus and Erasistratus, along with the Alexandrians and their experiments in anatomy and human vivisection. In Part 2, later Roman and Greek anatomical writers are discussed, with emphasis falling upon Galen's anatomical philosophy and achievements and his physiological system. Part 3 deals principally with the rise of the universities and the anatomical work of such figures as Mondino, da Vinci, Berengar, Estienne, Linacre, Sylvius and others. The final section is concerned with Vesalius as artist, humanist, naturalist; with a discussion of his *Fabrica;* and with his rivals and followers up to Harvey. A Vesalian Atlas contains nudes, skeletons and muscle tabulae from the *Epitome* and *Fabrica.*

Revision of 1925 edition entitled THE EVOLUTION OF ANATOMY. Index of names. 20 plates, 270 extremely interesting illustrations of medieval, ancient, renaissance, oriental origin. xii + 209pp. 5⅜ x 8.

T389 Paperbound **$1.50**

# AN INTRODUCTION TO THE STUDY OF EXPERIMENTAL MEDICINE

## by Claude Bernard

Here is the only major work of Claude Bernard now available in English. Ninety years ago, this great French physiologist saw that medicine could be a science rather than an art, and set down his observations in AN INTRODUCTION TO THE STUDY OF EXPERIMENTAL MEDICINE.

This classic of medical science records Bernard's far-reaching efforts to transform physiology into an exact science. Here he explains his principles of scientific research, illustrating them by specific case histories from his own work. He examines frankly the roles of chance and error, and even preliminary false conclusions, in leading eventually to scientific truth; and discusses with equal candor the use of hypothesis. Bernard is considered to be one of the fathers of biochemistry; and much of the modern application of mathematics to biology rests upon a foundation set down by him in this book.

Claude Bernard is remembered today for such major contributions to physiology as the discovery of the vasomotor system; the action of curare, carbon monoxide and other poisons; the functions of the pancreas in digestion; and the glycogenic function of the liver. These considerable achievements give authority to his description of a dedicated scientist attacking his problem some 90 years ago. This account, writes Professor I. Bernard Cohen, in a new Foreword, continues to be "as splendid a statement of the basic features of scientific research as has ever been written."

Translated by Henry C. Greene. Introduction by Lawrence J. Henderson. New Foreword by Professor I. Bernard Cohen of Harvard University. xxv + 266pp. 5⅜ x 8.

T400 Paperbound **$1.50**

# THE ORIGIN OF LIFE
## by A. I. Oparin

This is a classic of biochemistry—the first detailed exposition of the theory that living tissue was preceded upon earth by a long and gradual evolution of nitrogen and carbon compounds. It is still one of the basic works in any science library, as is proved by repeated reference to it in later books and monography.

A historical introduction first covers theories of the origin of life from the Greeks, through the middle ages and Renaissance, to moderns. Three basic theories are examined in light of modern knowledge: that life spontaneously arises perpetually; that life has always been present in the universe as a separate basic substance; that life arose once at some distant period of the earth's past.

Techniques of modern biochemistry are then applied to the problem by Dr. Oparin, and the topic is considered afresh in the following chapters: primary forms of carbon and nitrogen compounds; origin of organic substances, primary proteins; origin of primarily colloidal systems; origin and further evolution of primary organisms.

"Easily the most scholarly authority on the question . . . it will be a landmark for discussion for a long time to come," **NEW YORK TIMES.** "Every physiologist and biochemist should call it to the attention of his students . . . chemists will want to read this volume over and over again," **AMERICAN CHEMICAL SOCIETY JOURNAL**

231-item bibliography, especially strong on Russian and Eastern European publications. 16-page introduction by the translator, S. Morgulis, University of Nebraska, considers later discoveries exemplifying Oparin's theories. Index. xxv + 270pp. 5⅜ x 8.

S213 Paperbound **$1.75**

# ELEMENTS OF MATHEMATICAL BIOLOGY
## by Alfred J. Lotka

Formerly published as ELEMENTS OF PHYSICAL BIOLOGY, this classic work marks the major attempt to apply modern mathematics to the problems of ontology, phylogeny, ecology, physiology, endocrinology, psychology, and other branches of biology. One of the most seminal books ever published in its field, it has had enormous influence upon the later work of such scientists as Norbert Wiener and N. Rashevsky.

Partial contents. Evolution, a system in the course of irreversible transformation. Statistical meaning of irreversibility. Evolution as redistribution. KINETICS: fundamental equations of kinetics of evolving systems. General, special cases. Analysis of the growth function. STATICS. General principles of equilibrium. Chemical equilibrium, inter-species equilibrium, circulation of the elements, the carbon dioxide cycle, the nitrogen cycle, the phosphorus cycle, moving equilibria, displacement of equilibrium, parameters of state. DYNAMICS. Energy transformers of nature, relation of the transformation to available sources, correlating apparatus, adjustors, consciousness, function, origin, energy relations of consciousness. List of publications by A. J. Lotka. 36 tables. Analytical synopsis of chapters. 72 figures. xxx + 460pp. 5⅜ x 8.      Paperbound **$2.95**

# Catalogue of Dover
## SCIENCE BOOKS

### DIFFERENTIAL EQUATIONS
### (ORDINARY AND PARTIAL DIFFERENTIAL)

**INTRODUCTION TO THE DIFFERENTIAL EQUATIONS OF PHYSICS, L. Hopf.** Especially valuable to engineer with no math beyond elementary calculus. Emphasizes intuitive rather than formal aspects of concepts. Partial contents: Law of causality, energy theorem, damped oscillations, coupling by friction, cylindrical and spherical coordinates, heat source, etc. 48 figures. 160pp. 5⅜ x 8.　　　　　　　　　　　　　　　S120 Paperbound **$1.25**

**INTRODUCTION TO BESSEL FUNCTIONS, F. Bowman.** Rigorous, provides all necessary material during development, includes practical applications. Bessel functions of zero order, of any real order, definite integrals, asymptotic expansion, circular membranes, Bessel's solution to Kepler's problem, much more. "Clear . . . useful not only to students of physics and engineering, but to mathematical students in general," Nature. 226 problems. Short tables of Bessel functions. 27 figures. x + 135pp. 5⅜ x 8.　　　　　　S462 Paperbound **$1.35**

**DIFFERENTIAL EQUATIONS, F. R. Moulton.** Detailed, rigorous exposition of all non-elementary processes of solving ordinary differential equations. Chapters on practical problems; more advanced than problems usually given as illustrations. Includes analytic differential equations; variations of a parameter; integrals of differential equations; analytic implicit functions; problems of elliptic motion; sine-amplitude functions; deviation of formal bodies; Cauchy-Lipshitz process; linear differential equations with periodic coefficients; much more. Historical notes. 10 figures. 222 problems. xv + 395pp. 5⅜ x 8.　　S451 Paperbound **$2.00**

**PARTIAL DIFFERENTIAL EQUATIONS OF MATHEMATICAL PHYSICS, A. G. Webster.** Valuable sections on elasticity, compression theory, potential theory, theory of sound, heat conduction, wave propagation, vibration theory. Contents include: deduction of differential equations, vibrations, normal functions, Fourier's series. Cauchy's method, boundary problems, method of Riemann-Volterra, spherical, cylindrical, ellipsoidal harmonics, applications, etc. 97 figures. vii + 440pp. 5⅜ x 8.　　　　　　　　　　　S263 Paperbound **$2.00**

**ORDINARY DIFFERENTIAL EQUATIONS, E. L. Ince.** A most compendious analysis in real and complex domains. Existence and nature of solutions, continuous transformation groups, solutions in an infinite form, definite integrals, algebraic theory. Sturmian theory, boundary problems, existence theorems, 1st order, higher order, etc. "Deserves highest praise, a notable addition to mathematical literature," Bulletin, Amer. Math. Soc. Historical appendix. 18 figures. viii + 558pp. 5⅜ x 8.　　　　　　　　　　S349 Paperbound **$2.55**

**ASYMPTOTIC EXPANSIONS, A. Erdélyi.** Only modern work available in English; unabridged reproduction of monograph prepared for Office of Naval Research. Discusses various procedures for asymptotic evaluation of integrals containing a large parameter; solutions of ordinary linear differential equations. vi + 108pp. 5⅜ x 8.　　S318 Paperbound **$1.35**

**LECTURES ON CAUCHY'S PROBLEM, J. Hadamard.** Based on lectures given at Columbia, Rome, discusses work of Riemann, Kirchhoff, Volterra, and author's own research on hyperbolic case in linear partial differential equations. Extends spherical cylindrical waves to apply to all (normal) hyperbolic equations. Partial contents: Cauchy's problem, fundamental formula, equations with odd number, with even number of independent variables; method of descent. 32 figures. iii + 316pp. 5⅜ x 8.　　　　　　　　S105 Paperbound **$1.75**

# NUMBER THEORY

**INTRODUCTION TO THE THEORY OF NUMBERS, L. E. Dickson.** Thorough, comprehensive, witn adequate coverage of classical literature. Not beyond beginners. Chapters on divisibility, congruences, quadratic residues and reciprocity, Diophantine equations, etc. Full treatment of binary quadratic forms without usual restriction to integral coefficients. Covers infinitude of primes, Fermat's theorem, Legendre's symbol, automorphs, Recent theorems of Thue, Siegal, much more. Much material not readily available elsewhere. 239 problems. 1 figure. viii + 183pp. 5⅜ x 8.  S342 Paperbound **$1.65**

**ELEMENTS OF NUMBER THEORY, I. M. Vinogradov.** Detailed 1st course for persons without advanced mathematics; 95% of this book can be understood by readers who have gone no farther than high school algebra. Partial contents: divisibility theory, important number theoretical functions, congruences, primitive roots and indices, etc. Solutions to problems, exercises. Tables of primes, indices, etc. Covers almost every essential formula in elementary number theory! "Welcome addition . . . reads smoothly," Bull. of the Amer. Math. Soc. 233 problems. 104 exercises. viii + 227pp. 5⅜ x 8.  S259 Paperbound **$1.60**

# PROBABILITY THEORY AND INFORMATION THEORY

**SELECTED PAPERS ON NOISE AND STOCHASTIC PROCESSES,** edited by Prof. Nelson Wax, U. of Illinois. 6 basic papers for those whose work involves noise characteristics. Chandrasekhar, Uhlenback and Ornstein, Uhlenbeck and Ming, Rice, Doob. Included is Kac's Chauvenet-Prize winning "Random Walk." Extensive bibliography lists 200 articles, through 1953. 21 figures. 337pp. 6⅛ x 9¼.  S262 Paperbound **$2.35**

**A PHILOSOPHICAL ESSAY ON PROBABILITIES, Marquis de Laplace.** This famous essay explains without recourse to mathematics the principle of probability, and the application of probabiilty to games of chance, natural philosophy, astronomy, many other fields. Translated from 6th French edition by F. W. Truscott, F. L. Emory. Intro. by E. T. Bell. 204pp. 5⅜ x 8.  S166 Paperbound **$1.25**

**MATHEMATICAL FOUNDATIONS OF INFORMATION THEORY, A. I. Khinchin.** For mathematicians, statisticians, physicists, cyberneticists, communications engineers, a complete, exact introduction to relatively new field. Entropy as a measure of a finite scheme, applications to coding theory, study of sources, channels and codes, detailed proofs of both Shannon theorems for any ergodic source and any stationary channel with finite memory, much more. "Presents for the first time rigorous proofs of certain fundamental theorems . . . quite complete . . . amazing expository ability," American Math. Monthly. vii + 120pp. 5⅜ x 8.  S434 Paperbound **$1.35**

# VECTOR AND TENSOR ANALYSIS AND MATRIX THEORY

**VECTOR AND TENSOR ANALYSIS, G. E. Hay.** One of clearest introductions to increasingly important subject. Start with simple definitions, finish with sure mastery of oriented Cartesian vectors, Christoffel symbols, solenoidal tensors. Complete breakdown of plane, solid, analytical, differential geometry. Separate chapters on application. All fundamental formulae listed, demonstrated. 195 problems. 66 figures. viii + 193pp. 5⅜ x 8.  S109 Paperbound **$1.75**

**APPLICATIONS OF TENSOR ANALYSIS, A. J. McConnell.** Excellent text for applying tensor methods to such familiar subjects as dynamics, electricity, elasticity, hydrodynamics. Explains fundamental ideas and notation of tensor theory, geometrical treatment of tensor algebra, theory of differentiation of tensors, and a wealth of practical material. "The variety of fields treated and the presence of extremely numerous examples make this volume worth much more than its low price," Alluminio. Formerly titled "Applications of the Absolute Differential Calculus." 43 illustrations. 685 problems. xii + 381pp.  S373 Paperbound **$1.85**

**VECTOR AND TENSOR ANALYSIS, A. P. Wills.** Covers entire field, from dyads to non-Euclidean manifolds (especially detailed), absolute differentiation, the Riemann-Christoffel and Ricci-Einstein tensors, calculation of Gaussian curvature of a surface. Illustrations from electrical engineering, relativity theory, astro-physics, quantum mechanics. Presupposes only working knowledge of calculus. Intended for physicists, engineers, mathematicians. 44 diagrams. 114 problems. xxxii + 285pp. 5⅜ x 8.  S454 Paperbound **$1.75**

2

# DOVER SCIENCE BOOKS

# PHYSICS, ENGINEERING

## MECHANICS, DYNAMICS, THERMODYNAMICS, ELASTICITY

**MATHEMATICAL ANALYSIS OF ELECTRICAL AND OPTICAL WAVE-MOTION, H. Bateman.** By one of century's most distinguished mathematical physicists, a practical introduction to developments of Maxwell's electromagnetic theory which directly concern the solution of partial differential equation of wave motion. Methods of solving wave-equation, polar-cylindrical coordinates, diffraction, transformation of coordinates, homogeneous solutions, electromagnetic fields with moving singularities, etc. 168pp. 5⅜ x 8. S14 Paperbound **$1.60**

**THERMODYNAMICS, Enrico Fermi.** Unabridged reproduction of 1937 edition. Remarkable for clarity, organization; requires no knowledge of advanced math beyond calculus, only familiarity with fundamentals of thermometry, calorimetry. Partial Contents: Thermodynamic systems, 1st and 2nd laws, potentials; Entropy, phase rule; Reversible electric cells; Gaseous reactions: Van't Hoff reaction box, principle of LeChatelier; Thermodynamics of dilute solutions: osmotic, vapor pressures; boiling, freezing point; Entropy constant. 25 problems. 24 illustrations. x + 160pp. 5⅜ x 8. S361 Paperbound **$1.75**

**FOUNDATIONS OF POTENTIAL THEORY, O. D. Kellogg.** Based on courses given at Harvard, suitable for both advanced and beginning mathematicians. Proofs rigorous, much material here not generally available elsewhere. Partial contents: gravity, fields of force, divergence theorem, properties of Newtonian potentials at points of free space, potentials as solutions of LaPlace's equation, harmonic functions, electrostatics, electric images, logarithmic potential, etc. ix + 384pp. 5⅜ x 8. S144 Paperbound **$1.98**

**DIALOGUES CONCERNING TWO NEW SCIENCES, Galileo Galilei.** Classic of experimental science, mechanics, engineering, as enjoyable as it is important. Characterized by author as "superior to everything else of mine." Offers a lively exposition of dynamics, elasticity, sound, ballistics, strength of materials, scientific method. Translated by H. Grew, A. de Salvio. 126 diagrams. xxi + 288pp. 5⅜ x 8. S99 Paperbound **$1.65**

**THEORETICAL MECHANICS; AN INTRODUCTION TO MATHEMATICAL PHYSICS, J. S. Ames, F. D. Murnaghan.** A mathematically rigorous development for advanced students, with constant practical applications. Used in hundreds of advanced courses. Unusually thorough coverage of gyroscopic baryscopic material, detailed analyses of Corilis acceleration, applications of Lagrange's equations, motion of double pendulum, Hamilton-Jacobi partial differential equations, group velocity, dispersion, etc. Special relativity included. 159 problems. 44 figures. ix + 462pp. 5⅜ x 8. S461 Paperbound **$2.00**

**STATICS AND THE DYNAMICS OF A PARTICLE, W. D. MacMillan.** This is Part One of "Theoretical Mechanics." For over 3 decades a self-contained, extremely comprehensive advanced undergraduate text in mathematical physics, physics, astronomy, deeper foundations of engineering. Early sections require only a knowledge of geometry; later, a working knowledge of calculus. Hundreds of basic problems including projectiles to moon, harmonic motion, ballistics, transmission of power, stress and strain, elasticity, astronomical problems. 340 practice problems, many fully worked out examples. 200 figures. xvii + 430pp. 5⅜ x 8. S467 Paperbound **$2.00**

**THE THEORY OF THE POTENTIAL, W. D. MacMillan.** This is Part Two of "Theoretical Mechanics." Comprehensive, well-balanced presentation, serving both as introduction and reference with regard to specific problems, for physicists and mathematicians. Assumes no prior knowledge of integral relations, all math is developed as needed. Includes: Attraction of Finite Bodies; Newtonian Potential Function; Vector Fields, Green and Gauss Theorems; Two-layer Surfaces; Spherical Harmonics; etc. "The great number of particular cases . . . should make the book valuable to geo-physicists and others actively engaged in practical applications of the potential theory," Review of Scientific Instruments. xii + 469pp. 5⅜ x 8. S486 Paperbound **$2.25**

**DYNAMICS OF A SYSTEM OF RIGID BODIES (Advanced Section), E. J. Routh.** Revised 6th edition of a classic reference aid. Partial contents: moving axes, relative motion, oscillations about equilibrium, motion. Motion of a body under no forces, any forces. Nature of motion given by linear equations and conditions of stability. Free, forced vibrations, constants of integration, calculus of finite differences, variations, procession and mutation, motion of the moon, motion of string, chain, membranes. 64 figures. 498pp. 5⅜ x 8. S229 Paperbound **$2.35**

**THE DYNAMICS OF PARTICLES AND OF RIGID, ELASTIC, AND FLUID BODIES: BEING LECTURES ON MATHEMATICAL PHYSICS, A. G. Webster.** Reissuing of classic fills need for comprehensive work on dynamics. Covers wide range in unusually great depth, applying ordinary, partial differential equations. Partial contents: laws of motion, methods applicable to systems of all sorts; oscillation, resonance, cyclic systems; dynamics of rigid bodies; potential theory; stress and strain; gyrostatics; wave, vortex motion; kinematics of a point; Lagrange's equations; Hamilton's principle; vectors; deformable bodies; much more not easily found together in one volume. Unabridged reprinting of 2nd edition. 20 pages on differential equations, higher analysis. 203 illustrations. xi + 588pp. 5⅜ x 8. S522 Paperbound **$2.35**

3

**PRINCIPLES OF MECHANICS, Heinrich Hertz.** A classic of great interest in logic of science. Last work by great 19th century physicist, created new system of mechanics based upon space, time, mass; returns to axiomatic analysis, understanding of formal, structural aspects of science, taking into account logic, observation, a priori elements. Of great historical importance to Poincaré, Carnap, Einstein, Milne. 20 page introduction by R. S. Cohen, Wesleyan U., analyzes implications of Hertz's thought and logic of science. 13 page introduction by Helmholtz. xlii + 274pp. 5⅜ x 8.                            S316 Clothbound **$3.50**
                                                                                                                            S317 Paperbound **$1.75**

**MATHEMATICAL FOUNDATIONS OF STATISTICAL MECHANICS, A. I. Khinchin.** A thoroughly up-to-date introduction, offering a precise and mathematically rigorous formulation of the problems of statistical mechanics. Provides analytical tools to replace many commonly used cumbersome concepts and devices. Partial contents: Geometry, kinematics of phase space; ergodic problem; theory of probability; central limit theorem; ideal monatomic gas; foundation of thermodynamics; dispersion, distribution of sum functions; etc. "Excellent introduction . . . clear, concise, rigorous," Quarterly of Applied Mathematics. viii + 179pp. 5⅜ x 8.                                                                          S146 Clothbound **$2.95**
                                                                                                                            S147 Paperbound **$1.35**

**MECHANICS OF THE GYROSCOPE, THE DYNAMICS OF ROTATION, R. F. Deimel,** Prof. of Mechanical Engineering, Stevens Inst. of Tech. Elementary, general treatment of dynamics of rotation, with special application of gyroscopic phenomena. No knowledge of vectors needed. Velocity of a moving curve, acceleration to a point, general equations of motion, gyroscopic horizon, free gyro, motion of discs, the damped gyro, 103 similar topics. Exercises. 75 figures. 208pp. 5⅜ x 8.                                            S66 Paperbound **$1.65**

**MECHANICS VIA THE CALCULUS, P. W. Norris, W. S. Legge.** Wide coverage, from linear motion to vector analysis; equations determining motion, linear methods, compounding of simple harmonic motions, Newton's laws of motion, Hooke's law, the simple pendulum, motion of a particle in 1 plane, centers of gravity, virtual work, friction, kinetic energy of rotating bodies, equilibrium of strings, hydrostatics, sheering stresses, elasticity, etc. Many worked-out examples. 550 problems. 3rd revised edition. xii + 367pp.          S207 Clothbound **$3.95**

**A TREATISE ON THE MATHEMATICAL THEORY OF ELASTICITY, A. E. H. Love.** An indispensable reference work for engineers, mathematicians, physicists, the most complete, authoritative treatment of classical elasticity in one volume. Proceeds from elementary notions of extension to types of strain, cubical dilatation, general theory of strains. Covers relation between mathematical theory of elasticity and technical mechanics; equilibrium of isotropic elastic solids and aelotropic solid bodies; nature of force transmission, Volterra's theory of dislocations; theory of elastic spheres in relation to tidal, rotational, gravitational effects on earth; general theory of bending; deformation of curved plates; buckling effects; much more. "The standard treatise on elasticity," American Math. Monthly. 4th revised edition. 76 figures. xviii + 643pp. 6⅛ x 9¼.                                S174 Paperbound **$2.95**

# NUCLEAR PHYSICS, QUANTUM THEORY, RELATIVITY

**MESON PHYSICS, R. E. Marshak.** Presents basic theory, and results of experiments with emphasis on theoretical significance. Phenomena involving mesons as virtual transitions avoided, eliminating some of least satisfactory predictions of meson theory. Includes production study of $\pi$ mesons at nonrelativistic nucleon energies contracts between $\pi$ and $u$ mesons, phenomena associated with nuclear interaction of $\pi$ mesons, etc. Presents early evidence for new classes of particles, indicates theoretical difficulties created by discovery of heavy mesons and hyperons. viii + 378pp. 5⅜ x 8.                S500 Paperbound **$1.95**

**THE FUNDAMENTAL PRINCIPLES OF QUANTUM MECHANICS, WITH ELEMENTARY APPLICATIONS, E. C. Kemble.** Inductive presentation, for graduate student, specialists in other branches of physics. Apparatus necessary beyond differential equations and advanced calculus developed as needed. Though general exposition of principles, hundreds of individual problems fully treated. "Excellent book . . . of great value to every student . . . rigorous and detailed mathematical discussion . .. has succeeded in keeping his presentation clear and understandable," Dr. Linus Pauling, J. of American Chemical Society. Appendices: calculus of variations, math. notes, etc. 611pp. 5⅝ x 8⅜.                              T472 Paperbound **$2.95**

**WAVE PROPAGATION IN PERIODIC STRUCTURES, L. Brillouin.** General method, application to different problems: pure physics—scattering of X-rays in crystals, thermal vibration in crystal lattices, electronic motion in metals; problems in electrical engineering. Partial contents: elastic waves along 1-dimensional lattices of point masses. Propagation of waves along 1-dimensional lattices. Energy flow. 2, 3 dimensional lattices. Mathieu's equation. Matrices and propagation of waves along an electric line. Continuous electric lines. 131 illustrations. xii + 253pp. 5⅜ x 8.                                        S34 Paperbound **$1.85**

4

# DOVER SCIENCE BOOKS

**THEORY OF ELECTRONS AND ITS APPLICATION TO THE PHENOMENA OF LIGHT AND RADIANT HEAT, H. Lorentz.** Lectures delivered at Columbia Univ., by Nobel laureate. Unabridged, form historical coverage of theory of free electrons, motion, absorption of heat, Zeeman effect, optical phenomena in moving bodies, etc. 109 pages notes explain more advanced sections. 9 figures. 352pp. 5⅜ x 8.                                                                 S173 Paperbound **$1.85**

**SELECTED PAPERS ON QUANTUM ELECTRODYNAMICS, edited by J. Schwinger.** Facsimiles of papers which established quantum electrodynamics; beginning to present position as part of larger theory. First book publication in any language of collected papers of Bethe, Bloch, Dirac, Dyson, Fermi, Feynman, Heisenberg, Kusch, Lamb, Oppenheimer, Pauli, Schwinger, Tomonoga, Weisskopf, Wigner, etc. 34 papers: 29 in English, 1 in French, 3 in German, 1 in Italian. Historical commentary by editor. xvii + 423pp. 6⅛ x 9¼.
S444 Paperbound **$2.45**

**FOUNDATIONS OF NUCLEAR PHYSICS, edited by R. T. Beyer.** 13 of the most important papers on nuclear physics reproduced in facsimile in the original languages; the papers most often cited in footnotes, bibliographies. Anderson, Curie, Joliot, Chadwick, Fermi, Lawrence, Cockroft, Hahn, Yukawa. Unparalleled bibliography: 122 double columned pages, over 4,000 articles, books, classified. 57 figures. 288pp. 6⅛ x 9¼.                            S19 Paperbound **$1.75**

**THE THEORY OF GROUPS AND QUANTUM MECHANICS, H. Weyl.** Schroedinger's wave equation, de Broglie's waves of a particle, Jordon-Hoelder theorem, Lie's continuous groups of transformations, Pauli exclusion principle, quantization of Mawell-Dirac field equations, etc. Unitary geometry, quantum theory, groups, application of groups to quantum mechanics, symmetry permutation group, algebra of symmetric transformations, etc. 2nd revised edition. xxii + 422pp. 5⅜ x 8.                                                      S268 Clothbound **$4.50**
S269 Paperbound **$1.95**

**PHYSICAL PRINCIPLES OF THE QUANTUM THEORY, Werner Heisenberg.** Nobel laureate discusses quantum theory; his own work, Compton, Schroedinger, Wilson, Einstein, many others. For physicists, chemists, not specialists in quantum theory. Only elementary formulae considered in text; mathematical appendix for specialists. Profound without sacrificing clarity. Translated by C. Eckart, F. Hoyt. 18 figures. 192pp. 5⅜ x 8.
S113 Paperbound **$1.25**

**INVESTIGATIONS ON THE THEORY OF THE BROWNIAN MOVEMENT, Albert Einstein.** Reprints from rare European journals, translated into English. 5 basic papers, including Elementary Theory of the Brownian Movement, written at request of Lorentz to provide a simple explanation. Translated by A. D. Cowper. Annotated, edited by R. Fürth. 33pp. of notes elucidate, give history of previous investigations. 62 footnotes. 124pp. 5⅜ x 8.
S304 Paperbound **$1.25**

**THE PRINCIPLE OF RELATIVITY, E. Einstein, H. Lorentz, M. Minkowski, H. Weyl.** The 11 basic papers that founded the general and special theories of relativity, translated into English. 2 papers by Lorentz on the Michelson experiment, electromagnetic phenomena. Minkowski's "Space and Time," and Weyl's "Gravitation and Electricity." 7 epoch-making papers by Einstein: "Electromagnetics of Moving Bodies," "Influence of Gravitation in Propagation of Light," "Cosmological Considerations," "General Theory," 3 others. 7 diagrams. Special notes by A. Sommerfeld. 224pp. 5⅜ x 8.                                               S93 Paperbound **$1.75**


# STATISTICS

**ELEMENTARY STATISTICS, WITH APPLICATIONS IN MEDICINE AND THE BIOLOGICAL SCIENCES, F. E. Croxton.** Based primarily on biological sciences, but can be used by anyone desiring introduction to statistics. Assumes no prior acquaintance, requires only modest knowledge of math. All basic formulas carefully explained, illustrated; all necessary reference tables included. From basic terms and concepts, proceeds to frequency distribution, linear, nonlinear, multiple correlation, etc. Contains concrete examples from medicine, biology. 101 charts. 57 tables. 14 appendices. lv + 376pp. 5⅜ x 8.                        S506 Paperbound **$1.95**

**ANALYSIS AND DESIGN OF EXPERIMENTS, H. B. Mann.** Offers method for grasping analysis of variance, variance design quickly. Partial contents: Chi-square distribution, analysis of variance distribution, matrices, quadratic forms, likelihood ration tests, test of linear hypotheses, power of analysis, Galois fields, non-orthogonal data, interblock estimates, etc. 15pp. of useful tables. x + 195pp. 5 x 7⅜.                                          S180 Paperbound **$1.45**

**FREQUENCY CURVES AND CORRELATION, W. P. Elderton.** 4th revised edition of standard work on classical statistics. Practical, one of few books constantly referred to for clear presentation of basic material. Partial contents: Frequency Distributions; Pearsons Frequency Curves; Theoretical Distributions; Standard Errors; Correlation Ratio—Contingency; Corrections for Moments, Beta, Gamma Functions; etc. Key to terms, symbols. 25 examples. 40 tables. 16 figures. xi + 272pp. 5½ x 8½.                                     Clothbound **$1.49**

5

# HYDRODYNAMICS, ETC.

**HYDRODYNAMICS, Horace Lamb.** Standard reference work on dynamics of liquids and gases. Fundamental theorems, equations, methods, solutions, background for classical hydrodynamics. Chapters: Equations of Motion, Integration of Equations in Special Gases, Vortex Motion, Tidal Waves, Rotating Masses of Liquids, etc. Excellently planned, arranged, Clear, lucid presentation. 6th enlarged, revised edition. Over 900 footnotes, mostly bibliographical. 119 figures. xv + 738pp. 6⅛ x 9¼. S256 Paperbound **$2.95**

**HYDRODYNAMICS, A STUDY OF LOGIC, FACT, AND SIMILITUDE, Garrett Birkhoff.** A stimulating application of pure mathematics to an applied problem. Emphasis is on correlation of theory and deduction with experiment. Examines recently discovered paradoxes, theory of modelling and dimensional analysis, paradox and error in flows and free boundary theory. Classical theory of virtual mass derived from homogenous spaces; group theory applied to fluid mechanics. 20 figures, 3 plates. xiii + 186pp. 5⅜ x 8. S22 Paperbound **$1.85**

**HYDRODYNAMICS, H. Dryden, F. Murhaghan, H. Bateman.** Published by National Research Council, 1932. Complete coverage of classical hydrodynamics, encyclopedic in quality. Partial contents: physics of fluids, motion, turbulent flow, compressible fluids, motion in 1, 2, 3 dimensions; laminar motion, resistance of motion through viscous fluid, eddy viscosity, discharge of gases, flow past obstacles, etc. Over 2900-item bibliography. 23 figures. 634pp. 5⅜ x 8. S303 Paperbound **$2.75**

# ACOUSTICS AND OPTICS

**PRINCIPLES OF PHYSICAL OPTICS, Ernst Mach.** Classical examination of propagation of light, color, polarization, etc. Historical, philosophical treatment unequalled for breadth and readability. Contents: Rectilinear propagation, reflection, refraction, dioptrics, composition of light, periodicity, theory of interference, polarization, mathematical representation of properties, etc. 279 illustrations. 10 portraits. 324pp. 5⅜ x 8. S170 Paperbound $1.75

**THE THEORY OF SOUND, Lord Rayleigh.** Written by Nobel laureate, classical methods here will cover most vibrating systems likely to be encountered in practice. Complete coverage of experimental, mathematical aspects. Partial contents: Harmonic motions, lateral vibrations of bars, curved plates or shells, applications of Laplace's functions to acoustical problems, fluid friction, etc. First low-priced edition of this great reference-study work. Historical introduction by R. B. Lindsay. 1040pp. 97 figures. 5⅜ x 8.
S292, S293, Two volume set, paperbound **$4.00**

**THEORY OF VIBRATIONS, N. W. McLachlan.** Based on exceptionally successful graduate course, Brown University. Discusses linear systems having 1 degree of freedom, forced vibrations of simple linear systems, vibration of flexible strings, transverse vibrations of bars and tubes, of circular plate, sound waves of finite amplitude, etc. 99 diagrams. 160pp. 5⅜ x 8. S190 Paperbound **$1.35**

**APPLIED OPTICS AND OPTICAL DESIGN, A. E. Conrady.** Thorough systematic presentation of physical and mathematical aspects, limited mostly to "real optics." Stresses practical problem of maximum aberration permissible without affecting performance. Ordinary ray tracing methods; complete theory ray tracing methods, primary aberrations; enough higher aberration to design telescopes, low powered microscopes, photographic equipment. Covers fundamental equations, extra-axial image points, transverse chromatic aberration, angular magnification, similar topics. Tables of functions of N. Over 150 diagrams. x + 518pp. 5⅜ x 8⅝. S366 Paperbound **$2.98**

**RAYLEIGH'S PRINCIPLE AND ITS APPLICATIONS TO ENGINEERING, G. Temple, W. Bickley.** Rayleigh's principle developed to provide upper, lower estimates of true value of fundamental period of vibrating system, or condition of stability of elastic system. Examples, rigorous proofs. Partial contents: Energy method of discussing vibrations, stability. Perturbation theory, whirling of uniform shafts. Proof, accuracy, successive approximations, applications of Rayleigh's theory. Numerical, graphical methods. Ritz's method. 22 figures. ix + 156pp. 5⅜ x 8. S307 Paperbound **$1.50**

**OPTICKS, Sir Isaac Newton.** In its discussion of light, reflection, color, refraction, theories of wave and corpuscular theories of light, this work is packed with scores of insights and discoveries. In its precise and practical discussions of construction of optical apparatus, contemporary understanding of phenomena, it is truly fascinating to modern scientists. Foreword by Albert Einstein. Preface by I. B. Cohen, Harvard. 7 pages of portraits, facsimile pages, letters, etc. cxvi + 414pp. 5⅜ x 8. S205 Paperbound **$2.00**

# DOVER SCIENCE BOOKS

**ON THE SENSATIONS OF TONE, Hermann Helmholtz.** Using acoustical physics, physiology, experiment, history of music, covers entire gamut of musical tone: relation of music science to acoustics, physical vs. physiological acoustics, vibration, resonance, tonality, progression of parts, etc. 33 appendixes on various aspects of sound, physics, acoustics, music, etc. Translated by A. J. Ellis. New introduction by H. Margenau, Yale. 68 figures. 43 musical passages analyzed. Over 100 tables. xix + 576pp. 6⅛ x 9¼.
S114 Clothbound **$4.95**

## ELECTROMAGNETICS, ENGINEERING, TECHNOLOGY

**INTRODUCTION TO RELAXATION METHODS, F. S. Shaw.** Describes almost all manipulative resources of value in solution of differential equations. Treatment is mathematical rather than physical. Extends general computational process to include almost all branches of applied math and physics. Approximate numerical methods are demonstrated, although high accuracy is obtainable without undue expenditure of time. 48pp. of tables for computing irregular star first and second derivatives, irregular star coefficients for second order equations, for fourth order equations. "Useful. . . . exposition is clear, simple . . . no previous acquaintance with numerical methods is assumed," Science Progress. 253 diagrams. 72 tables. 400pp. 5⅜ x 8.
S244 Paperbound **$2.45**

**THE ELECTROMAGNETIC FIELD, M. Mason, W. Weaver.** Used constantly by graduate engineers. Vector methods exclusively; detailed treatment of electrostatics, expansion methods, with tables converting any quantity into absolute electromagnetic, absolute electrostatic, practical units. Discrete charges, ponderable bodies. Maxwell field equations, etc. 416pp. 5⅜ x 8.
S185 Paperbound **$2.00**

**ELASTICITY, PLASTICITY AND STRUCTURE OF MATTER, R. Houwink.** Standard treatise on rheological aspects of different technically important solids: crystals, resins, textiles, rubber, clay, etc. Investigates general laws for deformations; determines divergences. Covers general physical and mathematical aspects of plasticity, elasticity, viscosity. Detailed examination of deformations, internal structure of matter in relation to elastic, plastic behaviour, formation of solid matter from a fluid, etc. Treats glass, asphalt, balata, proteins, baker's dough, others. 2nd revised, enlarged edition. Extensive revised bibliography in over 500 footnotes. 214 figures. xvii + 368pp. 6 x 9¼.
S385 Paperbound **$2.45**

**DESIGN AND USE OF INSTRUMENTS AND ACCURATE MECHANISM, T. N. Whitehead.** For the instrument designer, engineer; how to combine necessary mathematical abstractions with independent observations of actual facts. Partial contents: instruments and their parts, theory of errors, systematic errors, probability, short period errors, erratic errors, design precision, kinematic, semikinematic design, stiffness, planning of an instrument, human factor, etc. 85 photos, diagrams. xii + 288pp. 5⅜ x 8.
S270 Paperbound **$1.95**

**APPLIED HYDRO- AND AEROMECHANICS, L. Prandtl, O. G. Tietjens.** Presents, for most part, methods valuable to engineers. Flow in pipes, boundary layers, airfoil theory, entry conditions, turbulent flow, boundary layer, determining drag from pressure and velocity, etc. "Will be welcomed by all students of aerodynamics," Nature. Unabridged, unaltered. An Engineering Society Monograph, 1934. Index. 226 figures. 28 photographic plates illustrating flow patterns. xvi + 311pp. 5⅜ x 8.
S375 Paperbound **$1.85**

**FUNDAMENTALS OF HYDRO- AND AEROMECHANICS, L. Prandtl, O. G. Tietjens.** Standard work, based on Prandtl's lectures at Goettingen. Wherever possible hydrodynamics theory is referred to practical considerations in hydraulics, unifying theory and experience. Presentation extremely clear. Though primarily physical, proofs are rigorous and use vector analysis to a great extent. An Engineering Society Monograph, 1934. "Still recommended as an excellent introduction to this area," Physikalische Blätter. 186 figures. xvi + 270pp. 5⅜ x 8.
S374 Paperbound **$1.85**

**GASEOUS CONDUCTORS: THEORY AND ENGINEERING APPLICATIONS, J. D. Cobine.** Indispensable text, reference, to gaseous conduction phenomena, with engineering viewpoint prevailing throughout. Studies kinetic theory of gases, ionization, emission phenomena; gas breakdown, spark characteristics, glow, discharges; engineering applications in circuit interrupters, rectifiers, etc. Detailed treatment of high pressure arcs (Suits); low pressure arcs (Langmuir, Tonks). Much more. "Well organized, clear, straightforward," Tonks, Review of Scientific Instruments. 83 practice problems. Over 600 figures. 58 tables. xx + 606pp. 5⅜ x 8.
S442 Paperbound **$2.75**

**PHOTOELASTICITY: PRINCIPLES AND METHODS, H. T. Jessop, F. C. Harris.** For engineer, specific problems of stress analysis. Latest time-saving methods of checking calculations in 2-dimensional design problems, new techniques for stresses in 3 dimensions, lucid description of optical systems used in practical photoelectricity. Useful suggestions, hints based on on-the-job experience included. Partial contents: strain, stress-strain relations, circular disc under thrust along diameter, rectangular block with square hold under vertical thrust, simply supported rectangular beam under central concentrated load, etc. Theory held to minimum, no advanced mathematical training needed. 164 illustrations. viii + 184pp. 6⅛ x 9¼.
S137 Clothbound **$3.75**

7

**MICROWAVE TRANSMISSION DESIGN DATA, T. Moreno.** Originally classified, now rewritten, enlarged (14 new chapters) under auspices of Sperry Corp. Of immediate value or reference use to radio engineers, systems designers, applied physicists, etc. Ordinary transmission line theory; attenuation; parameters of coaxial lines; flexible cables; tuneable wave guide impedance transformers; effects of temperature, humidity; much more. "Packed with information . . . theoretical discussions are directly related to practical questions," U. of Royal Naval Scientific Service. Tables of dielectrics, flexible cable, etc. ix + 248pp. 5⅜ x 8.
S549 Paperbound **$1.50**

**THE THEORY OF THE PROPERTIES OF METALS AND ALLOYS, H. F. Mott, H. Jones.** Quantum methods develop mathematical models showing interrelationship of fundamental chemical phenomena wtih crystal structure, electrical, optical properties, etc. Examines electron motion in applied field, cohesion, heat capacity, refraction, noble metals, transition and di-valent metals, etc. "Exposition is as clear . . . mathematical treatment as simple and reliable as we have become used to expect of . . . Prof. Mott," Nature. 138 figures. xiii + 320pp. 5⅜ x 8.
S456 Paperbound **$1.85**

**THE MEASUREMENT OF POWER SPECTRA FROM THE POINT OF VIEW OF COMMUNICATIONS ENGINEERING, R. B. Blackman, J. W. Tukey.** Pathfinding work reprinted from "Bell System Technical Journal." Various ways of getting practically useful answers in power spectra measurement, using results from both transmission and statistical estimation theory. Treats: Autocovariance, Functions and Power Spectra, Distortion, Heterodyne Filtering, Smoothing, Decimation Procedures, Transversal Filtering, much more. Appendix reviews fundamental Fourier techniques. Index of notation. Glossary of terms. 24 figures. 12 tables. 192pp. 5⅜ x 8⅝.
S507 Paperbound **$1.85**

**TREATISE ON ELECTRICITY AND MAGNETISM, James Clerk Maxwell.** For more than 80 years a seemingly inexhaustible source of leads for physicists, mathematicians, engineers. Total of 1082pp. on such topics as Measurement of Quantities, Electrostatics, Elementary Mathematical Theory of Electricity, Electrical Work and Energy in a System of Conductors, General Theorems, Theory of Electrical Images, Electrolysis, Conduction, Polarization, Dielectrics, Resistance, much more. "The greatest mathematical physicist since Newton," Sir James Jeans. 3rd edition. 107 figures, 21 plates. 1082pp. 5⅜ x 8.
S186 Clothbound **$4.95**

# CHEMISTRY AND PHYSICAL CHEMISTRY

**THE PHASE RULE AND ITS APPLICATIONS, Alexander Findlay.** Covers chemical phenomena of 1 to 4 multiple component systems, the "standard work on the subject" (Nature). Completely revised, brought up to date by A. N. Campbell, N. O. Smith. New material on binary, tertiary liquid equilibria, solid solutions in ternary systems, quinary systems of salts, water, etc. Completely revised to triangular coordinates in ternary systems, clarified graphic representation, solid models, etc. 9th revised edition. 236 figures. 505 footnotes, mostly bibliographic. xii + 449pp. 5⅜ x 8.
S92 Paperbound **$2.45**

**DYNAMICAL THEORY OF GASES, James Jeans.** Divided into mathematical, physical chapters for convenience of those not expert in mathematics. Discusses mathematical theory of gas in steady state, thermodynamics, Bolzmann, Maxwell, kinetic theory, quantum theory, exponentials, etc. "One of the classics of scientific writing . . . as lucid and comprehensive an exposition of the kinetic theory as has ever been written," J. of Institute of Engineers. 4th enlarged edition, with new material on quantum theory, quantum dynamics, etc. 28 figures. 444pp. 6⅛ x 9¼.
S136 Paperbound **$2.45**

**POLAR MOLECULES, Pieter Debye.** Nobel laureate offers complete guide to fundamental electrostatic field relations, polarizability, molecular structure. Partial contents: electric intensity, displacement, force, polarization by orientation, molar polarization, molar refraction, halogen-hydrides, polar liquids, ionic saturation, dielectric constant, etc. Special chapter considers quantum theory. "Clear and concise . . . coordination of experimental results with theory will be readily appreciated," Electronics Industries. 172pp. 5⅜ x 8.
S63 Clothbound **$3.50**
S64 Paperbound **$1.50**

**ATOMIC SPECTRA AND ATOMIC STRUCTURE, G. Herzberg.** Excellent general survey for chemists, physicists specializing in other fields. Partial contents: simplest line spectra, elements of atomic theory; multiple structure of line spectra, electron spin; building-up principle, periodic system of elements; finer details of atomic spectra; hyperfine structure of spectral lines; some experimental results and applications. 80 figures. 20 tables. xiii + 257pp. 5⅜ x 8.
S115 Paperbound **$1.95**

**TREATISE ON THERMODYNAMICS, Max Planck.** Classic based on his original papers. Brilliant concepts of Nobel laureate make no assumptions regarding nature of heat, rejects earlier approaches of Helmholtz, Maxwell, to offer uniform point of view for entire field. Seminal work by founder of quantum theory, deducing new physical, chemical laws. A standard text, an excellent introduction to field for students with knowledge of elementary chemistry, physics, calculus. 3rd English edition. xvi + 297pp. 5⅜ x 8.
S219 Paperbound **$1.75**

# DOVER SCIENCE BOOKS

**KINETIC THEORY OF LIQUIDS, J. Frenkel.** Regards kinetic theory of liquids as generalization, extension of theory of solid bodies, covers all types of arrangements of solids; thermal displacements of atoms; interstitial atoms, ions; orientational, rotational motion of molecules; transition between states of matter. Mathematical theory developed close to physical subject matter. "Discussed in a simple yet deeply penetrating fashion . . . will serve as seeds for a great many basic and applied developments in chemistry," J. of the Amer. Chemical Soc. 216 bibliographical footnotes. 55 figures. xi + 485pp. 5⅜ x 8.
S94 Clothbound **$3.95**
S95 Paperbound **$2.45**

# ASTRONOMY

**OUT OF THE SKY, H. H. Nininger.** Non-technical, comprehensive introduction to "meteoritics" —science concerned with arrival of matter from outer space. By one of world's experts on meteorites, this book defines meteors and meteorites; studies fireball clusters and processions, meteorite composition, size, distribution, showers, explosions, origins, much more. viii + 336pp. 5⅜ x 8.
T519 Paperbound **$1.85**

**AN INTRODUCTION TO THE STUDY OF STELLAR STRUCTURE, S. Chandrasekhar.** Outstanding treatise on stellar dynamics by one of greatest astro-physicists. Examines relationship between loss of energy, mass, and radius of stars in steady state. Discusses thermodynamic laws from Caratheodory's axiomatic standpoint; adiabatic, polytropic laws; work of Ritter, Emden, Kelvin, etc.; Stroemgren envelopes as starter for theory of gaseous stars; Gibbs statistical mechanics (quantum); degenerate stellar configuration, theory of white dwarfs; etc. "Highest level of scientific merit," Bulletin. Amer. Math. Soc. 33 figures. 509pp. 5⅜ x 8.
S413 Paperbound **$2.75**

**LES MÉTHODES NOVELLES DE LA MÉCANIQUE CÉLESTE, H. Poincaré.** Complete French text of one of Poincaré's most important works. Revolutionized celestial mechanics: first use of integral invariants, first major application of linear differential equations, study of periodic orbits, lunar motion and Jupiter's satellites, three body problem, and many other important topics. "Started a new era . . . so extremely modern that even today few have mastered his weapons," E. T. Bell. 3 volumes. Total 1282pp. 6⅛ x 9¼.
Vol. 1 S401 Paperbound **$2.75**
Vol. 2 S402 Paperbound **$2.75**
Vol. 3 S403 Paperbound **$2.75**
The set **$7.50**

**THE REALM OF THE NEBULAE, E. Hubble.** One of the great astronomers of our time presents his concept of "island universes," and describes its effect on astronomy. Covers velocity-distance relation; classification, nature, distances, general field of nebulae; cosmological theories; nebulae in the neighborhood of the Milky way; etc. 39 photos, including velocity-distance relations shown by spectrum comparison. "One of the most progressive lines of astronomical research," The Times, London. New Introduction by A. Sandage. 55 illustrations. xxiv + 201pp. 5⅜ x 8.
S455 Paperbound **$1.50**

**HOW TO MAKE A TELESCOPE, Jean Texereau.** Design, build an f/6 or f/8 Newtonian type reflecting telescope, with altazimuth Couder mounting, suitable for planetary, lunar, and stellar observation. Covers every operation step-by-step, every piece of equipment. Discusses basic principles of geometric and physical optics (unnecessary to construction), comparative merits of reflectors, refractors. A thorough discussion of eyepieces, finders, grinding, installation, testing, etc. 241 figures, 38 photos, show almost every operation and tool. Potential errors are anticipated. Foreword by A. Couder. Sources of supply. xiii + 191pp. 6¼ x 10.
T464 Clothbound **$3.50**

# BIOLOGICAL SCIENCES

**THE BIOLOGY OF THE AMPHIBIA, G. K. Noble,** Late Curator of Herpetology at Am. Mus. of Nat. Hist. Probably most used text on amphibia, most comprehensive, clear, detailed. 19 chapters, 85 page supplement: development; heredity; life history; speciation; adaptation; sex, integument, respiratory, circulatory, digestive, muscular, nervous systems; instinct, intelligence, habits, economic value classification, environment relationships, etc. "Nothing comparable to it," C. H. Pope, curator of Amphibia, Chicago Mus. of Nat. Hist. 1047 item bibliography. 174 illustrations. 600pp. 5⅜ x 8.
S206 Paperbound **$2.98**

**THE ORIGIN OF LIFE, A. I. Oparin.** A classic of biology. This is the first modern statement of theory of gradual evolution of life from nitrocarbon compounds. A brand-new evaluation of Oparin's theory in light of later research, by Dr. S. Margulis, University of Nebraska. xxv + 270pp. 5⅜ x 8.
S213 Paperbound **$1.75**

**THE BIOLOGY OF THE LABORATORY MOUSE, edited by G. D. Snell.** Prepared in 1941 by staff of Roscoe B. Jackson Memorial Laboratory, still the standard treatise on the mouse, assembling enormous amount of material for which otherwise you spend hours of research. Embryology, reproduction, histology, spontaneous neoplasms, gene and chromosomes mutations, genetics of spontaneous tumor formations, of tumor transplantation, endocrine secretion and tumor formation, milk influence and tumor formation, inbred, hybrid animals, parasites, infectious diseases, care and recording. "A wealth of information of vital concern. . . . recommended to all who could use a book on such a subject," Nature. Classified bibliography of 1122 items. 172 figures, including 128 photos. ix + 497pp. 6⅛ x 9¼.
S248 Clothbound **$6.00**

**THE TRAVELS OF WILLIAM BARTRAM, edited by Mark Van Doran.** Famous source-book of American anthropology, natural history, geography, is record kept by Bartram in 1770's on travels through wilderness of Florida, Georgia, Carolinas. Containing accurate, beautiful descriptions of Indians, settlers, fauna, flora, it is one of finest pieces of Americana ever written. 13 original illustrations. 448pp. 5⅜ x 8.                    T13 Paperbound **$2.00**

**BEHAVIOUR AND SOCIAL LIFE OF THE HONEYBEE, Ronald Ribbands.** Outstanding scientific study; a compendium of practically everything known of social life of honeybee. Stresses behaviour of individual bees in field, hive. Extends von Frisch's experiments on communication among bees. Covers perception of temperature, gravity, distance, vibration; sound production; glands; structural differences; wax production; temperature regulation; recognition, communication; drifting, mating behaviour, other highly interesting topics. "This valuable work is sure of a cordial reception by laymen, beekeepers and scientists," Prof. Karl von Frisch, Brit. J. of Animal Behaviour. Bibliography of 690 references. 127 diagrams, graphs, sections of bee anatomy, fine photographs. 352pp.                    S410 Clothbound **$4.50**

**ELEMENTS OF MATHEMATICAL BIOLOGY, A. J. Lotka.** Pioneer classic, 1st major attempt to apply modern mathematical techniques on large scale to phenomena of biology, biochemistry, psychology, ecology, similar life sciences. Partial contents: Statistical meaning of irreversibility; Evolution as redistribution; Equations of kinetics of evolving systems; Chemical, inter-species equilibrium; parameters of state; Energy transformers of nature, etc. Can be read with profit by even those having no advanced math; unsurpassed as study-reference. Formerly titled "Elements of Physical Biology." 72 figures. xxx + 460pp. 5⅜ x 8.
S346 Paperbound **$2.45**

**TREES OF THE EASTERN AND CENTRAL UNITED STATES AND CANADA, W. M. Harlow.** Serious middle-level text covering more than 140 native trees, important escapes, with information on general appearance, growth habit, leaf forms, flowers, fruit, bark, commercial use, distribution, habitat, woodlore, etc. Keys within text enable you to locate various species easily, to know which have edible fruit, much more useful, interesting information. "Well illustrated to make identification very easy," Standard Cat. for Public Libraries. Over 600 photographs, figures. xiii + 288pp. 5⅝ x 6½.                    T395 Paperbound **$1.35**

**FRUIT KEY AND TWIG KEY TO TREES AND SHRUBS (Fruit key to Northeastern Trees, Twig key to Deciduous Woody Plants of Eastern North America), W. M. Harlow.** Only guides with photographs of every twig, fruit described. Especially valuable to novice. Fruit key (both deciduous trees, evergreens) has introduction on seeding, organs involved, types, habits. Twig key introduction treats growth, morphology. In keys proper, identification is almost automatic. Exceptional work, widely used in university courses, especially useful for identification in winter, or from fruit or seed only. Over 350 photos, up to 3 times natural size. Index of common, scientific names, in each key. xvii + 125pp. 5⅝ x 8⅜.          T511 Paperbound **$1.25**

**INSECT LIFE AND INSECT NATURAL HISTORY, S. W. Frost.** Unusual for emphasizing habits, social life, ecological relations of insects rather than more academic aspects of classification, morphology. Prof. Frost's enthusiasm and knowledge are everywhere evident as he discusses insect associations, specialized habits like leaf-rolling, leaf mining, case-making, the gall insects, boring insects, etc. Examines matters not usually covered in general works: insects as human food; insect music, musicians; insect response to radio waves; use of insects in art, literature. "Distinctly different, possesses an individuality all its own," Journal of Forestry. Over 700 illustrations. Extensive bibliography. x + 524pp. 5⅜ x 8.
T519 Paperbound **$2.49**

**A WAY OF LIFE, AND OTHER SELECTED WRITINGS, Sir William Osler.** Physician, humanist, Osler discusses brilliantly Thomas Browne, Gui Patin, Robert Burton, Michael Servetus, William Beaumont, Laennec. Includes such favorite writing as title essay, "The Old Humanities and the New Science," "Books and Men," "The Student Life," 6 more of his best discussions of philosophy, literature, religion. "The sweep of his mind and interests embraced every phase of human activity," G. L. Keynes. 5 photographs. Introduction by G. L. Keynes, M.D., F.R.C.S. xx + 278pp. 5⅜ x 8.                    T488 Paperbound **$1.50**

**THE GENETICAL THEORY OF NATURAL SELECTION, R. A. Fisher.** 2nd revised edition of vital reviewing of Darwin's Selection Theory in terms of particulate inheritance, by one of greatest authorities on experimental, theoretical genetics. Theory stated in mathematical form. Special features of particulate inheritance are examined: evolution of dominance, maintenance of specific variability, mimicry, sexual selection, etc. 5 chapters on man's special circumstances as a social animal. 16 photographs. x + 310pp. 5⅜ x 8.
S466 Paperbound **$1.85**

# DOVER SCIENCE BOOKS

**THE AUTOBIOGRAPHY OF CHARLES DARWIN, AND SELECTED LETTERS, edited by Francis Darwin.** Darwin's own record of early life; historic voyage aboard "Beagle;" furore surrounding evolution, his replies; reminiscences of his son. Letters to Henslow, Lyell, Hooker, Huxley, Wallace, Kingsley, etc., and thoughts on religion, vivisection. We see how he revolutionized geology with concepts of ocean subsidence; how his great books on variation of plants and animals, primitive man, expression of emotion among primates, plant fertilization, carnivorous plants, protective coloration, etc., came into being. 365pp. 5⅜ x 8.
T479 Paperbound **$1.65**

**ANIMALS IN MOTION, Eadweard Muybridge.** Largest, most comprehensive selection of Muybridge's famous action photos of animals, from his "Animal Locomotion." 3919 high-speed shots of 34 different animals, birds, in 123 types of action; horses, mules, oxen, pigs, goats, camels, elephants, dogs, cats guanacos, sloths, lions, tigers, jaguars, raccoons, baboons, deer, elk, gnus, kangaroos, many others, walking, running, flying, leaping. Horse alone in over 40 ways. Photos taken against ruled backgrounds; most actions taken from 3 angles at once: 90°, 60°, rear. Most plates original size. Of considerable interest to scientists as biology classic, records of actual facts of natural history, physiology. "Really marvelous series of plates," Nature. "Monumental work," Waldemar Kaempffert. Edited by L. S. Brown, 74 page introduction on mechanics of motion. 340pp. of plates. 3919 photographs. 416pp. Deluxe binding, paper. (Weight: 4½ lbs.) 7⅛ x 10⅝.
T203 Clothbound **$10.00**

**THE HUMAN FIGURE IN MOTION, Eadweard Muybridge.** New edition of great classic in history of science and photography, largest selection ever made from original Muybridge photos of human action: 4789 photographs, illustrating 163 types of motion: walking, running, lifting, etc. in time-exposure sequence photos at speeds up to 1/6000th of a second. Men, women, children, mostly undraped, showing bone, muscle positions against ruled backgrounds, mostly taken at 3 angles at once. Not only was this a great work of photography, acclaimed by contemporary critics as work of genius, but it was also a great 19th century landmark in biological research. Historical introduction by Prof. Robert Taft, U. of Kansas. Plates original size, full of detail. Over 500 action strips. 407pp. 7¾ x 10⅝. Deluxe edition.
7204 Clothbound **$10.00**

**AN INTRODUCTION TO THE STUDY OF EXPERIMENTAL MEDICINE, Claude Bernard.** 90-year old classic of medical science, only major work of Bernard available in English, records his efforts to transform physiology into exact science. Principles of scientific research illustrated by specified case histories from his work; roles of chance, error, preliminary false conclusion, in leading eventually to scientific truth; use of hypothesis. Much of modern application of mathematics to biology rests on foundation set down here. "The presentation is polished . . . reading is easy," Revue des questions scientifiques. New foreword by Prof. I. B. Cohen, Harvard U. xxv + 266pp. 5⅜ x 8.
T400 Paperbound **$1.50**

**STUDIES ON THE STRUCTURE AND DEVELOPMENT OF VERTEBRATES, E. S. Goodrich.** Definitive study by greatest modern comparative anatomist. Exhaustive morphological, phylogenetic expositions of skeleton, fins, limbs, skeletal visceral arches, labial cartilages, visceral clefts, gills, vascular, respiratory, excretory, periphal nervous systems, etc., from fish to higher mammals. "For many a day this will certainly be the standard textbook on Vertebrate Morphology in the English language," Journal of Anatomy. 754 illustrations. 69 page biographical study by C. C. Hardy. Bibliography of 1186 references. Two volumes, total 906pp. 5⅜ x 8.
Two vol. set S449, 450 Paperbound **$5.00**

# EARTH SCIENCES

**THE EVOLUTION OF IGNEOUS BOOKS, N. L. Bowen.** Invaluable serious introduction applies techniques of physics, chemistry to explain igneous rock diversity in terms of chemical composition, fractional crystallization. Discusses liquid immiscibility in silicate magmas, crystal sorting, liquid lines of descent, fractional resorption of complex minerals, petrogen, etc. Of prime importance to geologists, mining engineers; physicists, chemists working with high temperature, pressures. "Most important," Times, London. 263 bibliographic notes. 82 figures. xviii + 334pp. 5⅜ x 8.
S311 Paperbound **$1.85**

**GEOGRAPHICAL ESSAYS, M. Davis.** Modern geography, geomorphology rest on fundamental work of this scientist. 26 famous essays present most important theories, field researches. Partial contents: Geographical Cycle; Plains of Marine, Subaerial Denudation; The Peneplain; Rivers, Valleys of Pennsylvania; Outline of Cape Cod; Sculpture of Mountains by Glaciers; etc. "Long the leader and guide," Economic Geography. "Part of the very texture of geography . . . models of clear thought," Geographic Review. 130 figures. vi + 777pp. 5⅜ x 8.
S383 Paperbound **$2.95**

**URANIUM PROSPECTING, H. L. Barnes.** For immediate practical use, professional geologist considers uranium ores, geological occurrences, field conditions, all aspects of highly profitable occupation. "Helpful information . . . easy-to-use, easy-to-find style," Geotimes. x + 117pp. 5⅜ x 8.
T309 Paperbound **$1.00**

11

**DE RE METALLICA, Georgius Agricola.** 400 year old classic translated, annotated by former President Herbert Hoover. 1st scientific study of mineralogy, mining, for over 200 years after its appearance in 1556 the standard treatise. 12 books, exhaustively annotated, discuss history of mining, selection of sites, types of deposits, making pits, shafts, ventilating, pumps, crushing machinery; assaying, smelting, refining metals; also salt alum, nitre, glass making. Definitive edition, with all 289 16th century woodcuts of original. Biographical, historical introductions. Bibliography, survey of ancient authors. Indexes. A fascinating book for anyone interested in art, history of science, geology, etc. Deluxe Edition. 289 illustrations. 672pp. 6¾ x 10. Library cloth.                                        S6 Clothbound **$10.00**

**INTERNAL CONSTITUTION OF THE EARTH, edited by Beno Gutenberg.** Prepared for National Research Council, this is a complete, thorough coverage of earth origins, continent formation, nature and behaviour of earth's core, petrology of crust, cooling forces in core, seismic and earthquake material, gravity, elastic constants, strain characteristics, similar topics. "One is filled with admiration . . . a high standard . . . there is no reader who will not learn something from this book," London, Edinburgh, Dublin, Philosophic Magazine. Largest Bibliography in print: 1127 classified items. Table of constants. 43 diagrams. 439pp. 6⅛ x 9¼.                                                  S414 Paperbound **$2.45**

**THE BIRTH AND DEVELOPMENT OF THE GEOLOGICAL SCIENCES, F. D. Adams.** Most thorough history of earth sciences ever written. Geological thought from earliest times to end of 19th century, covering over 300 early thinkers and systems; fossils and their explanation, vulcanists vs. neptunists, figured stones and paleontology, generation of stones, dozens of similar topics. 91 illustrations, including Medieval, Renaissance woodcuts, etc. 632 footnotes, mostly bibliographical. 511pp. 5⅜ x 8.                                     T5 Paperbound **$2.00**

**HYDROLOGY, edited by O. E. Meinzer,** prepared for the National Research Council. Detailed, complete reference library on precipitation, evaporation, snow, snow surveying, glaciers, lakes, infiltration, soil moisture, ground water, runoff, drought, physical changes produced by water hydrology of limestone terranes, etc. Practical in application, especially valuable for engineers. 24 experts have created "the most up-to-date, most complete treatment of the subject," Am. Assoc. of Petroleum Geologists. 165 illustrations. xi + 712pp. 6⅛ x 9¼.
S191 Paperbound **$2.95**

# LANGUAGE AND TRAVEL AIDS FOR SCIENTISTS

## SAY IT language phrase books

"SAY IT" in the foreign language of your choice! We have sold over ½ million copies of these popular, useful language books. They will not make you an expert linguist overnight, but they do cover most practical matters of everyday life abroad.

**Over 1000 useful phrases,** expressions, additional variants, substitutions.

**Modern! Useful!** Hundreds of phrases not available in other texts: "Nylon," "air-conditioned," etc.

The ONLY inexpensive phrase book **completely indexed.** Everything is available at a flip of your finger, ready to use.

Prepared by native linguists, travel experts.

Based on years of travel experience abroad.

May be used by itself, or to supplement any other text or course. Provides a living element. Used by many colleges, institutions: Hunter College; Barnard College; Army Ordinance School, Aberdeen; etc.

Available, 1 book per language:

| | |
|---|---|
| **Danish** (T818) 75¢ | **Italian** (T806) 60¢ |
| **Dutch** (T817) 75¢ | **Japanese** (T807) 75¢ |
| **English (for German-speaking people)** (T801) 60¢ | **Norwegian** (T814) 75¢ |
| **English (for Italian-speaking people)** (T816) 60¢ | **Russian** (T810) 75¢ |
| **English (for Spanish-speaking people)** (T802) 60¢ | **Spanish** (T811) 60¢ |
| **Esperanto** (T820) 75¢ | **Turkish** (T821) 75¢ |
| **French** (T803) 60¢ | **Yiddish** (T815) 75¢ |
| **German** (T804) 60¢ | **Swedish** (T812) 75¢ |
| **Modern Greek** (T813) 75¢ | **Polish** (T808) 75¢ |
| **Hebrew** (T805) 60¢ | **Portuguese** (T809) 75¢ |

# DOVER SCIENCE BOOKS

**MONEY CONVERTER AND TIPPING GUIDE FOR EUROPEAN TRAVEL, C. Vomacka.** Purse-size handbook crammed with information on currency regulations, tipping for every European country, including Israel, Turkey, Czechoslovakia, Rumania, Egypt, Russia, Poland. Telephone, postal rates; duty-free imports, passports, visas, health certificates; foreign clothing sizes; weather tables. What, when to tip. 5th year of publication. 128pp. 3½ x 5¼.     T260 Paperbound **60¢**

**NEW RUSSIAN-ENGLISH AND ENGLISH-RUSSIAN DICTIONARY, M. A. O'Brien.** Unusually comprehensive guide to reading, speaking, writing Russian, for both advanced, beginning students. Over 70,000 entries in new orthography, full information on accentuation, grammatical classifications. Shades of meaning, idiomatic uses, colloquialisms, tables of irregular verbs for both languages. Individual entries indicate stems, transitiveness, perfective, imperfective aspects, conjugation, sound changes, accent, etc. Includes pronunciation instruction. Used at Harvard, Yale, Cornell, etc. 738pp. 5⅜ x 8.     T208 Paperbound **$ 2.00**

**PHRASE AND SENTENCE DICTIONARY OF SPOKEN RUSSIAN, English-Russian, Russian-English.** Based on phrases, complete sentences, not isolated words—recognized as one of best methods of learning idiomatic speech. Over 11,500 entries, indexed by single words, over 32,000 English, Russian sentences, phrases, in immediately useable form. Shows accent changes in conjugation, declension; irregular forms listed both alphabetically, under main form of word. 15,000 word introduction covers Russian sounds, writing, grammar, syntax. 15 page appendix of geographical names, money, important signs, given names, foods, special Soviet terms, etc. Originally published as U.S. Gov't Manual TM 30-944. iv + 573pp. 5⅜ x 8.     T496 Paperbound **$2.75**

**PHRASE AND SENTENCE DICTIONARY OF SPOKEN SPANISH, Spanish-English, English-Spanish.** Compiled from spoken Spanish, based on phrases, complete sentences rather than isolated words—not an ordinary dictionary. Over 16,000 entries indexed under single words, both Castilian, Latin-American. Language in immediately useable form. 25 page introduction provides rapid survey of sounds, grammar, syntax, full consideration of irregular verbs. Especially apt in modern treatment of phrases, structure. 17 page glossary gives translations of geographical names, money values, numbers, national holidays, important street signs, useful expressions of high frequency, plus unique 7 page glossary of Spanish, Spanish-American foods. Originally published as U.S. Gov't Manual TM 30-900. iv + 513pp. 5⅝ x 8⅜.     T495 Paperbound **$1.75**

## SAY IT CORRECTLY language record sets

The best inexpensive pronunciation aids on the market. Spoken by native linguists associated with major American universities, each record contains:

> 14 minutes of speech—12 minutes of normal, relatively slow speech, 2 minutes of normal conversational speed.

> 120 basic phrases, sentences, covering nearly every aspect of everyday life, travel—introducing yourself, travel in autos, buses, taxis, etc., walking, sightseeing, hotels, restaurants, money, shopping, etc.

> 32 page booklet containing everything on record plus English translations easy-to-follow phonetic guide.

> Clear, high-fidelity recordings.

> Unique bracketing systems, selection of basic sentences enabling you to expand use of SAY IT CORRECTLY records with a dictionary, to fit thousands of additional situations.

Use this record to supplement any course or text. All sounds in each language illustrated perfectly—imitate speaker in pause which follows each foreign phrase in slow section, and be amazed at increased ease, accuracy of pronunciation. Available, one language per record for

| | | |
|---|---|---|
| French | Spanish | German |
| Italian | Dutch | Modern Greek |
| Japanese | Russian | Portuguese |
| Polish | Swedish | Hebrew |
| English (for German-speaking people) | | English (for Spanish-speaking people) |

7″ (33 1/3 rpm) record, album, booklet. **$1.00 each.**

**SPEAK MY LANGUAGE: SPANISH FOR YOUNG BEGINNERS, M. Ahlman, Z. Gilbert.** Records provide one of the best, most entertaining methods of introducing a foreign language to children. Within framework of train trip from Portugal to Spain, an English-speaking child is introduced to Spanish by native companion. (Adapted from successful radio program of N.Y. State Educational Department.) A dozen different categories of expressions,. including greeting, numbers, time, weather, food, clothes, family members, etc. Drill is combined with poetry and contextual use. Authentic background music. Accompanying book enables a reader to follow records, includes vocabulary of over 350 recorded expressions. Two 10″ 33 1/3 records, total of 40 minutes. Book. 40 illustrations. 69pp. 5¼ x 10½.     T890 The set **$4.95**

13

# LISTEN & LEARN language record sets

LISTEN & LEARN is the only extensive language record course designed especially to meet your travel and everyday needs. Separate sets for each language, each containing three 33 1/3 rpm long-playing records—1 1/2 hours of recorded speech by eminent native speakers who are professors at Columbia, New York U., Queens College.

Check the following features found only in LISTEN & LEARN:

> Dual language recording. 812 selected phrases, sentences, over 3200 words, spoken first in English, then foreign equivalent. Pause after each foreign phrase allows time to repeat expression.

> 128-page manual (196 page for Russian)—everything on records, plus simple transcription. Indexed for convenience. Only set on the market completely indexed.

> Practical. No time wasted on material you can find in any grammar. No dead words. Covers central core material with phrase approach. Ideal for person with limited time. Living, modern expressions, not found in other courses. Hygienic products, modern equipment, shopping, "air-conditioned," etc. Everything is immediately useable.

> High-fidelity recording, equal in clarity to any costing up to $6 per record.

"Excellent . . . impress me as being among the very best on the market," Prof. Mario Pei, Dept. of Romance Languages, Columbia U. "Inexpensive and well done . . . ideal present," Chicago Sunday Tribune. "More genuinely helpful than anything of its kind," Sidney Clark, well-known author of "All the Best" travel books.

UNCONDITIONAL GUARANTEE. Try LISTEN & LEARN, then return it within 10 days for full refund, if you are not satisfied. It is guaranteed after you actually use it.

6 modern languages—FRENCH, SPANISH, GERMAN, ITALIAN, RUSSIAN, or JAPANESE *—one language to each set of 3 records (33 1/3 rpm). 128 page manual. Album.

| **Spanish** | the set $4.95 | **German** | the set $4.95 | **Japanese*** | the set $5.95 |
| **French** | the set $4.95 | **Italian** | the set $4.95 | **Russian** | the set $5.95 |

* Available Oct. 1959.

# TRÜBNER COLLOQUIAL SERIES

These unusual books are members of the famous Trübner series of colloquial manuals. They have been written to provide adults with a sound colloquial knowledge of a foreign language, and are suited for either class use or self-study. Each book is a complete course in itself, with progressive, easy to follow lessons. Phonetics, grammar, and syntax are covered, while hundreds of phrases and idioms, reading texts, exercises, and vocabulary are included. These books are unusual in being neither skimpy nor overdetailed in grammatical matters, and in presenting up-to-date, colloquial, and practical phrase material. Bilingual presentation is stressed, to make thorough self-study easier for the reader.

COLLOQUIAL HINDUSTANI, A. H. Harley, formerly Nizam's Reader in Urdu, U. of London. 30 pages on phonetics and scripts (devanagari & Arabic-Persian) are followed by 29 lessons, including material on English and Arabic-Persian influences. Key to all exercises. Vocabulary. 5 x 7½. 147pp. Clothbound **$1.75**

COLLOQUIAL ARABIC, DeLacy O'Leary. Foremost Islamic scholar covers language of Egypt, Syria, Palestine, & Northern Arabia. Extremely clear coverage of complex Arabic verbs & noun plurals; also cultural aspects of language. Vocabulary. xviii + 192pp. 5 x 7½. Clothbound **$1.75**

COLLOQUIAL GERMAN, P. F. Doring. Intensive thorough coverage of grammar in easily-followed form. Excellent for brush-up, with hundreds of colloquial phrases. 34 pages of bilingual texts. 224pp. 5 x 7½. Clothbound **$1.75**

COLLOQUIAL SPANISH, W. R. Patterson. Castilian grammar and colloquial language, loaded with bilingual phrases and colloquialisms. Excellent for review or self-study. 164pp. 5 x 7½. Clothbound **$1.75**

COLLOQUIAL FRENCH, W. R. Patterson. 16th revised edition of this extremely popular manual. Grammar explained with model clarity, and hundreds of useful expressions and phrases; exercises, reading texts, etc. Appendixes of new and useful words and phrases. 223pp. 5 x 7½. Clothbound **$1.75**

# DOVER SCIENCE BOOKS

**COLLOQUIAL PERSIAN, L. P. Elwell-Sutton.** Best introduction to modern Persian, with 90 page grammatical section followed by conversations, 35 page vocabulary. 139pp.    Clothbound **$1.75**

**COLLOQUIAL CZECH, J. Schwarz,** former headmaster of Lingua Institute, Prague. Full easily followed coverage of grammar, hundreds of immediately useable phrases, texts. Perhaps the best Czech grammar in print. "An absolutely successful textbook," JOURNAL OF CZECHO-SLOVAK FORCES IN GREAT BRITAIN. 252pp. 5 x 7½.    Clothbound **$2.50**

**COLLOQUIAL RUMANIAN, G. Nandris,** Professor of University of London. Extremely thorough coverage of phonetics, grammar, syntax; also included 70 page reader, and 70 page vocabulary. Probably the best grammar for this increasingly important language. 340pp. 5 x 7½.
Clothbound **$2.50**

**COLLOQUIAL ITALIAN, A. L. Hayward.** Excellent self-study course in grammar, vocabulary, idioms, and reading. Easy progressive lessons will give a good working knowledge of Italian in the shortest possible time. 5 x 7½.    Clothbound **$1.75**

# MISCELLANEOUS

**TREASURY OF THE WORLD'S COINS, Fred Reinfeld.** Finest general introduction to numismatics; non-technical, thorough, always fascinating. Coins of Greece, Rome, modern countries of every continent, primitive societies, such oddities as 200-lb stone money of Yap, nail coinage of New England; all mirror man's economy, customs, religion, politics, philosophy, art. Entertaining, absorbing study; novel view of history. Over 750 illustrations. Table of value of coins illustrated. List of U.S. coin clubs. 224pp. 6½ x 9¼.
T433 Paperbound **$1.75**

**ILLUSIONS AND DELUSIONS OF THE SUPERNATURAL AND THE OCCULT, D. H. Rawcliffe.** Rationally examines hundreds of persistent delusions including witchcraft, trances, mental healing, peyotl, poltergeists, stigmata, lycanthropy, live burial, auras, Indian rope trick, spiritualism, dowsing, telepathy, ghosts, ESP, etc. Explains, exposes mental, physical deceptions involved, making this not only an exposé of supernatural phenomena, but a valuable exposition of characteristic types of abnormal psychology. Originally "The Psychology of the Occult." Introduction by Julian Huxley. 14 illustrations. 551pp. 5⅜ x 8.
T503 Paperbound **$2.00**

**HOAXES, C. D. MacDougall.** Shows how art, science, history, journalism can be perverted for private purposes. Hours of delightful entertainment, a work of scholarly value, often shocking. Examines nonsense news, Cardiff giant, Shakespeare forgeries, Loch Ness monster, biblical frauds, political schemes, literary hoaxers like Chatterton, Ossian, disumbrationist school of painting, lady in black at Valentino's tomb, over 250 others. Will probably reveal truth about few things you've believed, will help you spot more easily the editorial "gander" or planted publicity release. "A stupendous collection . . . and shrewd analysis," New Yorker. New revised edition. 54 photographs. 320pp. 5⅜ x 8.    T465 Paperbound **$1.75**

**YOGA: A SCIENTIFIC EVALUATION, Kovoor T. Behanan.** Book that for first time gave Western readers a sane, scientific explanation, analysis of yoga. Author draws on laboratory experiments, personal records of year as disciple of yoga, to investigate yoga psychology, physiology, "supernatural" phenomena, ability to plumb deepest human powers. In this study under auspices of Yale University Institute of Human Relations, strictest principles of physiological, psychological inquiry are followed. Foreword by W. A. Miles, Yale University. 17 photographs. xx + 270pp. 5⅜ x 8.    T505 Paperbound **$1.65**